GBBHunter

D i C

Logic 316

Methods of Logic

METHODS OF
LOGIC

By

WILLARD VAN ORMAN QUINE

Professor of Philosophy, Harvard University

LONDON
ROUTLEDGE & KEGAN PAUL

First published in England 1952
by Routledge & Kegan Paul Limited
Broadway House, Carter Lane
London, E.C.4

Printed in Great Britain
by lithography
by Jarrold & Sons Limited
Norwich

Second Impression 1958

To
MARJORIE

Preface

Logic is an old subject, and since 1879 it has been a great one. There is room in it for many books. But if each of five logic books is concerned, at least in its early portions, with the elements of the subject, and all are from the same hand, then space must be found in the fifth for an apology. Such is the purpose for which the present page and the next have been set aside.

This book undertakes both to convey a precise understanding of the formal concepts of modern logic and to develop convenient techniques of formal reasoning. Logic books exist which are strong in theory and rigorous and elegant in the matter of proofs, but the reader who would discover further proofs of his own has had painfully to develop his own method of discovery. In this book, though rigor has been preserved, the objective of inculcating technical facility has been allowed to prevail over that of elegance.

The logic of truth functions and the logic of one-place predicates, or monadic quantification theory, are provided here with mechanical tests of validity. Various such tests are known, but new ones are here presented which seem on the whole to terminate more quickly when applied to examples.

For the broader logic of predicates, or general quantification theory, comprehensive tests of validity are known to be impossible. Here one must resort to proofs rather than mere tests; and the discovery of proofs commonly depends on ingenuity. Here, therefore, efficacy is served by so framing the rules of proof as to make the discovery of proofs as easy on the average as we can. This objective, rather than that of conciseness of rules, has prompted the systematization of general quantification theory contained in this book.

This much makes the book a new manual of logical method. But theory also comes in for a share. The last five sections of the book deal with set theory and the foundations of mathematics, others deal with singular terms and descriptions, others grind the old ontological axe. These pages too turned out new in more than manner of expression.

Still, this is one more book which develops modern logic from the ground up. Unavoidably there have been patches where points explained in my earlier writings needed to be explained again in essentially the same old way. At these points I have adapted examples and expository passages from *Mathematical Logic*, *Elementary Logic*, and *O Sentido da Nova Lógica*, preferring not to obscure genuine points of contact by *ad hoc* shifts of example or of phrasing. But the points are few. §1 draws in part on §6 of *O Sentido*, and §3 draws in part on §2 of *Mathematical Logic*. In §§4, 8, 12, and 31, examples are borrowed from *Elementary Logic* but are handled differently.

About a sixth of the book is being printed small, as optional reading; the rest is intended as a text for a semester college course in deductive logic. The course in which I shall use it is not Freshman Thought, but it is a course for the general student and it does not presuppose Freshman Thought or other special training. Besides being intended for the general student, the course does double duty as a prerequisite for specialized courses in logic; and it is hoped correspondingly that this book may be useful as a foundation for further building. Finally, despite the presence of exercises, the book would fail of much of its purpose if it were not also taken up as a treatise by readers who have no commitments to a college logic course.

Acknowledgments

For helpful criticisms of earlier drafts I am grateful to Professors George D. W. Berry and George Burch, Dr. Joseph L. Cobitz, Professor Nelson Goodman, Drs. Oliver Straus and James W. Oliver, and the publishers' reader. Each of these seven has affected the book for the better; the last two were especially influential. To Mr. Robert F. McNaughton, Jr., I am indebted for a critical scrutiny of the book in its final stages, as well as for making the index and helping with the proofreading. I thank the Harvard University Press for permission to borrow portions of §2 of my *Mathematical Logic*, and I thank Ginn and Company for permission to adapt sundry examples from my *Elementary Logic*. The principal acknowledgment of all is due my wife for her untiring efforts, both secretarial and critical. But for her the book would have been slower to appear and slower and drearier to read.

Cambridge, March 8, 1950   W. V. Q.

ix

Introduction

Logic, like any science, has as its business the pursuit of truth. What are true are certain statements; and the pursuit of truth is the endeavor to sort out the true statements from the others, which are false.

Truths are as plentiful as falsehoods, since each falsehood admits of a negation which is true. But scientific activity is not the indiscriminate amassing of truths; science is selective and seeks the truths that count for most, either in point of intrinsic interest or as instruments for coping with the world.

For truth ordinarily attaches to statements by virtue of the nature of the world. It is a commonplace, inaccurate but not unfounded, that a statement is true when it corresponds to reality, when it mirrors the world. A fundamental way of deciding whether a statement is true is by comparing it, in some sense or other, with the world—or, which is the nearest we can come, by comparing it with our experience of the world.

Strictly speaking, what admit of truth and falsity are not statements as repeatable patterns of utterance, but individual events of statement utterance. For, utterances that sound alike can vary in meaning with the occasion of the utterance. This is due not only to careless ambiguities, but to systematic ambiguities which are essential to the nature of language. The pronoun 'I' changes its reference with every change of speaker; 'here' changes its reference with every significant movement through space; and 'now' changes its reference every time it is uttered.

So the crucial point of contact between description and reality is to be sought in the utterance of a statement on the occasion of an experience which that statement utterance directly reports. The seeing of a green patch, and the simultaneous utterance 'Green patch now', constitute the sort of composite event which, in its rare occurrences, gladdens the heart of the epistemologist.

Such events, fundamental though they are epistemologically, are rare because of the social nature of language. Language is a social institution serving, within its limitations, the social end of communication; so it is not to be wondered that the objects of our first and commonest utterances are socially shared physical objects rather than private experiences. Physical objects, if they did not exist, would (to transplant Voltaire's epigram) have had to be invented. They are indispensable as the public common denominators of private sense experience.

But utterances about physical objects are not verifiable or refutable by direct comparison with experience. They purport to describe, not experience, but the external world. They can be compared with the external world only through the medium of our experience of that world, but the connection between our experience and the world already involves a step of hypothesis or inference which precludes any direct and conclusive confrontation of the utterance with its subject matter. There is many a slip betwixt objective cup and subjective lip.

So statements, apart from an occasional collectors' item for epistemologists, are connected only deviously with experience. The latest scientific pronouncement about positrons and the statement that my pen is in my hand are equally statements about physical objects; and physical objects are known to us only as parts of a systematic conceptual structure which, taken as a whole, impinges at its edges upon experience. As far as knowledge is concerned, no more can be claimed for our whole body of affirmations than that it is a devious but convenient system for relating experiences to experiences. The system as a whole is under-determined by experience, but implies, given certain experiences, that certain others should be forthcoming. When such predictions of experience turn out wrong, the system has to be changed somehow. But we retain a wide latitude of choice as to what statements of the system to preserve and what ones to revise; any one of many revisions will be sufficient to unmake the particular implication which brought the system to grief. Our statements about external reality face the tribunal of sense experience not individually but as a corporate body.

But such choice of what to revise is subject to a vague scheme of priorities. Some statements about physical objects, e.g., 'My pen is in my hand', 'The mercury is at 80', are in some sense closer to possible experience than others; and such statements must be guarded pretty jealously once the appropriate experiences have appeared. Should revision of the system become necessary, other statements than these are to suffer. It is only by such an allocation of priority that we can hope to claim any empirical content or objective reference for the system as a whole.

There is also, however, another and somewhat opposite priority: the more fundamental a law is to our conceptual scheme, the less likely we are to choose it for revision. When some revision of our system of statements is called for, we prefer, other things being equal, a revision which disturbs the system least. Actually, despite the apparent opposition between this priority and the one previously noted, the one involves the other. For, the connection between a statement such as 'My pen is in my hand' and the experiences which are said to verify it is itself a matter of general principles central to the system.

Where the two priorities come into conflict, either is capable of prevailing. Statements close to experience and seemingly verified by the appropriate experiences may occasionally be given up, even by pleading hallucination, in the extreme case where their retention would entail a cataclysmic revision of fundamental laws. But to overrule a multiplicity of such statements, if they reinforce one another and are sustained by different observers, would invite criticism.

The priority on law, considered now apart from any competition with the priority on statements verified by experience, admits of many gradations. Conjectures of history and economics will be revised more willingly than laws of physics, and these more willingly than laws of mathematics and logic. Our system of statements has such a thick cushion of indeterminacy, in relation to experience, that vast domains of law can easily be held immune to revision on principle. We can always turn to other quarters of the system when revisions are called for by unexpected experiences. Mathematics and logic, central as they are to the conceptual scheme, tend to be accorded such immunity, in view of our conservative preference for revisions which disturb the system least; and herein, perhaps, lies the "necessity" which the laws of mathematics and logic are felt to enjoy.

In the end it is perhaps the same to say, as one often does, that the laws of mathematics and logic are true simply by virtue of our conceptual scheme. For, it is certainly by virtue of that scheme that those laws are central to it; and it is by virtue of being thus central that the laws are preserved from revision at the expense of statements less strategically situated.

It is also often said that the laws of mathematics and logic are true by virtue of the meanings of the words '+', '=', 'if', 'and', etc., which they contain. This also I can accept, for I expect it differs only in wording from saying that the laws are true by virtue of our conceptual scheme.

But it must now be remarked that our conservative preference for those revisions which disturb the system least is opposed by a significant contrary force, a force for simplification. Far-reaching revision of the fundamental laws of physics was elected in recent decades, by considerations of simplicity, in preference to the welter of *ad hoc* subsidiary laws which would otherwise have been needed to accommodate the wayward experiences of Michelson and Morley and other experimenters. Continued experiment "confirmed" the fundamental revisions, in the sense of increasing the simplicity differential.

Mathematical and logical laws themselves are not immune to revision if it is found that essential simplifications of our whole conceptual scheme will ensue. There have been suggestions, stimulated largely by quandaries of modern physics, that we revise the true-false dichotomy of current logic in favor of some sort of tri- or *n*-chotomy. Logical laws are the most central and crucial statements of our conceptual scheme, and for this reason the most protected from revision by the force of conservatism; but, because again of their crucial position, they are the laws an apt revision of which might offer the most sweeping simplification of our whole system of knowledge.

Thus the laws of mathematics and logic may, despite all "necessity", be abrogated. But this is not to deny that such laws are true by virtue of the conceptual scheme, or by virtue of meanings. Because these laws are so central, any revision of them is felt to be the adoption of a new conceptual scheme, the imposition of new meanings on old words. No such revolution, by the way, is envisaged in this book;

there will be novelties of approach and technique in these pages, but at bottom logic will remain unchanged.

For the most part, as has been stressed in the foregoing paragraphs, our statements relate only remotely to experience. The system of statements as a whole has its experiential implications; but the individual statements, apart from the peripheral few which directly describe experience as such, are relevant to experience only indirectly through their participation in the system. It is only by way of the relations of one statement to another that the statements in the interior of the system can figure at all in the prediction of experience, and can be found deserving of revision when prediction fails. Now of these relations of statements to statements, one of conspicuous importance is the relation of logical implication: the relation of any statement to any that follows logically from it. If one statement is to be held as true, each statement implied by it must also be held as true; and thus it is that statements internal to the system have their effects on statements at the periphery.

But for implication, our system of statements would for the most part be meaningless; nothing but the periphery would make sense. Yet implication is not really an added factor; for, to say that one statement logically implies a second is the same as saying that a third statement of the system, an 'if-then' compound formed from the other two, is logically true (or "valid.") Logical truths are statements on a par with the rest, but very centrally situated; they are statements of such forms as '$x = x$', 'p or not p', 'If p then p', 'If p and q then q', 'If everything is thus and so then something is thus and so', and others more complex and less quickly recognizable. Their characteristic is that they not only are true but stay true even when we make substitutions upon their component words and phrases as we please, provided merely that the so-called "logical" words '=', 'or', 'not', 'if-then', 'everything', 'something', etc., stay undisturbed. We may write any statements in the 'p' and 'q' positions and any terms in the 'thus and so' positions, in the forms cited above, without fear of falsity. All that counts, when a statement is logically true, is its structure in terms of logical words. Thus it is that logical truths are commonly said to be true by virtue merely of the meanings of the logical words.

The chief importance of logic lies in implication, which, therefore, will be the main theme of this book. Techniques are wanted for showing, given two statements, that the one implies the other; herein lies logical deduction. Such techniques will be developed, for increasingly inclusive portions of logic, as the book proceeds. The objects of deduction, the things related by implication, are statements; so statements will constitute not merely the medium of this book (as of most), but the primary subject matter.

Strictly speaking, as urged earlier, what admit of meaning and of truth and falsity are not the statements but the individual events of their utterance. However, it is a great source of simplification in logical theory to talk of statements in abstraction from the individual occasions of their utterance; and this abstraction, if made in full awareness and subject to a certain precaution, offers no difficulty. The precaution is merely that we must not apply our logical techniques to examples in which one and the same statement recurs several times with changed meanings, due to variations in immediate context. But such examples are easily enough adjusted to the purposes of logic by some preliminary paraphrasing, by way of bringing the implicit shifts of meaning into explicit form. (Cf. §8).

Logic and mathematics were coupled, in earlier remarks, as jointly enjoying a central position within the total system of discourse. Logic as commonly presented, and in particular as it will be presented in this book, seems to differ from mathematics in that in logic we talk about statements and their interrelationships, notably implication, whereas in mathematics we talk about abstract nonlinguistic things: numbers, functions, and the like. This contrast is in large part misleading. Logical truths, e.g., statements of the form 'If p and q then q', are not about statements; they may be about anything, depending on what statements we put in the blanks 'p' and 'q'. When we talk *about* such logical truths, and when we expound implications, we are indeed talking about statements; but so are we when we talk *about* mathematical truths.

But it is indeed the case that the truths of mathematics treat explicitly of abstract nonlinguistic things, e.g., numbers and functions, whereas the truths of logic, in a reasonably limited sense of the word 'logic', have no such entities as specific subject matter. This is an important difference. Despite this difference, however, logic in its higher reaches is found to bring us by natural stages into mathematics. For, it happens that certain unobtrusive extensions of logical theory carry us into a realm, commonly also called 'logic' in a broad sense of the word, which does have abstract entities of a special kind as subject matter. These entities are classes; and the logical theory of classes, or set theory, proves to be the basic discipline of pure mathematics. From it, as first came to be known through the work of Frege, Dedekind, Weierstrass, and their successors within the past seventy years, the whole of classical mathematics can be generated. Before the end of the book we shall have ascended through four grades of logic in the narrower sense, and emerged into set theory; and here we shall see, as examples of the derivation of classical mathematics, how the concept of number and various related notions can be defined.

Contents

PART III. GENERAL THEORY OF QUANTIFICATION

PART IV. GLIMPSES BEYOND

Methods of Logic

PART ONE

Truth Functions

§1. NEGATION, CONJUNCTION, AND ALTERNATION

The peculiarity of *statements* which sets them apart from other linguistic forms is that they admit of truth and falsity, and may hence be significantly affirmed and denied. To deny a statement is to affirm another statement, known as the *negation* or *contradictory* of the first. To deny 'The Taj Mahal is white' is to affirm 'The Taj Mahal is not white'. Note that this negation is opposed to the original not as black to white, but as non-white to white; it counts as true in every case except the case of whiteness.

The commonest method of forming the negation of statements in ordinary language is by attaching 'not' (or 'does not', etc.) to the main verb, as in the foregoing example. But if the verb is governed by 'sometimes' or 'always', the negation is formed rather by substituting 'never', or 'not always'. If the statement is compound and thus has no main verb, its negation has to be phrased more elaborately; e.g., 'It is not the case both that ... and that ...'. But, despite such irregularities of ordinary language, a little care suffices for constructing a clear negation of any given statement, the guiding consideration being simply this: the negation is to count as false if the given statement is true, and the negation is to count as true under any and all circumstances under which the given statement is false.

In logical studies it is convenient to adopt a single sign of negation, consisting of the prefix ' — ', applied to statements as wholes.[1] Thus ' —(Jones is away)' means 'Jones is not away'; the parentheses here serve to group, as a single whole, the statement to which ' — ' is applied. The sign ' — ' might be translated into words as 'it is not the

[1]Many authors prefer the tilde '∼'.

case that'; briefly it may be pronounced 'not'. When a statement is represented as a single letter 'p', as is commonly done in logical discussion, the sign of negation will be placed above instead of in front; thus we shall write '$\bar{p}$' instead of '$-p$' for the negation of 'p'.

Instead of affirming each of several statements we can, equivalently, affirm a single statement which is known to logicians (in contrast to grammarians) as the *conjunction* of the given statements. The conjunction of two or more statements is commonly expressed in English by linking the statements by 'and', or commas, or a combination of the two: 'Some are born great, some achieve greatness, and some have greatness thrust upon them.' In logical studies it is convenient to express the conjunction simply by writing the component statements in juxtaposition; e.g., '(some are born great)(some achieve greatness) (some have greatness thrust upon them)'—where again the parentheses serve merely to mark off the component statements as wholes. If we think of 'p', 'q', and 'r' as statements, their conjunction is represented as 'pqr'.

The meanings of negation and conjunction are summed up in these laws. *The negation of a true statement is false; the negation of a false statement is true; a conjunction of statements all of which are true is true; and a conjunction of statements not all of which are true is false.*

We see immediately that '$\bar{\bar{p}}$', the negation of '$\bar{p}$', will be true if and only if '$\bar{p}$' is false, hence if and only if 'p' is true; so there is no point in writing a double negation '$\bar{\bar{p}}$', amounting as it does simply to 'p'. It is equally evident that the conjunction 'pp' amounts simply to 'p'.

Consider now '$p(qr)$'. This, being the conjunction of 'p' and 'qr', is to be true if and only if 'p' and 'qr' are both true: and 'qr' in turn is to be true if and only if 'q' and 'r' are both true. Hence '$p(qr)$' is true if and only if 'p', 'q', and 'r' are all true; in other words, '$p(qr)$' amounts simply to the three-way conjunction 'pqr'. In the same way it may be seen that '$(pq)r$' amounts simply to 'pqr'. We may therefore drop parentheses and always write 'pqr', viewing this at will as the conjunction of 'pq' and 'r', as the conjunction of 'p' and 'qr', and as the conjunction of 'p', 'q', and 'r'. Conjunction is, in mathematical jargon, *associative*: internal grouping is immaterial in 'pqr', just as in the sum '$x + y + z$' or product 'xyz' of arithmetic. Conjunction contrasts in this respect with the arithmetical operation of division; for note that the parentheses in '12 ÷ (6 ÷ 2)' and '(12 ÷ 6) ÷ 2' make all the difference between 4 and 1.

Another respect in which conjunction resembles addition and multiplication, and differs from division, is that it is *commutative*; i.e., order is immaterial, there being no need to distinguish between '*pq*' and '*qp*'.

But conjunction was lately observed to enjoy also a third convenient property, not shared by addition and multiplication; viz., '*pp*' reduces to '*p*'. Conjunction is *idempotent*, to persist in the jargon. Taken together, these three properties of conjunction come simply to this: once we have an inventory of all the distinct components of a continued conjunction, no further details of the constitution of the conjunction need concern us.

Having touched on negation and conjunction, which correspond to 'not' and 'and', we turn now to a third way of forming statements from statements. It is called *alternation*, and corresponds to the connective 'or', or 'either-or'. This connective is subject in ordinary discourse to conflicting usages. One sense is the *nonexclusive*,[1] according to which the compound is true so long as at least one of the components is true. Under this usage the statement:

(Either) Jones is ill or Smith is away

is true if Jones is ill and Smith is away, true again if Jones is not ill but Smith is away, true again if Jones is ill but Smith is not away, and false only in case Jones is neither ill nor Smith away. The other sense in which 'or' is sometimes used, called the *exclusive*, construes the compound as true just in case *exactly* one of the components is true. In this sense of 'or', the compound becomes false not only when the components are both false (Jones neither ill nor Smith away) but also when the components are both true (Jones ill and Smith away).

The ambiguity of 'or' is commonly resolved, in ordinary usage, by adding the words 'or both' or 'but not both'. Thus the nonexclusive sense is expressible in the unambiguous fashion:

Jones is ill or Smith is away or both,

[1] I follow Cooley in preferring this awkward term to the more usual but somewhat misleading 'inclusive'.

and the exclusive sense thus:

> Jones is ill or Smith is away but not both.

When we are confronted with 'p or q' by itself, we do not in general know which interpretation to assign to it. Often the choice is immaterial, in that either sense would serve equally. For example, consider the expression '$x \leqq y$', i.e., '$x < y$ or $x = y$'. It makes no difference whether 'or' here is understood in the nonexclusive or the exclusive sense. The only difference between the two senses occurs in the case where both components are true; but when the components concerned are '$x < y$' and '$x = y$', the case of joint truth does not arise either in fact or in the mind of the speaker.

It is a common error to believe that examples like '$x < y$ or $x = y$' are clear cases of the use of 'or' in the exclusive sense, and in consequence of this error there is a tendency to overestimate the role which the exclusive sense of 'or' plays in everyday language. The clauses '$x < y$' and '$x = y$' are, of themselves, mutually exclusive or incompatible clauses; but this incompatibility, far from establishing that the context '$x < y$ or $x = y$' uses 'or' in the exclusive sense, deprives us of the one case in which we might hope to distinguish between the exclusive and nonexclusive senses. Since the clauses '$x < y$' and '$x = y$' are already of such nature as to exclude each other, it is immaterial whether we understand 'or' as repeating this exclusion or not.

If we want to establish indisputable instances of the exclusive use of 'or', we must imagine circumstances in which the person who uses 'or' has a positive purpose of denying, explicitly within the given statement, the joint truth of the components. Such examples are rare, but they exist. In an example given by Tarski it is supposed that a child asks his father to take him to the beach and afterwards to the movie. The father replies, in a tone of refusal, "We will go either to the beach or to the movie." Here the exclusive use is clear; the father means simultaneously to promise and to refuse. But it is much easier to find cases in which the nonexclusive interpretation is obligatory. For example, when it is decreed that passports will be issued only to persons who were born in the country or who are married to natives of the country, this does not mean that passports will be refused to persons who were born in the country and are married to natives. Most use of 'or' in everyday language is either of this type which admits only of the nonexclusive interpretation, or of the type of '$x < y$ or $x = y$', which admits both interpretations indifferently. Latin has distinct words for the two senses of 'or': *vel* for the nonexclusive and *aut* for the exclusive. In modern logic it is customary to write 'v', reminiscent of 'vel', for 'or' in the nonexclusive sense: '$p \lor q$'. It is this mode of compounding statements, and only this, that is called *alternation*. When the ambiguous 'or' of ordinary language appears hereafter in the book, let us agree to construe it in this nonexclusive sense. If occasions arise where the exclusive sense of 'or' is really wanted, it is easy enough to express it explicitly:

$$p \text{ or } q \text{ but not both,}$$

or equivalently:

$$\text{Either } p \text{ and not } q \text{ or } q \text{ and not } p,$$

i.e., in symbols:

$$p\bar{q} \lor \bar{p}q.^{[1]}$$

The meaning of alternation, then, is given by this rule: *An alternation is true if at least one of the components is true, and otherwise false.* Whereas a conjunction is true if and only if its components are all true, an alternation is false if and only if its components are all false. In a metaphor from genetics, conjunction and alternation may be contrasted thus: in conjunction, truth is recessive and falsity dominant; in alternation, truth is dominant and falsity recessive.

Because the explanation of alternation is just the same as that of conjunction except for interchanging the roles of truth and falsehood, it is evident that the formal properties of conjunction must reappear as properties of alternation; thus alternation, like conjunction, is associative, commutative, and idempotent. We can render '$(p \lor q) \lor r$' and '$p \lor (q \lor r)$' indifferently as '$p \lor q \lor r$'; we can interchange '$p \lor q$' with '$q \lor p$'; and we can reduce '$p \lor p$' to 'p'. All that matters in a continued alternation, as in a continued conjunction, is an inventory of the distinct components.

---

[1]After §3, this may be also written '$p \equiv \bar{q}$'.

Though the grouping of components is irrelevant within a continued conjunction and within a continued alternation, it is important
where conjunction and alternation are mixed; we must distinguish,
e.g., between '$pq \vee r$' and '$p(q \vee r)$'. In §5 a systematic technique will
appear whereby all complexes of conjunction, alternation, and negation can conveniently be analyzed; meanwhile, however, it is easy to
see in advance that '$pq \vee r$' and '$p(q \vee r)$' are bound to behave in
quite unlike ways. One clear point of divergence is this: '$p(q \vee r)$',
being a conjunction with 'p' as a component, cannot be true unless
'p' is true, whereas '$pq \vee r$', being an alternation with 'r' as one
component, will be true so long as 'r' is true, even if 'p' be false.

Grouping is likewise important when negation occurs in combination with conjunction or alternation. We are not likely, indeed, to
confuse '$\bar{p}q$' with '$-(pq)$', nor '$\bar{p} \vee q$' with '$-(p \vee q)$', for in the one
case only 'p' is negated while in the other case the whole compound
is negated. But what is less evident is that we must distinguish also
between '$-(pq)$' and '$\bar{p}\bar{q}$', and between '$-(p \vee q)$' and '$\bar{p} \vee \bar{q}$'. Let
us see what these distinctions are, taking 'p' as 'penicillin was flown
in' and 'q' as 'a quarantine was imposed'. There are four possible
situations:

pq: Penicillin was flown in and a quarantine was imposed.

$\bar{p}q$: Penicillin was not flown in but a quarantine was imposed.

$p\bar{q}$: Penicillin was flown in and no quarantine was imposed.

$\bar{p}\bar{q}$: Penicillin was not flown in nor was a quarantine imposed.

Now '$-(pq)$' denies just the first of the four situations, and so comes
out true in the second, third, and fourth. Thus '$-(pq)$' is quite
different from '$\bar{p}\bar{q}$', which holds in the fourth case only. As for
'$\bar{p} \vee \bar{q}$', this holds whenever one or both of '$\bar{p}$' and '$\bar{q}$' hold; hence in
the second, third, and fourth cases. We can therefore equate '$\bar{p} \vee \bar{q}$'
with '$-(pq)$'. Finally '$-(p \vee q)$' holds in the one case where '$p \vee q$'
fails—hence in the fourth case alone; so we may equate '$-(p \vee q)$'
with '$\bar{p}\bar{q}$'.

So '$-(pq)$' does not amount to '$\bar{p}\bar{q}$', but to '$\bar{p} \vee \bar{q}$'; and '$-(p \vee q)$'
does not amount to '$\bar{p} \vee \bar{q}$', but to '$\bar{p}\bar{q}$'. We may distribute the negation sign of '$-(pq)$' and '$-(p \vee q)$' over 'p' and 'q' individually only
on pain of changing conjunction to alternation and vice versa.[1]

----

[1] These equivalences are called DeMorgan's laws. See §10.

A little reflection reveals the same relationship in ordinary language. Clearly '$\bar{p}\bar{q}$', or 'Not p and not q', may be phrased 'Neither p nor q'; and it is scarcely surprising that 'Neither p nor q' should amount to '$-(p \lor q)$', the negation of 'Either p or q'. Again '$-(pq)$' may be read 'Not both p and q', and from this it is no leap to 'Either not p or not q'.

If we read the negation sign as 'it is not the case that', the distinctions of grouping become automatic.

$-(pq)$: It is not the case that both p and q.

$\bar{p}\bar{q}$: It is not the case that p and it is not the case that q.

$-(p \lor q)$: It is not the case that either p or q.

$\bar{p} \lor \bar{q}$: It is not the case that p or it is not the case that q.

Of these four the first and last, we have seen, come to the same thing; and similarly for the second and third.

EXERCISES

1. Which of the four cases:

   1 Jones ill, Smith away,   A.   2 3

   2 Jones not ill, Smith away,   B.   2 3 4

   3 Jones ill, Smith not away,

   4 Jones not ill, Smith not away

make the statement:

Jones is not ill or Smith is not away

come out true when 'or' is construed exclusively? nonexclusively?

2. Construing 'p' as 'penicillin was flown in' and 'q' as 'the quarantine was lifted', distinguish in phrasing between '$-(p \lor q)$' and '$\bar{p} \lor \bar{q}$'. Under what circumstances would one of these compounds come out true and the other false?

If the qu. was lifted, then C wd be false and D wd be true

§2. TRUTH FUNCTIONS

All that is strictly needed for a precise understanding of negation, conjunction, and alternation is stated in these laws:

'$\bar{p}$' is true if and only if 'p' is false,

'$pq...s$' is true if and only if all of 'p', 'q', ..., 's' are true,

'$p \lor q \lor ... \lor s$' is true if and only if 'p', 'q', ..., 's' are not all false.

Now it is evident from these laws that negation, conjunction, and alternation share the following important property: in order to be able to determine the truth or falsity of a negation, conjunction, or alternation, it is sufficient to know the truth or falsity of the component parts.

It is convenient to speak of truth and falsity as *truth values*; thus the truth value of a statement is said to be truth or falsity according as the statement is true or false. What we have just observed, then, is that the truth value of a negation, conjunction, or alternation is determined by the truth values of its components. This state of affairs is expressed by speaking of negation, conjunction, and alternation as *truth functions*. In general, a compound is called a *truth function of* its components if its truth value is determined in all cases by the truth values of the components. More precisely: a compound of given components is a truth function of them if its truth value remains unchanged under all changes of the components so long as the truth values of the components remain unchanged.

The property of truth-functionality which is thus enjoyed by negation, conjunction, and alternation may be better appreciated if for contrast we examine a non-truth-functional compound:

Jones died because he ate fish with ice cream.

Even agreeing that the components 'Jones died' and 'Jones ate fish with ice cream' are true, we may still dispute over the truth value of this compound. The truth value of the compound is not determined simply by the truth values of the component statements, but by these in company with further considerations; and very obscure those further considerations are. On the other hand the truth value of the conjunction:

Jones ate fish with ice cream and died

or of the alternation:

Jones ate fish with ice cream or died

or of the negation:

Jones did not die

admits of no dispute whatever once the truth values of 'Jones ate fish with ice cream' and 'Jones died' are known individually.

The compound 'p because q' is shown not to be a truth function of 'p' and 'q' by the fact that it comes out true when some truths are put for 'p' and 'q' and false when other truths are put for 'p' and 'q'. In the case of 'p v q', 'pq', and '$\bar{p}$', on the other hand, one true component is as good as another and one false component is as bad as another so far as the truth or falsity of the compound is concerned.

Any particular truth function can be adequately described by presenting a schedule showing what truth values the compound will take on for each choice of truth values for the components. Our three basic truth functions themselves, indeed, were summarily so described in the opening lines of the present section. Any unfamiliar fourth truth-functional symbol could likewise be introduced and adequately explained simply by saying what truth values on the part of the components are to make the new compound true and what ones are to make it false. A symbol 'excl-or' for the exclusive 'or', e.g., would be fully explained by a stipulation that 'p excl-or q' is to be false when 'p' and 'q' are taken as both true or both false, and true in the remaining two cases ('p' true and 'q' false or vice versa).

This question now arises: do our negation, conjunction, and alternation constitute a sufficient language for *all* truth-functional purposes? Given an explanation of a new truth-functional symbol (e.g., 'excl-or'), can we always be sure that the new symbol will be translatable into our existing notation? The answer is that negation and conjunction are always sufficient, without even alternation!

E.g., consider again 'p excl-or q'. This has been explained as false in just the case (a) where 'p' and 'q' are both true and the case (b) where 'p' and 'q' are both false. Therefore 'p excl-or q' amounts simply to denying, simultaneously, 'pq' and '$\bar{p}\bar{q}$'; for 'pq' holds in case (a) and there alone, and '$\bar{p}\bar{q}$' holds in case (b) and there alone. Therefore 'p excl-or q' amounts to:

$$-(pq) \ -(\bar{p}\bar{q}),$$

the conjunction of '$-(pq)$' and '$-(\bar{p}\bar{q})$'; for this conjunction simultaneously denies 'pq' and '$\bar{p}\bar{q}$' and nothing more. The compound 'p excl-or q' is false in the two cases where '$-(pq) \ -(\bar{p}\bar{q})$' is false, and true in the two cases where '$-(pq) - (\bar{p}\bar{q})$' is true. So the symbol 'excl-or' is superfluous; conjunction and negation suffice.

In the same way the symbol '$\vee$' of alternation itself can be seen to be superfluous. The one case where '$p \vee q$' is to be false is the case where 'p' and 'q' are both false; i.e., the case where '$\bar{p}\bar{q}$' holds. So instead of writing '$p \vee q$' we may simply deny '$\bar{p}\bar{q}$', writing '$-(\bar{p}\bar{q})$'.

These two simple examples of translating truth functions into negation and conjunction illustrate a general method which works for almost any truth function. Given a description of a truth function— i.e., given simply a schedule showing what truth values the compound is to take on for each choice of truth values for the components—we can construct a truth function out of negation and conjunction which answers the description. The general method will become evident if illustrated once more, this time with a less simple and more arbitrary example than 'excl-or' and '$\vee$'. This time a certain truth function of 'p', 'q', and 'r' is described as follows, let us say. It is to come out true in the five cases:

'p' false,	'q' true,	'r' true,
'p' true,	'q' false,	'r' true,
'p' true,	'q' true,	'r' false,
'p' false,	'q' true,	'r' false,
'p' false,	'q' false,	'r' false

and false in the remaining three cases:

'p' true,	'q' true,	'r' true,
'p' false,	'q' false,	'r' true,
'p' true,	'q' false,	'r' false.

Now these three latter cases are the cases respectively where 'pqr' is true, where '$\bar{p}\bar{q}r$' is true, and where '$p\bar{q}\bar{r}$' is true; so the compound which we are seeking is obtained simply by simultaneously negating these three unwanted cases, in a conjunction thus:

$$-(pqr) - (\bar{p}\bar{q}r) - (p\bar{q}\bar{r}).$$

Our compound thus denies, explicitly, just those cases in which it was to come out false; in all other cases it comes out true.

Clearly this same method will work for any example so long as there are *some* cases, one or more, in which the desired compound is to come out false. We thus have a routine whereby *almost* any described truth function can be written out in terms of negation and conjunction. The only truth functions which our routine fails to take care of are the ones which are to be true in *all* cases, regardless of the truth values of the components. These trivial exceptions call, then, for separate treatment; and a treatment is straightway forthcoming which is correspondingly trivial. If our problem is to express a truth function of '*p*', '*q*', '*r*', and '*s*' (say) which will come out true regardless of what truth values are assigned to '*p*', '*q*', '*r*', and '*s*', we may solve it simply by writing:

$$- (p\bar{p}qrs).$$

Clearly '*p$\bar{p}$qrs*' will come out false in all cases, on account of '*p$\bar{p}$*'; therefore '$- (p\bar{p}qrs)$' will come out true in all cases.

So it is now clear that negation and conjunction constitute a sufficient language for all truth-functional purposes. Far from needing ever to add further notations for hitherto inexpressible truth functions, we can even drop the notation '**v**' which is already at hand. But we shall not drop it, for it facilitates certain technical manipulations (cf. §§10–11).

It should be remarked that conjunction is really no less superfluous than alternation; for the fact is that an adequate notation for truth functions is constituted not only by negation and conjunction, but equally by negation and alternation. To see this it is sufficient to observe that the conjunction '*pq*' itself is translatable into terms of negation and alternation, as '$- (\bar{p} \mathbf{v} \bar{q})$'. This expression is equivalent to '*pq*', in the sense that it comes out true where '*p*' and '*q*' are both true, and otherwise false. For, '$- (\bar{p} \mathbf{v} \bar{q})$' is true if and only if '$\bar{p} \mathbf{v} \bar{q}$' is false, hence if and only if '*$\bar{p}$*' and '*$\bar{q}$*' are both false, and hence if and only if '*p*' and '*q*' are both true.

In lieu of negation and conjunction, or negation and alternation, a *single* connective can be made to suffice—viz., '|', construed as follows: '*p* | *q*' is to be true if and only if '*p*' and '*q*' are not both true. '*p* | *q*' amounts to what would be expressed in terms of conjunction and negation as '$- (pq)$'; but, if we start rather with '|' as basic, we can express '*$\bar{p}$*' in terms of '|' as '*p* | *p*', and '*pq*' as '(*p* | *q*) | (*p* | *q*)'. Another connective which would suffice by itself is '↓', or 'neither-nor'. '*p* ↓ *q*' amounts to what would be expressed in terms of conjunction and negation as '*$\bar{p}\bar{q}$*'; but, if we start rather with '↓' as basic, we can express '*$\bar{p}$*' as '*p* ↓ *p*' and '*pq*' as '(*p* ↓ *p*) ↓ (*q* ↓ *q*)'.

The logic of alternation, conjunction, and negation was investigated systematically in ancient times by the Stoics,[1] in the Middle Ages by Petrus Hispanus, Duns Scotus, and others,[1] and in modern times mainly by Boole (1847 onward) and Schröder (1877 onward). The concept of truth function becomes explicit in Frege (1879). The reductions to '|' and ' ↓ ' are due to Sheffer (1913).

EXERCISE

Obtain a compound of 'p', 'q', and 'r', using only conjunction and negation, which will come out true whenever exactly two of 'p', 'q', and 'r' are true, and otherwise false.

$$\sim \left(pqr\right) \sim \left(\bar{p}\bar{q}\bar{r}\right) \sim \left(\bar{p}\bar{q}r\right) \sim \left(\bar{p}q\bar{r}\right) \sim \left(p\bar{q}\bar{r}\right)$$

§3. THE CONDITIONAL

Besides 'and' and 'or', another connective of statements which plays an important part in everyday language is 'if-then'. A statement of the form 'if p then q' is called a *conditional*. The component in the position of 'p' here is called the *antecedent* of the conditional, and the component in the position of 'q' is called the *consequent*.

A conjunction of two statements is true, we know, just in case both components are true: and an alternation is true just in case one or both components are true. Now under what circumstances is a conditional true? Even to raise this question is to depart from everyday attitudes. An affirmation of the form 'if p then q' is commonly felt less as an affirmation of a conditional than as a conditional affirmation of the consequent.[2] If, after we have made such an affirmation, the antecedent turns out true, then we consider ourselves committed to the consequent, and are ready to acknowledge error if it proves false. If on the other hand the antecedent turns out to have been false, our conditional affirmation is as if it had never been made.

Departing from this usual attitude, however, let us think of conditionals simply as compound statements which, like conjunctions and alternations, admit as wholes of truth and falsity. Under what circumstances, then, should a conditional as a whole be regarded as true, and under what circumstances false? Where the antecedent is true, the above account of common attitudes suggests equating the truth value of the conditional with that of the consequent; thus a conditional

---

[1]See Łukasiewicz, "Zur Geschichte," cited in the Bibliography.

[2]I am indebted here to Dr. Philip Rhinelander. Elsewhere in this section I draw upon §2 of my *Mathematical Logic* (Cambridge, Mass.: Harvard University Press, 1947, reprint edition), by permission of the publishers.

with true antecedent and true consequent will count as true, and a conditional with true antecedent and false consequent will count as false. Where the antecedent is false, on the other hand, the adoption of a truth value for the conditional becomes rather more arbitrary; but the decision which proves most convenient is to regard all conditionals with false antecedents as true. The conditional 'if p then q', so construed, is written '$p \supset q$' and called the *material conditional*. It is construed as true where 'p' and 'q' are true, also where 'p' is false and 'q' true, and also where 'p' and 'q' are both false; and it is construed as false only in the remaining case, viz., where 'p' is true and 'q' false.

The sign '$\supset$', like '$\mathbf{v}$', is superfluous. We know from §2 how to construct, by means of conjunction and negation alone, a compound which shall be false in just the one case where 'p' is true and 'q' false; viz., '$-(p\bar{q})$'. We could dispense with '$\supset$' altogether, always writing '$-(p\bar{q})$' instead of '$p \supset q$'. Yet another rendering, readily seen to come to the same thing, is '$\bar{p} \mathbf{v} q$'. However, the superfluous sign '$\supset$' will prove eventually to facilitate technical manipulations.

Now consider the statement:

(1)   If anything is a vertebrate, it has a heart.

This, to begin with, is not a conditional in the sense with which we have been concerned above, for it is not really a compound of two statements 'anything is a vertebrate' and 'it has a heart'. The form of words 'it has a heart' is not a statement, true or false, which can be entertained in its own right, and be mooted to be true in case there are vertebrates. Rather, (1) must be viewed as affirming a bundle of individual conditionals: If a is a vertebrate, a has a heart; if b is a vertebrate, b has a heart; and so on. In short:

(2) No matter what x may be, if x is a vertebrate then x has a heart.

But it is important to note that, of the bundle of conditionals which (2) affirms, each individual conditional can quite suitably be interpreted as a material conditional. For, if we reflect that the material conditional '$p \supset q$' amounts to '$-(p\bar{q})$', and then rewrite (2) accordingly, we have:

No matter what x may be, it is not the case that x both is a vertebrate and does not have a heart,

14   TRUTH FUNCTIONS   [§3]

or briefly:

(3)   Nothing is a vertebrate and yet does not have a heart

—which does full justice to the original (1). So a *generalized conditional*, such as (1), can in full accordance with common usage be construed as affirming a bundle of material conditionals. Taken as a whole, the generalized conditional is a topic for Part II; it lies beyond the present phase of analysis, which concerns only the compounding of statements explicitly from blocklike components which are self-contained statements in turn.

Another use of 'if-then' which is certainly not to be construed in the fashion of '$p \supset q$' is the *contrafactual conditional*; e.g.:

(4)   If Eisenhower had run, Truman would have lost.

Whoever affirms a conditional thus in the subjunctive mood is already prepared in advance to maintain also, unconditionally, the falsehood of the antecedent, but still he thinks the conditional adds some information. Surely, then, he does not consider that such a conditional is automatically verified (like '$p \supset q$') simply by the falsity of the antecedent. This kind of conditional is not subject to the earlier remark to the effect that in ordinary usage a conditional is dropped from consideration, as empty and uninteresting, once its antecedent proves false.

The contrafactual conditional is best dissociated from the ordinary conditional in the indicative mood. Whatever the proper analysis of the contrafactual conditional may be, we may be sure in advance that it cannot be truth-functional; for, obviously ordinary usage demands that some contrafactual conditionals with false antecedents and false consequents be true and that other contrafactual conditionals with false antecedents and false consequents be false. Any adequate analysis of the contrafactual conditional must go beyond mere truth values and consider causal connections, or kindred relationships, between matters spoken of in the antecedent of the conditional and matters spoken of in the consequent. It may be wondered, indeed, whether any really coherent theory of the contrafactual conditional of ordinary usage is possible at all, particularly when we imagine trying to adjudicate between such examples as these:

If Bizet and Verdi had been compatriots, Bizet would have been
  Italian;
If Bizet and Verdi had been compatriots, Verdi would have
  been French.

The problem of contrafactual conditionals is in any case a perplexing
one,[1] and it belongs not to pure logic but to the theory of meaning
or possibly the philosophy of science. We shall not recur to it here.
So the material conditional '$p \supset q$' is put forward not as an analysis
of general conditionals such as (1), nor as an analysis of contrafactual
conditionals such as (4), but, at most, as an analysis of the ordinary
singular conditional in the indicative mood. Even as an analysis of
such conditionals the version '$p \supset q$' (or '$-(p\bar{q})$') is sometimes felt
to be unnatural, for it directs us to construe a conditional as true no
matter how irrelevant its antecedent may be to its consequent, so
long as it is not the case that the antecedent is true and the consequent
false. The following conditionals, e.g., qualify as true:

(5)   If France is in Europe then the sea is salt,

(6)   If France is in Australia then the sea is salt,

(7)   If France is in Australia then the sea is sweet.

No doubt this result seems strange; but I do not think it would be any
less strange to construe (5)–(7) as false. The strangeness is intrinsic
rather to the statements (5)–(7) themselves, regardless of their truth
or falsity; for it is not usual in practice to form conditionals out of
component statements whose truth or falsity is already known unconditionally. The reason this is not usual is readily seen: Why affirm a
long statement like (5) or (6) when we are in position to affirm the
shorter and stronger statement 'The sea is salt'? And why affirm a
long statement like (6) or (7) when we are in position to affirm the
shorter and stronger statement 'France is not in Australia'?

In practice, one who affirms 'If p then q' is ordinarily uncertain as
to the truth or falsehood individually of 'p' and of 'q' but has some
reason merely for disbelieving the combination 'p and not q' as a
whole. We say:

If Jones has malaria then he needs quinine,

[1]See Nelson Goodman, "The problem of counterfactual conditionals."

because we know about malaria but are in doubt both of Jones' ailment and of his need of quinine. Only those conditionals are worth affirming which follow from some manner of relevance between antecedent and consequent—some law, perhaps, connecting the matters which these two component statements describe. But such connection underlies the useful application of the conditional without needing to participate in its meaning. Such connection underlies the useful application of the conditional even though the meaning of the conditional be understood precisely as '$-(p\bar{q})$'.

The situation is quite similar, indeed, in the case of the connective 'or'. The statement:

France is in Europe or the sea is sweet

is as little worth affirming as (5)–(7) and for the same reason: we can save breath and yet convey more information by affirming simply 'France is in Europe'. In practice one who affirms 'p or q' is ordinarily uncertain as to the truth or falsehood individually of 'p' and of 'q', but believes merely that at least one of the two is true because of a law or some other manner of relevance connecting the matters which the two component statements describe. Yet clearly no meaning need be imputed to 'or' itself beyond the purely truth-functional meaning "not both false".

The question how well '$p \supset q$' conforms to the ordinary indicative 'if-then' is in any case one of linguistic analysis, and of little consequence for our purposes. What is important to note is that '$p \supset q$', the so-called material conditional, is to have precisely the meaning '$-(p\bar{q})$' (or '$\bar{p} \vee q$'); and it will become evident enough, as we proceed, how well adapted this concept is to purposes for which the idiom 'if-then' naturally suggests itself. In particular, as already noted, the material conditional is precisely what is wanted for the individual instances covered by a general conditional of the type (1).

No

The idiom 'p if and only if q', called the *biconditional*, amounts obviously to the conjunction of two conditionals, 'if p then q' and 'if q then p'. All that has been said regarding the interpretation of the conditional applies *mutatis mutandis* to the biconditional; whatever use 'if-then' may be put to, and whatever meaning it may be conceived to have, a corresponding use and a corresponding meaning must accrue to 'if and only if'. When in particular the conditional is construed as the material conditional '$p \supset q$', the corresponding biconditional is called the *material biconditional* and written '$p \equiv q$'. Since '$p \equiv q$' may be regarded simply as an abbreviation of '$(p \supset q)$ $(q \supset p)$', or '$-(p\bar{q}) - (q\bar{p})$', it is evidently false in two and only two cases: in the case where 'p' is true and 'q' false, and in the case where 'q' is true and 'p' false. In other words, a material biconditional is true if the components are alike in truth value (both true or both false), and it is false if the components differ in truth value.

The sign '$\equiv$', like '$\supset$' and '$\vee$', is dispensable; indeed, we have already seen that '$p \equiv q$' may be expressed in terms of conjunction and negation as '$-(p\bar{q}) - (q\bar{p})$'. But, as will appear in due course, each of these three dispensable signs plays a special part in facilitating the techniques of logic.

The material conditional goes back to Philo of Megara. It was revived in modern logic by Frege (1879) and Peirce (1885). The conditional sign '$\supset$' was used by Gergonne as early as 1816, though not in the material sense. The appropriateness of the material version was vigorously debated in ancient times (cf. Peirce, 3.441 ff; Łukasiewicz, "Zur Geschichte", p. 116), and has become a current topic of controversy as well. The issue has been clouded, however, by failure to distinguish clearly between the conditional and implication (cf. §7).

EXERCISE

It was said in a footnote in §1 that 'p or q' in the exclusive sense could be written '$p \equiv \bar{q}$'. Explain why.

$$p \equiv \bar{q} \;=\; (p \supset \bar{q})(\bar{q} \supset p) \;=\; (\bar{p} \vee \bar{q})(q \vee p)$$
$$\sim(p\bar{q}) \sim(\bar{q}p)$$

§4. GROUPING

A conspicuous type of ambiguity in ordinary language is ambiguity of grouping. The statement:

Rutgers will get the pennant and Hobart will be runner-up if Rzymski is disqualified,

e.g., is hopelessly ambiguous in point of grouping; there is no telling whether Rutgers' getting the pennant is supposed to be contingent upon Rzymski's being disqualified. If so the logical form is '$p \supset qr$', and otherwise it is 'q $(p \supset r)$', where 'p' represents 'Rzymski is disqualified', 'q' represents 'Rutgers gets the pennant', and 'r' represents 'Hobart is runner-up'.

In complex statements of ordinary language the intended grouping sometimes has to be guessed, as above, and sometimes has to be inferred from unsystematic cues, as illustrated by the following example:

(1) If the new mail-order campaign does not break the Dripsweet monopoly and restore freedom of competition then Jones will sell his car and mortgage his home.

The words 'if' and 'then' here are helpful in determining the grouping, for they frame the complex antecedent of the conditional just as clearly as if they were parentheses. But they do not show how much text is intended for the consequent of the conditional. Should we stop the consequent of the conditional at the last 'and', or construe it as running clear to the end? The proper answer is evident at a glance; however, let us note explicitly why. The clauses 'Jones will sell his car' and 'Jones will mortgage his home' have been telescoped by omitting the repetition of 'Jones will'; and this affords conclusive evidence that the 'and' here is intended to coördinate just these two clauses, rather than reaching farther back to include a whole conditional as one component of the conjunction. So we know that (1) is to be construed as a conditional, having as antecedent:

the new mail-order campaign does not break the Dripsweet monopoly and restore freedom of competition

and as consequent:

Jones will sell his car and mortgage his home.

But there remains a question of grouping within the antecedent: is the 'not' to govern the whole, or is it to goven just the part preceding 'and'? Obviously the whole. And note that the obviousness of this choice is due to much the same telescoping device as was observed before: the words 'restore freedom of competition' which follow the 'and' must, because of their fragmentary character, be construed as coördinate with 'break the Dripsweet monopoly'. So (1) is a conditional of the form '$-(pq) \supset rs$', where 'p' means 'the new mail-order campaign breaks the Dripsweet monopoly', 'q' means 'the new mail-order campaign restores freedom of competition', 'r' means 'Jones will sell his car', and 's' means 'Jones will mortgage his home'.

We all have an extraordinary finesse at ordinary language; and thus it is that the correctness of the above interpretation of (1) is bound to have been more immediately evident to all of us than the reasons why. But an examination of the reasons affords some notion of the sorts of unsystematic devices whereby ordinary language succeeds in its indications of grouping, such times as it succeeds at all.

We noted the effectiveness of 'if' and 'then' in marking the boundaries of the antecedent of a conditional. In similar fashion 'either' and 'or' may be used to mark the boundaries of the first component of an alternation; and similarly 'both' and 'and' may be used to mark the boundaries of the first component of a conjunction. Thus the ambiguity of:

> Jones came and Smith stayed or Robinson left

can, by inserting 'either' at the appropriate point, be resolved in favor of '$pq \mathbin{v} r$' or '$p(q \mathbin{v} r)$' at will:

> Either Jones came and Smith stayed or Robinson left,
> Jones came and either Smith stayed or Robinson left.

Grouping may also be indicated in ordinary language by inserting a vacuous phrase such as 'it is the case that', balanced with another 'that' to show coordination of clauses. A further device is the insertion of emphatic particles such as 'else' after 'or', or 'also' or 'furthermore' after 'and'; such reinforcement of a connective has the effect of suggesting that it is a major one.

It is evident by now that the artificial notations of logic and mathematics enjoy a great advantage over ordinary language, in their use of parentheses to indicate grouping. Parentheses show groupings unfailingly, and are simple to use. They have the further virtue of allowing complex clauses to be dropped mechanically into place without distortion of clause or of context. This particular virtue has been of incalculable importance; without it mathematics could never have developed beyond a rudimentary stage.

Even so, parentheses can be a nuisance. Unless conventions are adopted for omitting some of them, our longer formulas tend to bristle with them and we find ourselves having to count them in order to pair them off. Actually two conventions for minimizing parentheses have been tacitly in use now for some pages; it is time they were stated. One is this: the connectives 'v', '⊃', and '≡' are treated as marking a greater break than conjunction. Thus 'pq v r' is understood as having the grouping '(pq) v r', and not '$p(q$ v $r)$'—as is well suggested by the typographical pattern itself. Similarly 'p v qr' means 'p v (qr)', 'pq ⊃ r' means '(pq) ⊃ r', etc. The other convention to which we have been tacitly adhering is this: the negation sign is understood as governing as little as possible of what follows it. Thus '$-(pq)r$' means '$(-(pq))r$', not '$-((pq)r)$'; similarly '$-(p$ v $q)r$' means '$(-(p$ v $q))r$', not '$-((p$ v $q)r)$'; and so on.

An auxiliary notation of dots will now be adopted which will have the effect of eliminating *all* parentheses, so far as Part I is concerned, except those directly connected with negation. Perhaps this expedient will seem to reduce parentheses beyond the point of diminishing returns; actually its main value lies in clearing the way for a new influx of parentheses in Part II and beyond.

Dots are reinforcements. They may be thought of as a systematic counterpart of the practice in ordinary language, noted above, of inserting 'else', 'also', etc. To begin with, if we want to convey the meaning '$p(q$ v $r)$' and thus create a greater break at the point of conjunction than at the point of alternation, we shall insert a dot at the point of conjunction thus: '$p . q$ v r'. For '$(p$ v $q)r$' similarly we shall write 'p v $q . r$', for '$p(q$ ⊃ $r)$' we shall write '$p . q$ ⊃ r', etc.

Next, if at some occurrence of 'v' or '⊃' or '≡' we want to create a still greater break than is expressed by the dot of conjunction, we shall insert a dot alongside 'v' or '⊃' or '≡'; thus '$(p . q$ v $r) ≡ s$' becomes '$p . q$ v $r .≡ s$'. Just as the undotted 'v' or '⊃' or '≡' marks a greater break than the undotted conjunction, so the dotted 'v' or '⊃' or '≡' marks a greater break than the dot of conjunction. The dot which is thus added to reinforce 'v' or '⊃' or '≡' goes on the side where the reinforcement is needed; thus '$(p$ ⊃ $q . r)$ v s' becomes

'$p \supset q . r . \mathbf{v} s$', but '$p \supset (q . r \equiv s)$' becomes '$p \supset . q . r \equiv s$'. Again '$(p . q \equiv r) \mathbf{v} (p \supset q . r)$', calling for reinforcement on both sides of the central '$\mathbf{v}$', becomes '$p . q \equiv r . \mathbf{v} . p \supset q . r$'.

When we want to create a still greater break at some point of conjunction than is expressed by a dotted '$\mathbf{v}$' or '$\supset$' or '$\equiv$' in the neighborhood, we shall put a double dot '$:$' for the conjunction. When we want to create a still greater break than this at '$\mathbf{v}$' or '$\supset$' or '$\equiv$', we shall put a double dot alongside '$\mathbf{v}$' or '$\supset$' or '$\equiv$'; and so on to larger groups of dots. What might be written fully in terms of parentheses as:

$$ s \mathbf{v} (p(q \supset r) \equiv (p \mathbf{v} q)r)t, $$

e.g., is written with help of dots as follows:

$$ s \mathbf{v} : p . q \supset r . \equiv . p \mathbf{v} q . r : t. $$

In general thus the connectives '$\mathbf{v}$', '$\supset$', and '$\equiv$' fare alike. Any group of dots alongside any of these connectives represents a greater break than is represented by the same number of dots standing alone as a sign of conjunction, but a lesser break than is represented by any larger group of dots.

Parentheses will continue to be used to enclose a compound governed by a negation sign; the notations '$-(pq)$', '$-(p \mathbf{v} q)$', etc. thus persist unchanged. Dots have no power, of course, to transcend parentheses; in '$-(p \mathbf{v} q . r)s$', e.g., the dot is powerless to group the 's' with the 'r'.

EXERCISES

1. Show how the ambiguous statement:

John will play or John will sing and Mary will sing

could be rendered unambiguous, in either of two senses, by telescoping clauses.

2. Indicate and justify the appropriate grouping of:

If they either drain the swamp and reopen the road or dredge the harbor, they will provide the uplanders with a market and themselves with a bustling trade.

3. Rewrite these using dots:

$p . q/\vee \vee . \supset s . \equiv : pq \supset s . p \vee \supset s$

$(p(q \vee r) \supset s) \equiv (pq \supset s)(pr \supset s),$

$-(p \vee q)(r \vee s) \supset -(p \vee q)s.$

$\sim (p \vee q) . \vee \vee s : \supset : \sim (p \vee q) s$

4. Rewrite this using parentheses:

$p \supset . q \vee r . p \vee qs : \equiv : . \bar{q}\bar{r} \vee . \bar{p} . \bar{q} \vee \bar{s} : \supset \bar{p}.$

$(p \supset ((q \vee r)(p \vee qs))) \equiv ((\bar{q}\bar{r} \vee (\bar{p} (\bar{q} \vee \bar{s})))) \supset \bar{p})$

§5. TRUTH-VALUE ANALYSIS

In §2 a compound was said to be a truth function of its components when its truth value is determined by those of the components; and it was then observed that conjunction and negation constitute an adequate notation for truth functions. In view of this latter circumstance it is natural and convenient hereafter to conceive the notion of truth function in a purely notational way: the *truth functions of* given components are all the compounds constructed from them by means exclusively of conjunction and negation (and the dispensable further connectives '$\vee$', '$\supset$', '$\equiv$'). Thus '$\bar{p}$' is a truth function of 'p', and '$- (p \vee \bar{r}. \equiv pq) \supset r$' is a truth function of 'p', 'q', and 'r'. We also count 'p' itself a truth function of 'p'.

A truth function of letters 'p', 'q', etc., is strictly speaking not a statement, of course, since the letters are themselves not actual statements but mere dummies in place of which any desired statements may be imagined. Hereafter the letters 'p', 'q', etc., and all truth functions of them will be called *schemata* (singular: schema). More specifically they will be called *truth-functional schemata* when it becomes necessary to distinguish them from schemata involving logical devices of other than truth-functional kind. Schemata are logical diagrams of statements; the letters 'p', 'q', etc., by supplanting the component clauses of a statement, serve to blot out all the internal matter which is not germane to the broad outward structures with which our logical study is concerned.

By *interpretation* of the letter 'p' (or 'q', etc.) may be meant specification of an actual statement which is to be imagined in place of the letter. By interpretation of 'p' may also be meant simply specification of a truth value for 'p'. The two senses of 'interpretation' can be used pretty interchangeably because each actual statement S has a specific truth value (known or unknown) and that truth value is all that matters to the truth value of any truth function of S.

A convenient graphic method of imposing interpretations, of the second of the above varieties, is simply to supplant the letters in a schema by the mark 'T' for truths and '⊥' for falsehoods.[1] Computing then directly with these marks, we can quickly determine what truth value the whole schema takes on under the imposed interpretations. Thus, suppose our problem is to determine the truth value of the schema '$-(pq \vee \bar{p}\bar{q})$' for the case where '$p$' is interpreted as true and 'q' as false. We simply put 'T' for 'p' and '⊥' for 'q' in the schema, getting '$-(\text{T}⊥ \vee \overline{\text{T}⊥})$'. But, since 'T̄' reduces to '⊥' and '⊥̄' to 'T', this becomes '$-(\text{T}⊥ \vee ⊥\text{T})$'. Further, since a conjunction with false component is false, 'T⊥' reduces to '⊥' and so does '⊥T'. So the whole is now down to '$-(⊥ \vee ⊥)$'. But, an alternation of falsehoods being false, '⊥ ∨ ⊥' reduces to '⊥'; the whole thus becomes 'T', or 'T'. This outcome means that our original schema '$-(pq \vee \bar{p}\bar{q})$' comes out true when '$p$' is interpreted as true and 'q' as false.

The process whereby '$-(\text{T}⊥ \vee \overline{\text{T}⊥})$' was reduced to 'T' will be called *resolution*. The simplest of the steps involved in resolution, viz. reduction of 'T̄' to '⊥' and of '⊥̄' to 'T', will always be tacit hereafter; we shall never write 'T̄' nor '⊥̄', but immediately '⊥' and 'T', as if the notation of negation as applied to 'T' and '⊥' consisted simply in inverting. The other steps of resolution illustrated in the above example were reduction of 'T⊥', '⊥T', and '⊥ ∨ ⊥' to '⊥'. These steps, and all further ones for which there might be occasion in other examples, may conveniently be codified in the form of eight *rules of resolution*:

(i) *Delete 'T' as component of conjunction.* (Thus 'TTT' reduces to 'TT' and thence to 'T'; '⊥T' reduces to '⊥'; etc. Reason: a conjunction with a true component is true or false according as the rest of it is true or false.)

(ii) *Delete '⊥' as component of alternation.* (Thus '⊥ ∨ ⊥ ∨ ⊥' re-

---

[1] We need not fumble for a pronunciation of '⊥' coördinate with the pronunciation 'tee' of 'T', for the words 'true' and 'false' themselves are short enough to serve conveniently as pronunciations of the two signs. Before deploring my preference of '⊥' to the initial 'F' of 'false', note the urgent need of 'F' for other purposes in Parts II–IV.

duces to '⊥ ∨ ⊥' and thence to '⊥'; '⊥ ∨ ⊤' reduces to '⊤'; etc. Reason: an alternation with a false component is true or false according as the rest of it is true or false.)

    (iii) *Reduce a conjunction with '⊥' as component to '⊥'.*

    (iv) *Reduce an alternation with '⊤' as component to '⊤'.*

    (v) *If a conditional has '⊤' as antecedent or consequent, drop the antecedent.* (Thus '⊤ ⊃ ⊤' and '⊥ ⊃ ⊤' reduce to '⊤', and '⊤ ⊃ ⊥' reduces to '⊥'. Reason: a conditional with true antecedent is true or false according as the consequent is true or false; and a conditional with true consequent is true.)

    (vi) *If a conditional has '⊥' as antecedent or consequent, negate the antecedent and drop the consequent.* (Thus '⊥ ⊃ ⊤' and '⊥ ⊃ ⊥' reduce to '⊤', and '⊤ ⊃ ⊥' reduces to '⊥'. Reason: a conditional with false antecedent is true, and a conditional with false consequent is true or false according as the antecedent is false or true.)

    (vii) *Drop '⊤' as component of a biconditional.* (Thus '⊤ ≡ ⊤' reduces to '⊤', and '⊤ ≡ ⊥' and '⊥ ≡ ⊤' reduce to '⊥'.)

    (viii) *Drop '⊥' as component of a biconditional and negate the other side.* (Thus '⊥ ≡ ⊥' reduces to '⊤', and '⊤ ≡ ⊥' and '⊥ ≡ ⊤' reduce to '⊥'.)

Set up according to these rules, our original example of resolution amounts to no more than this:

$$-(\top\!\bot \lor \bot\!\top)$$
$$-(\bot \lor \bot) \quad \text{(changing '⊤⊥' and '⊥⊤' each to '⊥' by (i) or (iii))}$$
$$\top \quad\quad \text{(changing '⊥ ∨ ⊥' to '⊥' by (ii))}$$

Turning to a more elaborate example, let us determine the truth value of '$pq \lor \bar{p}\bar{r} . \supset . q \equiv r$' for the case where '$p$' and '$q$' are interpreted as false and 'r' as true.

$$\bot\!\bot \lor \top\!\bot . \supset . \bot \equiv \top$$
$$\bot\!\bot \lor \top\!\bot . \supset \bot \quad \text{(changing '⊥ ≡ ⊤' to '⊥' by (vii) or (viii))}$$
$$-(\bot\!\bot \lor \top\!\bot) \quad \text{(by (vi))}$$
$$-(\bot \lor \bot) \quad \text{(by (iii) twice)}$$
$$\top \quad \text{(changing '⊥ ∨ ⊥' to '⊥' by (ii))}$$

Thus '$pq \lor \bar{p}\bar{r} . \supset . q \equiv r$' comes out true when false statements are put for 'p' and 'q' and a true one for 'r'.

Let us feign contact with reality by considering an actual statement of the form 'pq v $\bar{p}\bar{r}$.⊃. $q \equiv r$':

(1) If either the resident and the deputy resident both resign or the resident neither resigns nor exposes the *chargé d'affaires*, in either case the deputy resident will resign if and only if the resident exposes the *chargé d'affaires*.

What we have found is that (1) comes out true in the case where neither the resident nor the deputy resident resigns and the resident exposes the *chargé d'affaires*.

We have evaluated the schema 'pq v $\bar{p}\bar{r}$.⊃. $q \equiv r$' for one interpretation: 'p' and 'q' as false and 'r' as true. There remain seven other interpretations that might be considered: 'p', 'q', and 'r' all true, 'p' and 'q' true and 'r' false, 'p' and 'r' true and 'q' false, and so on. The eight cases can be systematically explored, with evaluation of the schema for each case, by the following method. First we put '⊤' for 'p', leaving 'q' and 'r' unchanged, and make all possible resolutions by (i)–(viii):

$$\top q \text{ v } \bot \bar{r} .⊃. q \equiv r$$
$$q \text{ v } \bot \bar{r} .⊃. q \equiv r \quad \text{(changing '}\top q\text{' to '}q\text{' by (i))}$$
$$q \text{ v } \bot .⊃. q \equiv r \quad \text{(changing '}\bot \bar{r}\text{' to '}\bot\text{' by (iii))}$$
$$q ⊃. q \equiv r \quad \text{(changing '}q \text{ v } \bot\text{' to '}q\text{' by (ii))}$$

Then we put '⊤' for 'q' in this result and resolve further:

$$\top ⊃. \top \equiv r$$
$$\top \equiv r \quad \text{(by (v))}$$
$$r \quad \text{(by (vii))}$$

We have now found that whenever 'p' and 'q' are both interpreted as true, our original schema resolves to 'r'—hence becomes true or false according as 'r' is true or false. This disposes of two of the eight cases. Next we return to our intermediate result '$q ⊃. q \equiv r$' and put '⊥' for 'q':

$$\bot ⊃. \bot \equiv r$$
$$\top \quad \text{(by (vi))}$$

This shows that our original schema comes out true whenever 'p' is interpreted as true and 'q' as false, regardless of 'r'. This disposes of two more of our eight cases. Now we go all the way back to our original schema and put '⊥' for 'p':

$$\underline{\mathrm{L}}q \vee \overline{\mathrm{T}r} . \supset . q \equiv r$$
$$\perp \vee \overline{\mathrm{T}r} . \supset . q \equiv r \quad \text{(by (iii))}$$
$$\overline{\mathrm{T}r} \supset . q \equiv r \quad \text{(by (ii))}$$
$$\bar{r} \supset . q \equiv r \quad \text{(by (i))}$$

Putting '⊤' for 'r' here and resolving further, we have:

$$\perp \supset . q \equiv \top$$
$$\top \quad \text{(by (vi))}$$

This shows that our original schema comes out true whenever 'p' is interpreted as false and 'r' as true, regardless of 'q'. Two more cases are disposed of. Finally we go back to '$\bar{r} \supset . q \equiv r$' and put '⊥' for '$r$':

$$\top \supset . q \equiv \perp$$
$$q \equiv \perp \quad \text{(by (v))}$$
$$\bar{q} \quad \text{(by (viii))}$$

So whenever 'p' and 'r' are both interpreted as false, our schema resolves to '$\bar{q}$'—hence becomes false or true according as 'q' is interpreted as true or false.

The foregoing analysis might conveniently have been carried out in a single array as follows:

$$pq \vee \bar{p}\bar{r} . \supset . q \equiv r$$

$\top q \vee \underline{\mathrm{L}}\bar{r} . \supset . q \equiv r$	$\underline{\mathrm{L}}q \vee \overline{\mathrm{T}r} . \supset . q \equiv r$
$q \vee \underline{\mathrm{L}}\bar{r} . \supset . q \equiv r$	$\perp \vee \overline{\mathrm{T}r} . \supset . q \equiv r$
$q \vee \perp . \supset . q \equiv r$	$\overline{\mathrm{T}r} \supset . q \equiv r$
$q \supset . q \equiv r$	$\bar{r} \supset . q \equiv r$
$\top \supset . \top \equiv r \quad \perp \supset . \perp \equiv r$	$\perp \supset . q \equiv \top \quad \top \supset . q \equiv \perp$
$\top \equiv r \qquad \top$	$\top \qquad q \equiv \perp$
r	$\bar{q}$
$\top \quad \perp$	$\perp \quad \top$

This is called a *truth-value analysis*. The general method may be summed up as follows. We make a grand dichotomy of cases by putting first '⊤' and then '⊥' for some chosen letter, say 'p'. The expressions thus formed are the respective headings of a bipartite analysis.

Then we resolve both expressions, by (i)–(viii), until we end up with '⊤' or '⊥' or some schema. If a schema results, we then proceed to develop, under that schema, a new bipartite analysis with respect to a chosen one of its letters. We continue thus until all end results are single marks — '⊤' or '⊥'. Each end result shows what truth value the original schema will take on when its letters are interpreted according to the marks which have there supplanted them.

Actually all intermediate steps of resolution are so obvious, and so readily reconstructed at will, that they may hereafter be left to the imagination. Thus the above truth-value analysis would in future be condensed as follows:

$$pq \vee \bar{p}\bar{r} .\supset. q \equiv r$$

$$\begin{array}{cc}
\top q \vee \bot \bar{r} .\supset. q \equiv r & \qquad \bot q \vee \top \bar{r} .\supset. q \equiv r \\
q \supset. q \equiv r & \qquad \bar{r} \supset. q \equiv r \\
\top \supset. \top \equiv r \quad \bot \supset. \bot \equiv r & \qquad \bot \supset. q \equiv \top \quad \top \supset. q \equiv \bot \\
r \qquad\qquad \top & \qquad \top \qquad\qquad \bar{q} \\
\top \quad \bot & \qquad\qquad\qquad \bot \quad \top
\end{array}$$

There is no need always to choose '*p*' as the first letter for which to put '⊤' and '⊥'. It is better to choose the letter which has the most repetitions, if repetitions there be, and to adhere to this plan also at each later stage. Thus it was, indeed, that whereas in the second stage on the left side of the above analysis '*q*' was chosen for replacement by '⊤' and '⊥', on the other hand in the second stage on the right side '*r*' was chosen. This strategy tends to hasten the disappearance of letters, and thus to minimize work.

A method of truth-value analysis which has been usual in the literature since 1920–21 (Łukasiewicz, Post, Wittgenstein) is that of *truth tables*. Under this method all combinations of truth values for the letters of a schema are listed, and for each combination the truth value of the schema is computed by a process of reasoning tantamount to what I have called resolution. This method has the shortcoming of cumbersomeness when many letters are involved. Where '*p*', '*q*', and '*r*' are concerned, eight combinations of truth values have to be dealt with. Where four letters are concerned, as in the example three pages hence, sixteen combinations have to be dealt with. The advantage of the technique presented in the present pages is that the various combinations of truth values concerned tend to group themselves to form a smaller number of cases.

EXERCISES

1. Suppose they drain the swamp but neither reopen the road nor dredge the harbor nor provide the uplanders with a market; and suppose nevertheless they do provide themselves with a bustling trade. Determine, under these circumstances, the truth value of the statement in Exercise 2 of the preceding section. Method: represent the components as 'p', 'q', 'r', 's', 't'; put 'T' and '⊥' appropriately for the letters; resolve.

2. Make a truth-value analysis of each of the schemata:

$$p \supset pq, \qquad p \supset . p \vee q, \qquad p \supset . p \supset q, \qquad p \supset . p \equiv q.$$

Present your work in full, showing intermediate steps of resolution; afterward circle those intermediate lines for omission, to show how the work would look in the condensed style.

3. For comparison perform two truth-value analyses of '$p \supset q . q \supset r$', first following and then flouting the strategy of choosing the most frequent letter.

§6. CONSISTENCY AND VALIDITY

A truth-functional schema is called *consistent* if it comes out true under some interpretation of its letters; otherwise *inconsistent*. A truth-functional schema is called *valid* if it comes out true under every interpretation of its letters. The schema '$p\bar{q}$', for example, is consistent, for it comes out true when 'p' is interpreted as true and 'q' as false; but it is not valid, since there are other interpretations of 'p' and 'q' which make it come out false.

The way to test a truth-functional schema for validity and consistency is obvious: we carry out a truth-value analysis and see whether we get 'T' in every case (showing validity) or '⊥' in every case (showing inconsistency) or neither. Two examples of validity and inconsistency are respectively '$p \supset p$' and '$p\bar{p}$':

$$
\begin{array}{cc}
p \supset p & p\bar{p} \\
\mathsf{T} \supset \mathsf{T} \qquad \bot \supset \bot & \mathsf{T}\bot \qquad \bot\mathsf{T} \\
\mathsf{T} \qquad\qquad \mathsf{T} & \bot \qquad\qquad \bot
\end{array}
$$

Valid schemata were already exploited at one point in the argument of §2, where '$-(p\bar{p}qrs)$' was cited.

$$-(p\bar{p}qrs)$$

$$-(\top\!\!\downarrow qrs) \qquad\qquad -(\downarrow\!\!\top qrs)$$
$$\top \qquad\qquad\qquad\qquad \top$$

In general, obviously, a schema is valid if and only if its negation is inconsistent, and a schema is inconsistent if and only if its negation is valid. Thus the negations '$-(p\bar{p})$' and '$-(p\bar{p}qrs)$' of the inconsistent schemata '$p\bar{p}$' and '$p\bar{p}qrs$' are valid, and the negation '$-(p \supset p)$' of the valid schema '$p \supset p$' is inconsistent.

A test of validity may be stopped short, with negative outcome, as soon as we come to a case yielding '$\downarrow$'; and a test of consistency may be stopped, with affirmative outcome, as soon as we come to a case yielding '$\top$'. Thus the analysis of '$pq \vee \bar{p}\bar{r} . \supset . q \equiv r$' in §5 might, if we had been interested only in consistency and validity, have been discontinued in this fragmentary state:

$$pq \vee \bar{p}\bar{r} . \supset . q \equiv r$$
$$\top q \vee \downarrow\bar{r} . \supset . q \equiv r$$
$$q \supset . q \equiv r$$
$$\top \supset . \top \equiv r$$
$$r$$
$$\top \qquad \perp$$

This much already suffices to show both that '$pq \vee \bar{p}\bar{r} . \supset . q \equiv r$' is consistent and that it is not valid.

'Validity' is not to be thought of as a term of praise. When a schema is valid, any statement whose form that schema depicts is bound to be, in some sense, trivial. It will be trivial in the sense that it conveys no real information regarding the subject matter whereof its component clauses speak. The statement:

(1)   If the Bruins win then the Bruins win,

whose form is depicted in the valid schema '$p \supset p$', gives us no information about the outcome of the game; indeed, any other clause, on any other subject matter, could be used here in place of 'the Bruins win' with as much and as little effect. Valid schemata are important not as an end but as a means. We shall see in another page or two that simple cases of validity afford short-cuts in the truth-value analysis of other schemata; and we shall see in the next section that the determination of certain complex cases of validity is tantamount to determining relations of equivalence and implication between other schemata.

Though the statements illustrative of valid schemata are always trivial in the sense noted above, they are not always trivial in the sense of being, like (1), recognizable on sight. Valid schemata may run to any length and any degree of complexity; and some even of moderate length cannot be recognized as valid without substantial computation. The same is true of consistency. Below is a schema of quite moderate complexity which, though by no means recognizable as valid on sight, is found to be valid by truth-value analysis.

$$pq \vee p\bar{r} \vee \bar{p}r \vee \bar{p}s \vee \bar{q}r \vee \bar{r}s$$

$$\lceil q \vee \lceil \bar{r} \vee \lfloor r \vee \lfloor s \vee \bar{q}r \vee \bar{r}s \qquad \lfloor q \vee \lfloor \bar{r} \vee \lceil r \vee \lceil s \vee \bar{q}r \vee \bar{r}s$$

$$q \vee \bar{r} \vee \bar{q}r \vee \bar{r}s \qquad r \vee s \vee \bar{q}r \vee \bar{r}s$$

$$q \vee \lfloor \vee \bar{q}\rceil \vee \lfloor \bar{s} \quad q \vee \lceil \vee \bar{q}\lfloor \vee \lceil\bar{s} \quad \lceil \vee s \vee \bar{q}\rceil \vee \lfloor\bar{s} \quad \lfloor \vee s \vee \bar{q}\lfloor \vee \lceil\bar{s}$$

$$q \vee \bar{q} \qquad \lceil \qquad \lceil \qquad s \vee \bar{s}$$

$$\lceil \vee \lfloor \quad \lfloor \vee \lceil \qquad\qquad\qquad \lceil \vee \lfloor \quad \lfloor \vee \lceil$$

$$\lceil \qquad \lceil \qquad\qquad\qquad\qquad \lceil \qquad \lceil$$

The test shows validity, but unimplimented inspection would have availed little.

Taking advantage of the really evident cases of validity and inconsistency, however, we may speed up our truth-value analyses hereafter. Schemata like '$q \vee \bar{q}$' and '$s \vee \bar{s}$', which emerged in the course of the above analysis, are now known to be valid, and hence to reduce to '⌐' in all cases; hereafter, therefore, we may as well agree to reduce any such result directly to '⌐', without further ceremony. Thus, in place of the configurations:

$$q \vee \bar{q} \qquad\qquad\qquad s \vee \bar{s}$$

$$\lceil \vee \lfloor \quad \lfloor \vee \lceil \qquad\qquad \lceil \vee \lfloor \quad \lfloor \vee \lceil$$

$$\lceil \qquad \lceil \qquad\qquad\qquad \lceil \qquad \lceil$$

which appeared in the lower corners of the above analysis, we shall in future write simply:

$$q \vee \bar{q} \qquad\qquad\qquad s \vee \bar{s}$$

$$\lceil \qquad\qquad\qquad\qquad \lceil$$

In general, any such patently valid schema may be reduced immediately to '⊤' whenever it occurs in a truth-value analysis, whether in isolation or as component of a longer formula. Similarly any patently inconsistent schema such as '$p\bar{p}$', '$p\bar{p}qrs$', '$\bar{q}pqr$', etc. may be reduced immediately to '⊥' whenever it turns up in an analysis.

With these shortcuts in mind, let us analyze a really complex schema:

$$p \text{ v } q . p \text{ v } \bar{q} . \text{v } \bar{p}q := q .:\supset. pr \text{ v } \bar{p}r$$

$$\begin{array}{ll} \top vq.\top v\bar{q}.\text{v}\llcorner q:\equiv q.:\supset.\top rv\llcorner \bar{r} & \qquad \llcorner vq.\llcorner v\bar{q}.\text{v}\top q:\equiv q.:\supset.\llcorner rv\llcorner \bar{r} \\ \quad q \supset. r \text{ v } \bar{r} & \qquad\qquad -(q\bar{q} \text{ v } q .\equiv q) \\ \qquad q \supset \top & \qquad\qquad -(\llcorner \text{ v } q .\equiv q) \\ \qquad\quad \top & \qquad\qquad -(q \equiv q) \\ & \qquad\qquad\qquad \llcorner \end{array}$$

The reduction of the left side to '$q \supset . r \text{ v } \bar{r}$' proceeded by various steps of resolution, as usual. But in the next step, using our new shortcut, we put '⊤' for the patently valid '$r \text{ v } \bar{r}$' and got '$q \supset \top$', which then resolved into '⊤'. On the right-hand side of the analysis, the reduction to '$-(q\bar{q} \text{ v } q .\equiv q)$' proceeded by resolution as usual; then, using our new shortcut, we put '⊥' for the patently inconsistent '$q\bar{q}$', and got '$-(\bot \text{ v } q .\equiv q)$', which resolved in turn into '$-(q \equiv q)$'. Here, using our new shortcut again, we put '⊤' for the patently valid '$q \equiv q$' and conclude our work.

Where to draw the line between what is patently valid or inconsistent and what is not patently so is quite arbitrary. The '$-(q\bar{q} \text{ v } q .\equiv q)$' in the right-hand part of the above analysis is itself an inconsistent schema, and so might have been supplanted immediately by '⊥' if its inconsistency had been felt to be sufficiently obvious. Similarly the '$q \supset . r \text{ v } \bar{r}$' in the left-hand part of the analysis might have been supplanted directly by '⊤'. For uniformity of classroom work, however, it is convenient to limit the category of "patently inconsistent" schemata to conjunctions such as '$p\bar{p}$', '$\bar{q}pqr$', etc., in which some letter appears both plain and negated as component of the conjunction. It is convenient to limit the category of "patently valid" schemata to these two kinds: (a) alternations such as '$p \text{ v } \bar{p}$', '$\bar{q} \text{ v } p \text{ v } q \text{ v } r$', etc., in which some letter appears both plain and negated as component of the alternation; (b) conditionals or biconditionals whose two sides are alike, e.g., '$q \equiv q$', '$qr \equiv qr$', '$p \text{ v } q .\supset. p \text{ v } q$'.

It is only to such schemata, then, that our shortcut is to be applied; these, and only these, will be reduced appropriately to '⊥' or '⊤' on sight.

From the validity of a schema we may infer, without separate test, the validity of any schema which is formed from it by *substitution*. From the validity, e.g., of 'p v $\bar{p}$' we may infer the validity of the schema 'qr v $-(qr)$', which is formed from 'p v $\bar{p}$' by substituting 'qr' for 'p'. This is apparent from the definition of validity. Validity of 'p v $\bar{p}$' means that 'p v $\bar{p}$' is bound to come out true no matter what statement be put for 'p'; so it follows, as a special case, that 'qr v $-(qr)$' will come out true no matter what statement 'qr' be made to represent—hence no matter what statements be put for 'q' and 'r'. *Substitution of schemata for letters preserves validity.* But it is clearly essential that 'substitution for a letter' be construed as meaning uniform substitution for every occurrence of the letter. From the validity of 'p v $\bar{p}$', e.g., we are not entitled to infer validity of 'qr v $\bar{p}$', nor of 'qr v $-(qs)$'. It is permissible to put the same or different schemata for different letters, but we must always put the same schema for recurrences of the same letter.

Since inconsistency of a schema is simply validity of its negation, we may conclude further that *substitution of schemata for letters preserves inconsistency.* But note on the other hand that substitution cannot be depended upon to preserve consistency. The mere fact that the more general schema has *some* true instances (which is what consistency means) gives us no reason to suppose that the special case will share any of the true instances. The schema 'p v pq', e.g., is consistent (as may be verified by truth-value analysis), but substitution of '$r\bar{r}$' for 'p' therein yields an inconsistent schema '$r\bar{r}$ v $r\bar{r}q$'. Similarly, substitution for a letter in a nonvalid schema cannot be depended upon to yield a nonvalid schema; it may yield a valid or nonvalid one.

EXERCISES

1. Test each of these for validity by truth-value analysis, exploiting the new short-cut regarding patently valid and patently inconsistent clauses:

$p \supset q$ .v. $q \supset p$, p v qr v. $\bar{p}$. $\bar{q}$ v $\bar{r}$,

$p \equiv q$ .v. $p \equiv \bar{q}$, $p \equiv q$ .v. $q \equiv r$ .v. $p \equiv r$.

2. In each of the above four schemata, substitute 'p v q' for 'p'. This is chiefly an exercise in adjusting dots to preserve proper grouping.

3. Given a schema, can it ever happen that by one set of substitutions we get a valid schema from it, and by another set of substitutions an inconsistent schema? Illustrate or explain.

§7. IMPLICATION

The most conspicuous purpose of logic, in its applications to science and everyday discourse, is the justification and criticism of inference. Logic is largely concerned with devising techniques for showing that a given statement does, or does not, "follow logically" from another. The statement 'No dropped freshman is eligible for the Bowdoin Prize', e.g., follows logically from 'No freshman is eligible for the Bowdoin or Bechtel Prize'; and the statement 'Cassius is not both lean and hungry' follows logically from 'Cassius is not hungry'. Now the first of these two examples lies beyond the scope of the truth-functional part of logic with which we are concerned in Part I, but the second example can already be treated here.

From the point of view of logical theory, the fact that the statement 'Cassius is not both lean and hungry' follows from 'Cassius is not hungry' is conveniently analyzed into these two circumstances: (a) the two statements have the respective logical forms '$-(pq)$' and '$\bar{q}$' (with 'Cassius is lean' and 'Cassius is hungry' supplanting 'p' and 'q'); and (b) there are no two statements which, put respectively for 'p' and 'q', make '$\bar{q}$' true and '$-(pq)$' false. Circumstance (b) will hereafter be phrased in this way: '$\bar{q}$' *implies* '$-(pq)$'. In general, one truth-functional schema is said to *imply* another if there is no way of so interpreting the letters as to make the first schema true and the second false.

Whether a truth-functional schema S_1 implies another, S_2, can be decided always by taking S_1 as antecedent and S_2 as consequent of a conditional, and testing the conditional for validity. For, according to our definition, S_1 implies S_2 if and only if no interpretation makes S_1 true and S_2 false, hence if and only if no interpretation falsifies the material conditional whose antecedent is S_1 and whose consequent is

S_2. In a word, *implication is validity of the conditional.* To determine that '*q*' implies '$-(pq)$', e.g., we check the validity of the corresponding conditional:

$$\bar{q} \supset -(pq)$$

$$\bot \supset -(p\top) \qquad\qquad \top \supset -(p\bot)$$
$$\top \qquad\qquad\qquad\qquad \top$$

Next let us note an example which turns out negatively. That '*p* v *q*' does *not* imply '*pq*' is found thus:

$$p \vee q \, . \supset pq$$

$$\top \vee q \, . \supset \top q$$
$$q$$
$$\top \qquad \bot$$

Once having come out with a '$\bot$', we discontinue our test in the knowledge that '*p* v *q* . $\supset$ *pq*' is not valid; i.e., that '*p* v *q*' does not imply '*pq*'. This result does not mean that '*p* v *q* . $\supset$ *pq*' does not come out true under *some* interpretations of '*p*' and '*q*', nor does it mean that '*p* v *q*' and '*pq*' themselves do not come out simultaneously true under some interpretations of '*p*' and '*q*'. The failure of implication means merely that *some* interpretations which make '*p* v *q*' true make '*pq*' false; or, what comes to the same thing, that some interpretations make '*p* v *q* . $\supset$ *pq*' false.

By reflecting briefly on our methods of testing for implication, validity, and inconsistency, one sees that these four general laws hold:

(i) Any schema implies itself.

(ii) If one schema implies a second and the second a third then the first implies the third.

(iii) An inconsistent schema implies every schema and is implied by inconsistent ones only.

(iv) A valid schema is implied by every schema and implies valid ones only.

An easy familiarity with simple cases of implication between truth-functional schemata will be found to facilitate construction of proofs at even as advanced a level of logic as §§29 ff. At that stage it will not be enough to be able to answer raised questions of implication, which we can do by truth-value analysis as above; we must also be able to raise the questions. We must be able to think up schemata which imply or are implied by a given schema and promise well as links in a proposed chain of argument. Such products of imagination can be checked mechanically by truth-value analysis, but thinking them up is an unmechanical activity. Facility in it depends on grasping the sense of simple schemata clearly enough to be able, given a schema, to conjure up quite an array of fairly simple variants which imply or are implied by it. Given '$p \lor q$', it should occur to us immediately that 'p' and 'q' and 'pq' and '$\bar{p} \supset q$' imply it and that '$p \lor q \lor r$' and '$\bar{p} \supset q$' are implied by it. Given '$p \supset q$', it should occur to us immediately that each of:

$$\bar{p}, \quad q, \quad qr, \quad \bar{p} \lor q, \quad \bar{q} \supset \bar{p}, \quad p \supset qr, \quad p \lor r . \supset q$$

implies it and that each of:

$$\bar{p} \lor q, \quad \bar{q} \supset \bar{p}, \quad p \supset . q \lor r, \quad p \supset q . \lor r$$

is implied by it. Such flashes need not be highly accurate, for we can check each hunch afterward by truth-value analysis. What is important is that they be prolific, and accurate enough to spare excessive lost motion.

No doubt repertoire is an aid to virtuosity in contriving implications, but understanding is the principal thing. When simple schemata are sufficiently transparent to us, we can see through them by the light of pure reason to other schemata which must come out true if these do, or which can not come out true unless these do. It is well to reflect upon the above examples and succeeding ones until it becomes obvious from the sheer meanings of signs that the implications must hold.

Readiness with implications is aided also, no doubt, by ease of checking. Accordingly a quick implication test called the *fell swoop* will now be explained which, though not general, works for an important range of simple cases.

Some schemata are visibly verifiable by one and only one interpretation of their letters. E.g., '$p\bar{q}$' comes out true when and only when 'T' is put for 'p' and '⊥' for 'q'. Now when S is such a schema, the question whether S implies a schema S' can be settled simply by supplanting 'p', 'q', etc., in S' by the values which make for truth of S, and resolving. If we come out with 'T' or a valid schema, then S implies S'; otherwise not. E.g., to determine that '$p\bar{q}$' implies

'$p \supset q . \supset r$' we put '$\top$' for 'p' and '$\bot$' for 'q' in '$p \supset q . \supset r$' and resolve the result '$\top \supset \bot . \supset r$', getting '$\top$'.

In particular a fell swoop will settle any question of implication on the part of 'p' or '$\bar{p}$'. To find that 'p' implies '$q \supset p$' we put '$\top$' for 'p' in '$q \supset p$' and resolve the result '$q \supset \top$' to '$\top$'. To find that 'p' implies '$p \supset q . \supset q$' we put '$\top$' for 'p' in '$p \supset q . \supset q$' and resolve the result '$\top \supset q . \supset q$', coming out with the valid schema '$q \supset q$'. To find that '$\bar{q}$' implies '$-(pq)$', which was the example of Cassius, we could have simply put '$\bot$' for 'q' in '$-(pq)$' and resolved the result '$-(p\bot)$' to '$\top$'.

Some schemata, on the other hand, are visibly falsifiable by one and only one interpretation of their letters. E.g., '$-(pr)$' comes out false when and only when '$\top$' is put for 'p' and 'r'; '$p \supset r$' comes out false when and only when '$\top$' is put for 'p' and '$\bot$' for 'r'; '$p \vee r$' comes out false when and only when '$\bot$' is put for 'p' and 'r'; '$pr \supset s$' comes out false when and only when '$\top$' is put for 'p' and 'r' and '$\bot$' for 's'; and '$p \supset . r \vee s$' comes out false when and only when '$\top$' is put for 'p' and '$\bot$' for 'r' and 's'. Now when S' is a schema thus falsifiable by one and only one interpretation, the question whether a schema S implies S' can be settled simply by supplanting 'p', 'q', etc. in S by the values which make for falsity of S', and resolving. If we come out with '$\bot$' or an inconsistent schema, then S implies S'; otherwise not. For, the implication can fail only through truth of S where S' is false.

E.g., to find that '$p \supset q . q \supset r$' implies '$p \supset r$' we put '$\top$' for '$p$' and '$\bot$' for '$r$' in '$p \supset q . q \supset r$' and resolve the result '$\top \supset q . q \supset \bot$', getting the inconsistent schema '$q\bar{q}$'. To find that '$p \vee q . q \supset r$' implies '$p \vee r$' we put '$\bot$' for 'p' and 'r' in '$p \vee q . q \supset r$' and resolve, getting '$q\bar{q}$' again. To find that '$p \supset q . qr \supset s$' implies '$pr \supset s$' we put '$\top$' for '$p$' and '$r$' and '$\bot$' for '$s$' in '$p \supset q . qr \supset s$' and resolve.

In particular this backward variety of the fell swoop is convenient when we want to know whether a schema S implies 'p', or '$\bar{p}$'. To find that '$pq \vee p\bar{q}$' implies 'p' we put '$\bot$' for 'p' in '$pq \vee p\bar{q}$' and resolve the result '$\bot q \vee \bot\bar{q}$', getting '$\bot$'. To find that '$p \vee q . p \vee \bar{q}$' implies '$p$' we put '$\bot$' for '$p$' in '$p \vee q . p \vee \bar{q}$' and resolve the result '$\bot \vee q . \bot \vee \bar{q}$', getting the inconsistent schema '$q\bar{q}$'.

Fell swoops are possible only where the schema which is to do the implying clearly comes out true under one and only one interpretation, or else the schema which is to be implied comes out false under one and only one interpretation. The general test of implication, applicable in every case, is truth-value analysis of the conditional; the *full sweep* as opposed to the fell swoop.

Implication may be made to relate statements as well as schemata. When one schema implies another, and a pair of statements are obtained from the schemata by interpretation, we may say by extension that the one statement implies the other. Thus, besides saying that '$\bar{q}$' implies '$-(pq)$', we may make interpretations and say that 'Cassius is not hungry' implies 'Cassius is not lean and hungry'. But it is well here to say more explicitly that the one statement implies the other *truth-functionally*, adding the adverb as a reminder that the schemata which brought the two statements into an implication relationship were truth-functional schemata rather than schemata of kinds which have yet to be taken up in Part II and beyond. Truth-functional implication is, in other words, the relation which one statement bears to another when the second follows from the first by logical considerations within the scope of the logic of truth functions. The terms 'truth-functionally valid' and 'truth-functionally inconsistent' may be applied to statements in similar fashion.

Implication, as we have seen, is intimately related to the conditional. Implication holds when and only when the conditional is valid. This important connection has engendered a tendency among writers on logic to adopt 'implies', confusingly, as a reading of the conditional sign '⊃' itself. Then, since '$p \supset q$' has been explained as coming out true whenever 'p' is interpreted as false or 'q' as true, it is concluded with an air of paradox that every falsehood implies every statement and that every truth is implied by every statement. It is not perceived that '⊃' is at best an approximation to 'if-then', not to 'implies'.

In order fully to appreciate the distinction which I intend between '⊃', or 'if-then', and 'implies', it is necessary to become clearly aware of the difference between use and mention. When we say that Cambridge adjoins Boston we mention Cambridge and Boston, but use the names 'Cambridge' and 'Boston'; we write the verb 'adjoins' not between Cambridge and Boston, but between their names. When the mentioned objects are cities, as here, use and mention are unlikely to be confused. But the same distinction holds when the mentioned objects are themselves linguistic expressions. When we write:

The fifth word of "The Raven" rimes with the eleventh

we mention the words 'dreary' and 'weary', but what we use are names of them. We write 'rimes with' not between the riming words but between their names. We may also write:

'dreary' rimes with 'weary',

but here again we are using names of the riming words in question—the names being in this case formed by adding single quotation marks. It would be not merely untrue but ungrammatical and meaningless to write:

Dreary rimes with weary.

Now when we say that one statement or schema implies another, similarly, we are not to write 'implies' between the statements or schemata concerned, but between their names. In this way we mention the schemata or statements, we talk *about* them, but use their names. These names are usually formed by adding single quotation marks.[1] Validity and consistency are in this respect on the same footing with implication; we say that a schema or statement is valid or consistent by appending 'is valid' or 'is consistent' not to the schema or statement in question but to a name of it.

When on the other hand we compound a statement or schema from two others by means of 'if-then', or '⊃', we use the statements or schemata themselves and not their names. Here we do not *mention* the statements or schemata. There is no reference to them; they merely occur as parts of a longer statement or schema. The conditional:

If Cassius is not hungry then he is not lean and hungry

mentions Cassius, and says something quite trivial about him, but it mentions no statements at all. The situation here is the same as with conjunction, alternation, and negation.

We have made a point of handling 'if-then' truth-functionally. Among our topics of logical analysis, indeed, no place has been made for non-truth-functional ways of compounding statements. But the fact remains that implication, as a relation between statements, imputes intimate structural connections; it involves far more than the mere truth values of the two statements. This fact conflicts in no way with a strict adherence to truth-functional ways of *compounding* statements and schemata, insofar as statements or schemata are to be compounded at all. The verbs 'implies', 'is longer than', 'is clearer than', and 'rimes with' are all on a par so far as the present contrasts are concerned: they connect, not statements to form compound statements, but names of statements to form statements about statements.

---

[1] When the expression to be named is displayed in an isolated line or lines, I make a colon do the work of single quotation marks; see above.

EXERCISES

1. Determine which of the four schemata:

$$p \cdot p \supset q, \qquad \bar{q} \cdot p \supset q, \qquad p \cdot \bar{p} \supset q, \qquad p \supset q\bar{q}$$

imply 'q' and which imply '$\bar{p}$'. This means eight fell swoops.

2. Determine what implications hold between these:

$$p \supset q, \qquad p \vee q . \supset r, \qquad p \supset . q \vee r.$$

Note that '$p \supset . q \vee r$', like '$p \supset q$', becomes false under just one interpretation of its letters.

3. Find as many schemata as you can, containing one occurrence each of 'p' and 'q' and no further letters, such that each implies '$\bar{p}$'. Also find as many as you can which are implied by '$\bar{p}$'.

4. Determine whether either of these statements implies the other:

> The company is responsible if and only if the unit was an Interplex and installed since January.
>
> If the unit was an Interplex, then it was installed since January and the company is responsible; and if the unit was not an Interplex then it was not installed since January and the company is not responsible.

Method: Obtain schemata representing the logical forms of these statements by using 'p', 'q', and 'r' for the component statements; then test the schemata for implication. Be sure to use 'p' for one and the same component throughout both compounds and similarly for 'q' and 'r'. Be sure also to keep the proper groupings.

§8. WORDS INTO SYMBOLS

Logical inference leads from *premisses*—statements assumed or believed for whatever reason—to *conclusions* which can be shown on purely logical grounds to be true if the premisses are true. Techniques to this end are a primary business of logic, and have already begun to occupy our attention. But whereas the connection between premisses and conclusions is thus grounded in logic, ordinarily the premisses and conclusions themselves are not; and herein precisely lies the *application* of logic to fields other than itself.

The premisses and conclusions may treat of any topics and are couched, to begin with, in ordinary language rather than in the technical ideography of modern logic. It is as an aid to establishing implications that we then proceed to mutilate and distort the statements, introducing schematic letters in order to bring out relevant skeletal structures, and translating varied words into a few fixed symbols such as '⊃' and 'v' in order to gain a manageable economy of structural elements. The task of thus suitably paraphrasing a statement and isolating the relevant structure is just as essential to the application of logic as is the test or proof of implication for which that preliminary task prepares the way.

An example of how such paraphrasing reduces varied idioms to uniformity has already been noted in the notation of negation (cf. §1). The notation of conjunction has a similar effect; for in ordinary language conjunction is expressed not only by 'and' but also by 'but', by 'although', by unspoken punctuation, and in various other ways. Consideration of 'but' and 'although' is instructive, for it brings out a distinction between what may be called the logical and the rhetorical aspects of language. We are likely to say:

> Jones is here but Smith is away,

rather than:

> Jones is here and Smith is away,

because of the contrast between being here and being away; or, if the contrast between 'Jones is here' and 'Smith is away' attains such proportions as to cause surprise, as it might, e.g., if Jones is not in the habit of coming except to see Smith, we are likely to say:

> Jones is here although Smith is away.

But the circumstances which render the compound true are always the same, viz., joint truth of the two components, regardless of whether 'and', 'but', or 'although' is used. Use of one of these words rather than another may make a difference in naturalness of idiom and may also provide some incidental evidence as to what is going on in the speaker's mind, but it is incapable of making the difference between truth and falsehood of the compound. The difference in meaning between 'and', 'but', and 'although' is rhetorical, not logical. Logical notation, unconcerned with rhetorical distinctions, expresses conjunction uniformly.

For a further example of the reduction of manifold idioms of ordinary language to uniformity in logical notations, consider the idiomatic variants of 'if-then':

If p then q, p only if q, q if p, q provided that p, q in case p.

The notation '$p \supset q$', insofar as it may be admitted as a version of 'if p then q' at all, is a version at once of all those variant idioms.

Note that the antecedent of a conditional, corresponding to the 'p' of '$p \supset q$', is not always the part which comes first in the vernacular. It is the part rather that is governed by 'if' (or by 'in case', 'provided that', etc.), regardless of whether it comes early or late in the conditional. Thus it is that 'p if q' goes over into '$q \supset p$', not '$p \supset q$'. But whereas 'if' is thus ordinarily a sign of the antecedent, the attachment of 'only' reverses it; 'only if' is a sign of the consequent. Thus 'p only if q' means, not 'p if q', but 'if p then q'; not '$q \supset p$', but '$p \supset q$'. E.g., 'You will graduate only if your bills have been paid' does not mean 'If your bills have been paid you will graduate'; it means 'If you will graduate, your bills (will) have been paid'.

The reader may have found 'if p then q' awkward as a pronunciation of '$p \supset q$', because of the separation of 'if' from 'then'. If so, the above observation on 'only if' deserves special attention; '$\supset$' may be read 'only if'.

It is particularly to be noted that 'only if' does not have the sense of '$\equiv$', which is '*if and* only if'. As the words suggest, 'p if and only if q' is a conjunction of 'p if q' and 'p only if q'—hence of '$q \supset p$' and '$p \supset q$'.

Among the linguistic variants of 'if p then q' listed above, one more might have been included: 'not p unless q'. This variant leads to the following curious reflection: if 'not p unless q' means '$p \supset q$', and '$p \supset q$' means '$\bar{p} \vee q$', then 'not p unless q' must mean '$\bar{p} \vee q$', which makes 'unless' answer to '$\vee$' and hence to 'or'. Whatever strangeness there may be in equating 'unless' to 'or' is precisely the strangeness of equating 'if-then' to 'ᗞ'. It is sometimes felt that 'if-then' suggests a causal connection, or the like; and, insofar as it does, so also does 'unless'. But when we distill a truth function out of 'if-then' we have 'ᗞ', and when we distill a truth function out of 'unless' we have 'v', 'or'.

The evident commutativity of 'or', i.e., the equivalence of 'p or q' with 'q or p', is less evident with 'unless'. The statements:

(1)   Smith will sell unless he hears from you,

(2)   Smith will hear from you unless he sells

seem divergent in meaning. However, this divergence may be attributed in part to a subtle tendency in 'unless' compounds to mention the earlier event last when time relationships are important. Because of this tendency, we are likely to construe the vague 'hears from you' in (1) as meaning 'hears from you that he should not sell', and in (2) as meaning 'hears from you that he should have sold'. But if we are to compare (1) and (2) as genuine compounds of statements, we must first render each component unambiguous and durable in its meaning—if not absolutely, at least sufficiently to exclude shifts of meaning within the space of the comparison. Thus we should perhaps revise (1) and (2) to read:

> Smith will sell unless you restrain him,
> Smith will be reprimanded by you unless he sells,

and so consider them to be related not as 'p unless q' and 'q unless p', but merely as 'p unless q' and 'r unless p'.

Thus far we have been surveying in a cursory way that aspect of paraphrasing which turns on mere vocabulary. We have been correlating connective words of ordinary language with the connective symbols of symbolic logic. The last example, however, has brought to light another and subtler aspect of the task of paraphrasing: on occasion we must not only translate connectives but also rephrase the component clauses themselves, to the extent anyway of insuring them against material shifts of meaning within the space of the argument in hand. The necessity of this operation is seen more simply and directly in the following example. The two conjunctions:

(3)   He went to Pawcatuck and I went along,

(4)   He went to Saugatuck but I did not go along

may both be true; yet if we represent them as of the forms 'pq' and '$r\bar{q}$', as seems superficially to fit the case, we come out with an inconsistent combination '$pqr\bar{q}$'. Actually of course the 'I went along' in (3) must be distinguished from the 'I went along' whose negation appears in (4); the one is 'I went along to Pawcatuck' and the other is 'I went along to Saugatuck'. When (3) and (4) are completed in this fashion they can no longer be represented as related in the manner of 'pq' and '$r\bar{q}$', but only in the manner of 'pq' and '$r\bar{s}$'; and the apparent inconsistency disappears. In general, the trustworthiness of logical analysis and inference depends on our not giving one and the same expression different interpretations in the course of the reasoning. Violation of this principle was known traditionally as the *fallacy of equivocation*.

Insofar as the interpretation of ambiguous expressions depends on circumstances of the argument as a whole—speaker, hearer, scene, date, and underlying problem and purpose—the fallacy of equivocation is not to be feared; for, those background circumstances may be expected to influence the interpretation of an ambiguous expression uniformly wherever the expression recurs in the course of the argument. This is why words of ambiguous reference such as 'I', 'you', 'here', 'Smith', and 'Elm Street' are ordinarily allowable in logical arguments without qualification; their interpretation is indifferent to the logical soundness of an argument, provided merely that it stays the same throughout the space of the argument.

The fallacy of equivocation arises rather when the interpretation of an ambiguous expression is influenced in varying ways by immediate contexts, as in (3) and (4), so that the expression undergoes changes of meaning within the limits of the argument. In such cases we have to rephrase before proceeding; not rephrase to the extent of resolving all ambiguity, but to the extent of resolving such part of the ambiguity as might, if left standing, end up by being resolved in dissimilar ways by different immediate contexts within the proposed logical argument. The logical connectives by which components are joined in compounds must be thought of as insulating each component from

5

whatever influences its neighbors might have upon its meaning; each component is to be wholly on its own, except insofar as its meaning may depend on those broader circumstances which condition the meanings of words in the compound as a whole or in the logical argument as a whole.

It often becomes evident, when this warning is borne in mind, that a compound which superficially seems analyzable in terms merely of conjunction and negation really calls for logical devices of a more advanced nature. The statement:

(5)   We saw Stromboli but it was not erupting

is not adequately analyzed as a simple conjunction, for the construction 'was...-ing' in the second clause involves an essential temporal reference back to the first clause. A more adequate analysis would construe (5) rather as:

Some moment of our seeing Stromboli was a moment of its not erupting,

which involves logical structures taken up in Part II.

The general enterprise of paraphrasing statements so as to isolate their logical structures has, we have thus far seen, two aspects: the direct translating of appropriate words into logical symbols (comprising just truth-functional symbols at this level of logic), and the rephrasing of component clauses to circumvent the fallacy of equivocation. Now a third aspect, of equal importance with the other two when our examples are of any considerable complexity, is determination of how to organize paraphrased fragments properly into a structured whole. Here we face the problem of determining the intended grouping. A few clues to grouping in statements of ordinary language have been noted (§4), but in the main we must rely on our good sense of everyday idiom for a sympathetic understanding of the statement and then re-think the whole in logical symbols. When a statement is complex, it is a good plan to look for the outermost structure first and then *paraphrase inward*, step by step. This procedure has the double advantage of dividing the problem up into manageable parts, and of keeping the complexities of grouping under control. E.g., consider the statement:

(6) If Jones is ill or Smith is away then neither will the Argus deal
be concluded nor will the directors meet and declare a dividend
unless Robinson comes to his senses and takes matters into his
own hands.

First we seek the main connective of (6). Reasoning as in §4, we can
narrow the choice down to 'if-then' and 'unless'; suppose we decide
on 'if-then'. The outward structure of (6), then, is that of a conditional; so let us impose just this much structure explicitly upon (6),
postponing minuter analysis. We have:

(7) Jones is ill or Smith is away $\supset$ neither will the Argus deal be
concluded nor will the directors meet and declare a dividend
unless Robinson comes to his senses and takes matters into his
own hands.

Next we may consider, as if it were a separate problem removed from
(7), just the long compound 'neither ... hands'. We decide, let us
suppose, that its main connective is 'unless'. Treating 'unless' as 'v',
we turn (7) as a whole into:

(8) Jones is ill or Smith is away $\supset$. neither will the Argus deal
be concluded nor will the directors meet and declare a dividend
v Robinson will come to his senses and take matters into his
own hands.

Now we take up, as if it were a separate problem removed from (8),
the longest component not yet analyzed; viz., 'neither ... dividend'.
The main connective here is clearly 'neither-nor'. Reflecting then
that 'neither r nor s' in general goes into symbols as '$\bar{r}\bar{s}$', we rewrite
'neither ... dividend' accordingly; (8) thus becomes:

(9) Jones is ill or Smith is away $\supset$. $-$(the Argus deal will be concluded) $-$(the directors will meet and declare a dividend) v
Robinson will come to his senses and take matters into his own
hands.

Directing our attention finally to the various short compounds which
remain unanalyzed in (9), we turn the whole into:

(10) Jones is ill v Smith is away .$\supset$: $-$(the Argus deal will be concluded) $-$(the directors will meet . the directors will declare a

dividend) v. Robinson will come to his senses . Robinson will take matters into his own hands.

Put schematically, the total structure is:

(11) $p \lor q . \supset . \bar{r} - (st) \lor uv.$

EXERCISES

1. Justify inference of the conclusion:

If Smith is away and Robinson does not come to his senses then the Argus deal will not be concluded

from (6). *Method:* Find the schema which corresponds to this conclusion as (11) does to (6); then show that this schema is implied by (11).

2. Determine which of these statements implies which:

Jones is not eligible unless he has resigned his commission and signed a waiver.

Jones is eligible if he has resigned his commission or signed a waiver.

Jones is eligible only if he has signed a waiver.

Method: Paraphrase both statements, represent their structure schematically, and test the schemata. Show all steps.

3. Paraphrase inward, showing and justifying each step:

If the tree rings have been correctly identified and the mace is indigenous, then the Ajo culture antedated the Tula if and only if the Tula culture was contemporary with or derivative from that of the present excavation.

§9. EQUIVALENCE

Two truth-functional schemata are called *equivalent* if they agree with each other in point of truth value under every interpretation of their letters, or in other words if they agree case by case under truth-value analysis. In anticipation, various cases of equivalence were noted in §§1–3:

'p' to '$\overset{=}{p}$', 'pp', and '$p \lor p$',   '$pq \cdot r$' to '$p \cdot qr$',

'pq' to 'qp' and '$-(\bar{p} \lor \bar{q})$',   '$p \lor q \cdot \lor r$' to '$p \lor . q \lor r$',

'$p \lor q$' to '$q \lor p$' and '$-(\bar{p}\bar{q})$',   '$-(pq)$' to '$\bar{p} \lor \bar{q}$',

'$p \supset q$' to '$-(p\bar{q})$' and '$\bar{p} \lor q$',   '$-(p \lor q)$' to '$\bar{p}\bar{q}$',

'$p \equiv q$' to '$p \supset q \cdot q \supset p$' and '$-(p\bar{q}) -(q\bar{p})$'.

To test two schemata for equivalence, we might make truth-value analyses of the two schemata and see if they agree case by case. But there is another way which tends to be easier: we may form a biconditional of the two schemata, and test it for validity. For, according to our definition, two schemata S_1 and S_2 are equivalent if and only if no interpretation makes S_1 and S_2 unlike in truth value; hence if and only if no interpretation falsifies the biconditional whose sides are S_1 and S_2. Thus, just as implication is validity of the conditional, so equivalence is validity of the biconditional.[1]

To determine the equivalence of '$p \cdot q \lor r$' to '$pq \lor pr$', e.g., we check the validity of the corresponding biconditional:[2]

$$p \cdot q \lor r \cdot \equiv \cdot pq \lor pr$$

$$\top \cdot q \lor r \cdot \equiv \cdot \top q \lor \top r \qquad\qquad \bot \cdot q \lor r \cdot \equiv \cdot \bot q \lor \bot r$$

$$q \lor r \cdot \equiv \cdot q \lor r \qquad\qquad\qquad\qquad \top$$

$$\top$$

In similar fashion it may be checked that 'p' is equivalent to each of:

(1) $\overset{=}{p}, \quad pp, \quad p \lor p, \quad p \lor pq, \quad p \cdot p \lor q, \quad pq \lor pq, \quad p \lor q \cdot p \lor \bar{q}.$

It has been said that the most conspicuous purpose of logic, in its application to ordinary discourse, is the justification and criticism of inference. But a second purpose, almost as important, is transformation of statements. It is often desirable to transform one statement into another which "says the same thing" in a different form—a form which is simpler, perhaps, or more convenient for the particular

---

[1]Accordingly the tendency to confuse 'implies' with 'if-then' (§7) carries with it a tendency to confuse 'is equivalent to' with 'if and only if'. The proper contrast between equivalence and the biconditional is quite the same as was stressed in §7 between implication and the conditional.

[2]In pursuance of the policy announced in §5, all intermediate steps of resolution in this analysis are left to the reader to fill in. The reason an intermediate stage '$q \lor r \cdot \equiv \cdot q \lor r$' is shown in the left-hand part of the analysis is that the passage from this to '$\top$' is not by resolution but by the rule of patently valid clauses, §6.

purposes in hand. Now insofar as such transformations are justifiable by considerations purely of truth-functional structure (rather than turning upon other sorts of logical structure which lie beyond the scope of Part I), a technique for their justification is at hand in our test of equivalence of truth-functional schemata. Transformation, e.g., of:

(2) The admiral will speak and either the dean or the president will introduce him

into:

(3) Either the admiral will speak and the dean will introduce him or the admiral will speak and the president will introduce him,

or vice versa, is justified by the equivalence of '$p . q \vee r$' to '$pq \vee pr$', and this equivalence is verified by mechanical test as above. The statements (2) and (3) may, by an extension of terminology similar to that made in §7, be spoken of as truth-functionally equivalent.

It is evident from our definitions and testing techniques that

(i) Equivalence is mutual implication.

From this law and (i)–(iv) of §7, these clearly follow:

(ii) Any schema is equivalent to itself.

(iii) If one schema is equivalent to a second and the second is equivalent to a third then the first is equivalent to the third.

(iv) If one schema is equivalent to a second then the second is equivalent to the first. (Not so for implication!)

(v) Valid schemata are equivalent to one another and to no others; and similarly for inconsistent schemata.

Substitution was observed in §6 to preserve validity. Since implication and equivalence are merely validity of a conditional and a biconditional, it follows that substitution also preserves implication and equivalence. From the equivalence of 'p' to each of the schemata in (1), e.g., we may infer by substitution that '$\bar{r}$' is equivalent to each of '$\bar{\bar{r}}$', '$\bar{r}\bar{r}$', '$\bar{r} \vee \bar{r}$', '$\bar{r} \vee \bar{r}s$', etc.; also that '$\bar{q}r$' is equivalent to each of '$- -(\bar{q}r)$', '$\bar{q}r\bar{q}r$', '$\bar{q}r \vee \bar{q}r$', etc.; and correspondingly for any other substitution upon 'p' and 'q' in (1). The particular family of equivalences thus generated will be made use of later as a means of simplifying schemata.

Substitution consists always in putting schemata for single letters, and for all recurrences of the letters. When these restrictions are not met, the putting of one schema for another will be called not substitution but *interchange*. Thus interchange consists in putting one schema for another which need not be a single letter, and which need not be supplanted in all its recurrences. What has been said of substitution, that it preserves implication, equivalence, and inconsistency, cannot of course be said in general of interchange. But there are useful laws of interchange, the least of which is this *first law of interchange:* Think of '...p...' as any schema containing 'p', and of '...q...' as formed from '...p...' by putting 'q' for one or more occurrences of 'p'; then

$$\text{'}p \equiv q\text{'} \quad \text{implies} \quad \text{'}...p... .\equiv. ...q...\text{'}.$$

(Similarly for any other letters instead of 'p' and 'q'.) Let us see why the law holds. We want to show that any interpretation of letters which makes 'p ≡ q' come out true will make '...p... .≡. ...q...' come out true. But to make 'p ≡ q' come out true we must either put '⊤' for both 'p' and 'q' or else '⊥' for both 'p' and 'q'; and in either case '...p...' and '...q...', which differed only in 'p' and 'q', become indistinguishable from each other, so that their biconditional reduces to '⊤'.

Now we can establish a more important *second law of interchange*: If S_1 and S_2 are equivalent, and S_2' is formed from S_1' by putting S_2 for one or more occurrences of S_1, then S_1' and S_2' are equivalent. E.g., this law enables us to argue from the equivalence of 'p ⊃ q' and '−(p$\bar{q}$)' to the equivalence of 'p ⊃ q .v r' and '−(p$\bar{q}$) v r'. The rough idea is, in school jargon, that putting equals for equals yields equals.

This second law of interchange is established as follows. Choose any two letters not appearing in S_1' nor in S_2'. They are, let us imagine, 'p' and 'q'. Then put 'p' for the occurrences of S_1 in question in S_1'; the result may be represented as '...p...', and the result of similarly using 'q' may be represented as '...q...'. By the first law of interchange, 'p ≡ q' implies '...p... .≡. ...q...'. By substitution of S_1 for 'p' and S_2 for 'q' in this implication, we may conclude that the biconditional of S_1 and S_2 implies the biconditional of S_1' and S_2'. But the biconditional of S_1 and S_2 is valid, since S_1 and S_2 are equivalent. Therefore the biconditional of S_1' and S_2' is valid; cf. (iv) of §7. Therefore S_1' and S_2' are equivalent.

This second law assures us that we can interchange equivalents S_1 and S_2 in any schema S_1' without affecting the outcome of a truth-value analysis; for, S_1' and the result S_2' will be equivalent, and equivalent schemata are schemata that agree case by case under truth-value analysis. There thus follows this *third law of interchange*: Interchange of equivalents preserves validity, implication, equivalence, and inconsistency; and, unlike substitution for letters, it even preserves consistency, nonvalidity, nonimplication, and nonequivalence.

Substitution for letters must, we saw, be construed as uniform and exhaustive; but there is no such requirement in the case of interchanging equivalents. If in the valid schema '$p \vee \bar{p}$' we substitute 'qr' for 'p', we may infer the validity of '$qr \vee -(qr)$' and this only; but if in that same valid schema '$p \vee \bar{p}$' we elect rather to put 'pp' for its *equivalent* 'p', we are entitled thereby to infer the validity not merely of '$pp \vee -(pp)$', but equally of '$pp \vee \bar{p}$' and '$p \vee -(pp)$'.

Since interchange of equivalents does not affect the outcome of a truth-value analysis, it proves to be a convenient adjunct to the technique of truth-value analysis; for, if we supplant schemata by simpler equivalents in the course of such analyses, our computations are reduced. In particular, accordingly, whenever a configuration of any of the seven forms depicted in (1) makes its appearance in the course of a truth-value analysis, let us immediately simplify it before proceeding. We are not only to put 'p' for its equivalents '$\bar{\bar{p}}$', 'pp', '$p \vee p$', '$p \vee pq$', etc., but correspondingly '$\bar{r}$' for '$\bar{\bar{\bar{r}}}$', '$\bar{r}\bar{r}$', '$\bar{r} \vee \bar{r}$', '$\bar{r} \vee \bar{r}s$', etc., and '$\bar{q}r$' for '$- -(\bar{q}r)$', '$\bar{q}r\bar{q}r$', '$\bar{q}r \vee \bar{q}r$', etc.

With our new policy in mind let us take another turn at the long schema which was analyzed in §6:

$$p \vee q . p \vee \bar{q} .\vee \bar{p}q :\equiv q .: \supset . pr \vee p\bar{r}$$

$$p \vee \bar{p}q .\equiv q :\supset p$$

$$\top \vee {\downarrow} q .\equiv q :\supset \top \qquad\qquad {\downarrow} \vee \top q .\equiv q :\supset {\downarrow}$$

$$\top \qquad\qquad\qquad\qquad -(q \equiv q)$$

$$\qquad\qquad\qquad\qquad\qquad {\downarrow}$$

Here the original schema is subjected to some simplifications before the substitution of signs for 'p' is even begun. The simplifications consist in reducing both '$p \lor q . p \lor \bar{q}$' and '$pr \lor p\bar{r}$' to '$p$'; for '$p \lor q . p \lor \bar{q}$' is the last of the schemata in (1), and '$pr \lor p\bar{r}$' is the next to last with 'r' substituted for 'q'.

Next let us turn back to the first long truth-value analysis of §6. Under the new procedure it would run rather thus:

```
                    pq ∨ p̄r̄ ∨ p̄r ∨ p̄s ∨ q̄r ∨ r̄s̄
⊤q ∨ ⊤r̄ ∨ ⌊r ∨ ⌊s ∨ q̄r ∨ r̄s̄         ⌊q ∨ ⌊r̄ ∨ ⊤r ∨ ⊤s ∨ q̄r ∨ r̄s̄
       q ∨ r̄ ∨ q̄r ∨ r̄s̄                       r ∨ s ∨ q̄r ∨ r̄s̄
          q ∨ r̄ ∨ q̄r                            r ∨ s ∨ r̄s̄
  ⊤ ∨ r̄ ∨ ⌊r      ⊥ ∨ r̄ ∨ ⊤r        ⊤ ∨ s ∨ ⌊s̄      ⊥ ∨ s ∨ ⊤s̄
     ⊤                r̄ ∨ r          ⊤                  s ∨ s̄
                       ⊤                                 ⊤
```

In this case none of the seven forms listed in (1) is visible in the original schema as it stands, but some emerge as the analysis proceeds. On the left side, '$q \lor \bar{r} \lor \bar{q}r \lor \bar{r}\bar{s}$' is reduced to '$q \lor \bar{r} \lor \bar{q}r$' by putting '$\bar{r}$' for '$\bar{r} \lor \bar{r}\bar{s}$'. On the right side, similarly, '$r \lor s \lor \bar{q}r \lor \bar{r}\bar{s}$' is reduced to '$r \lor s \lor \bar{r}\bar{s}$' by putting '$r$' for '$r \lor \bar{q}r$'.

Both of the simplifications last noted are based on the equivalence of '$p \lor pq$' to 'p'; but they involve also a mental switching of conjunctions and alternations. The clause '$\bar{r} \lor \bar{r}\bar{s}$' which is to give way to '$\bar{r}$' is not even visible in '$q \lor \bar{r} \lor \bar{q}r \lor \bar{r}\bar{s}$' until we think of the part '$\bar{q}r \lor \bar{r}\bar{s}$' as switched to read '$\bar{r}\bar{s} \lor \bar{q}r$'; nor is the clause '$r \lor \bar{q}r$' visible in '$r \lor s \lor \bar{q}r \lor \bar{r}\bar{s}$' until we think of the part '$s \lor \bar{q}r$' as switched to read '$\bar{q}r \lor s$'. Even when this clause '$r \lor \bar{q}r$' has been isolated, moreover, its equivalence to 'r' is not inferred from the equivalence of '$p \lor pq$' to 'p' *merely* by substitution; we have also, mentally, to reread '$r \lor \bar{q}r$' as '$r \lor r\bar{q}$' by switching the conjunction. Such preparatory switching of alternations and conjunctions involves a tacit appeal to further equivalences: the equivalence of '$p \lor q$' to '$q \lor p$' and of 'pq' to 'qp'. But these steps drop out of consciousness if we school ourselves, as we well may, to disregard typographical order among the components of a conjunction and of an alternation.

It is arbitrary to single out just these seven equivalences, viz., the equivalence of 'p' to each of the seven schemata in (1), as a basis for simplifications auxiliary to truth-value analyses. A further convenient equivalence, which could in fact have been exploited in both of the truth-value analyses last set forth, is the equivalence of '$p \lor \bar{p}q$' to '$p \lor q$'. Another convenient one is the equivalence of '$p \,.\, \bar{p} \lor q$' to 'pq'. However, a long catalogue of simplification rules would cost more trouble in the mastery than it would save in the abridging of truth-value analyses. The seven equivalences singled out in (1) were chosen for their simplicity and their especial utility, and, incidentally, for a certain family resemblance: all are equivalences to 'p'.

EXERCISES

1. Determine which of these are equivalent to '$pq \supset r$' and which to '$p \lor q \,.\, \supset r$':

$$p \supset .\, q \supset r, \quad q \supset .\, p \supset r, \quad p \supset r \,.\, q \supset r, \quad p \supset r \,.\lor.\, q \supset r.$$

2. Determine which of these are equivalent to '$p \supset qr$' and which to '$p \supset .\, q \lor r$':

$$p \supset q \,.\, p \supset r, \qquad\qquad p \supset q \,.\lor.\, p \supset r.$$

3. Determine any equivalent pairs from among these:

$$p \supset q, \quad \bar{p} \supset \bar{q}, \quad \bar{p} \supset q, \quad q \supset p, \quad \bar{q} \supset \bar{p}, \quad \bar{q} \supset p.$$

This means fifteen short tests.

4. Making full use of the new simplification procedure, test each of the following three pairs for equivalence by truth-value analysis:

$pq \lor pr \lor qr$,	$p \lor q \,.\, p \lor r \,.\, q \lor r$;
$pqr \lor pqs \lor prs \lor qrs$,	$p \lor q \lor r \,.\, p \lor q \lor s \,.\, p \lor r \lor s \,.\, q \lor r \lor s$;
$pqr \lor p\bar{q}\bar{r} \lor p\bar{q}r \lor p\bar{q}\bar{r}$,	$p \lor q \lor r \,.\, p \lor q \lor \bar{r} \,.\, p \lor \bar{q} \lor r \,.\, p \lor \bar{q} \lor \bar{r}$.

§10. NORMAL SCHEMATA

The notations '$\lor$', '$\supset$', and '$\equiv$' are superfluous, we know, in that all use of them can be paraphrased into terms of conjunction and negation. The sign '$\supset$', however, has been seen to have a special utility in the testing of implication; for, to test implication we form a conditional (with help of '$\supset$') and test its validity. The sign '$\equiv$'

has been seen to be of similar use in the testing of equivalence. So there is good reason for having added the strictly superfluous signs '⊃' and '≡'. Now the advantages of retaining 'v' are of quite a different kind, and will become evident in the course of the present section and the next.

What are known as DeMorgan's laws, because they were stated by Augustus DeMorgan in the nineteenth century (as well as by William of Ockham in the fourteenth century and Petrus Hispanus in the thirteenth[1]), affirm the equivalence of

(i)   '$-(p$ v q v ... v $s)$'   to   '$\bar{p}\bar{q}...\bar{s}$'   and

(ii)   '$-(pq...s)$'   to   '$\bar{p}$ v $\bar{q}$ v ... v $\bar{s}$'.

For the case of just 'p' and 'q', these laws were already noted in §1. The further cases follow by substitution and interchange. E.g., from the equivalence of '$-(p$ v $q)$' to '$\bar{p}\bar{q}$' we have, by substitution of 'p v q' for 'p' and 'r' for 'q', the equivalence of '$-(p$ v q v $r)$' to '$-(p$ v $q)\bar{r}$'; and thence, putting '$\bar{p}\bar{q}$' for its equivalent '$-(p$ v $q)$', we obtain the equivalence of '$-(p$ v q v $r)$' to '$\bar{p}\bar{q}\bar{r}$'.

DeMorgan's laws are useful in enabling us to avoid negating conjunctions and alternations. We never need apply negation to the whole of an alternation, since '$-(p$ v q v ... v $s)$' is equivalent to '$\bar{p}\bar{q}...\bar{s}$'; and we never need apply negation to the whole of a conjunction, since '$-(pq...s)$' is equivalent to '$\bar{p}$ v $\bar{q}$ v ... v $\bar{s}$'. Also of course we never need apply negation to a negation, since '$\bar{\bar{p}}$' is equivalent to 'p'. For that matter, we also never need apply negation to a conditional or biconditional; for, by the method of the preceding section it is easy to verify the equivalence of

(iii)   '$-(p \supset q)$'   to   '$p\bar{q}$'   and of

(iv)   '$-(p \equiv q)$'   to   '$\bar{p} \equiv q$'   and to   '$p \equiv \bar{q}$'.

So any truth-functional schema can be put over into an equivalent in which negation never applies to anything but individual letters. Transformation of this kind is generally conducive to easy intelligibility.

[1] Cf. Łukasiewicz, "Zur Geschichte."

E.g., consider the forbidding schema:

(1) $-\{p \supset \bar{s}q \,.\supset\, -(sq \supset p) : -[\, -(rp) -(p \supset \bar{s})]\}.$

(It is of some help to vary parentheses thus with brackets and braces when they are deeply nested.) Now since (1) has the outward form '$-(tu)$', it can be transformed by (ii) to read:

$$-[p \supset \bar{s}q \,.\supset\, -(sq \supset p)] \text{ v } - -[\, -(rp) -(p \supset \bar{s})].$$

Cancellation of '$- -$' reduces this to:

(2) $-[p \supset \bar{s}q \,.\supset\, -(sq \supset p)] \text{ v } -(rp) -(p \supset \bar{s}).$

Then by (iii) we transform the first half of (2) into:

$$p \supset \bar{s}q \,.\, - -(sq \supset p), \qquad \text{or}$$

$$p \supset \bar{s}q \,.\, sq \supset p,$$

so that (2) becomes:

(3) $p \supset \bar{s}q \,.\, s\acute{q} \supset p \,.\text{v} -(rp) -(p \supset \bar{s}).$

By (ii) again, '$-(rp)$' here becomes '$\bar{r} \text{ v } \bar{p}$', and, by (iii) again, '$-(p \supset \bar{s})$' becomes '$p\bar{\bar{s}}$' or 'ps', so that (3) comes down to:

(4) $p \supset \bar{s}q \,.\, sq \supset p \,.\text{v}.\, \bar{r} \text{ v } \bar{p} \,.\, ps,$

in which, finally, all negation signs are limited to single letters. (4) is far easier to grasp than (1).

Such is the advantage of confining negation to single letters. Now it will be found in general that still further perspicuity can be gained by confining conjunction to single letters and negations of letters; and it will be found also that such confinement of conjunction can, like the confinement of negation to single letters, always be accomplished. The law which makes this possible is known as the *law of distributivity of conjunction through alternation*, and runs as follows:

'$p \,.\, q \text{ v } r \text{ v } ... \text{ v } t$' is equivalent to '$pq \text{ v } pr \text{ v } ... \text{ v } pt$'.

Regardless of the number of letters involved, the equivalence is readily verified by the method of the preceding section:

$$p \,.\, q \vee r \vee ... \vee t \,.\!\equiv\!.\, pq \vee pr \vee ... \vee pt$$

$$\top \,.\, qvrv...vt \,.\!\equiv\!.\, \top qv\top rv...v\top t \qquad \bot \,.\, qvrv...vt \,.\!\equiv\!.\, \lfloor qv\lfloor rv...v\lfloor t$$

$$\frac{qvrv...vt \,.\!\equiv\!.\, qvrv...vt}{\top} \qquad\qquad \frac{\bot \equiv \bot}{\top}$$

This law, like the familiar identity:

$$x(y + z + ... + w) = xy + xz + ... + xw$$

of algebra, authorizes the convenient operation of "multiplying out." Thanks to it, we need never acquiesce in a conjunction which has an alternation as component; we can always distribute the other part of the conjunction through the alternation, as above, so as to come out with an alternation of simpler conjunctions.

Since order is immaterial to conjunction, such distribution can be worked equally well in reverse: not only is '$p \,.\, q \vee r \vee ... \vee t$' equivalent to '$pq \vee pr \vee ... \vee pt$', but also '$q \vee r \vee ... \vee t \,.\, p$' is equivalent to '$qp \vee rp \vee ... \vee tp$'. These two sorts of distribution are indeed one and the same, once we learn to ignore order of conjunction.

When we have a conjunction of two alternations, distribution takes the form of the familiar "cross-multiplying" of algebra; e.g., '$p \vee t \,.\, q \vee r \vee s$' comes out '$pq \vee pr \vee ps \vee tq \vee tr \vee ts$'. For, we begin by handling '$q \vee r \vee s$' as we might a single letter 'u'; thus, just as '$p \vee t \,.\, u$' would become '$pu \vee tu$' by (reverse) distribution, so '$p \vee t \,.\, q \vee r \vee s$' becomes '$p \,.\, q \vee r \vee s \,.\vee.\, t \,.\, q \vee r \vee s$'. Afterward, distribution of 'p' turns the part '$p \,.\, q \vee r \vee s$' into '$pq \vee pr \vee ps$', and distribution of 't' turns the part '$t \,.\, q \vee r \vee s$' into '$tq \vee tr \vee ts$'.

Let us now go back to (4) and improve it by distributing. We thereby change the part '$\bar{r} \vee \bar{p} \,.\, ps$' of (4) to '$\bar{r}ps \vee \bar{p}ps$', so that (4) becomes:

$$(5) \qquad\qquad p \supset \bar{s}q \,.\, sq \supset p \,.\vee\, \bar{r}ps \vee \bar{p}ps.$$

We can open the way to further distribution if we get rid of '$\supset$', translating '$t \supset u$' in general as '$\bar{t} \vee u$'. Such translation turns (5) into:

$$\bar{p} \vee \bar{s}q \,.\, -(sq) \vee p \,.\vee\, \bar{r}ps \vee \bar{p}ps,$$

which, when '$-(sq)$' is changed to '$\bar{s} \vee \bar{q}$' by (ii), becomes:

$$\bar{p} \vee \bar{s}q \,.\, \bar{s} \vee \bar{q} \vee p \,.\vee\, \bar{r}ps \vee \bar{p}ps.$$

Now the part '$\bar{p}$ v $\bar{s}q$. $\bar{s}$ v $\bar{q}$ v p' can be "cross-multiplied," so that the whole becomes:

(6) $\bar{p}\bar{s}$ v $\bar{p}\bar{q}$ v $\bar{p}p$ v $\bar{s}q\bar{s}$ v $\bar{s}q\bar{q}$ v $\bar{s}qp$ v $\bar{r}ps$ v $\bar{p}ps$.

We can quickly shorten this result by deleting the patently inconsistent clauses '$\bar{p}p$', '$\bar{s}q\bar{q}$', and '$\bar{p}ps$'. We then have:

(7) $\bar{p}\bar{s}$ v $\bar{p}\bar{q}$ v $\bar{s}q\bar{s}$ v $\bar{s}qp$ v $\bar{r}ps$.

Such deletion is a case of the procedure explained in §6: each of the patently inconsistent clauses may be thought of as supplanted by '⊥', which afterward drops by resolution ((ii) of §5).

Also we may drop any duplications from conjunctions—thus reducing '$\bar{s}q\bar{s}$' to '$\bar{s}q$'. This was the second of the seven forms of simplification noted in (1) of the preceding section. So (7) becomes:

(8) $\bar{p}\bar{s}$ v $\bar{p}\bar{q}$ v $\bar{s}q$ v $\bar{s}qp$ v $\bar{r}ps$,

which wears its meaning on its sleeve. This its equivalents (1) and (4) could scarcely have been said to do.

The result (8) has the following four noteworthy properties: '⊃' and '≡' do not occur; negation is confined to single letters; conjunction is confined to letters and negations of letters; and no letter appears more than once inside any conjunction. Schemata having these four properties will be called *normal*.

This essentially negative characterization of normality may be reformulated in more positive terms as follows. Let us speak of single letters and negations of single letters collectively as *literals*; thus 'p', 'q', '$\bar{p}$', etc. are literals. Let us speak of any literal, and also any conjunction of literals wherein no letter appears twice, as a *fundamental schema*; thus 'pq', '$\bar{p}\bar{s}$', '$\bar{s}qp$', etc., are fundamental schemata, and so are 'p', '$\bar{p}$', 'q', etc., themselves. A *normal schema*, finally, may now be defined as any fundamental schema or alternation of fundamental schemata.

Most of the process whereby (1) was transformed into its normal equivalent (8) can be reproduced for all schemata, and all of the process can be reproduced for most schemata. Given any schema, we can rid it of '⊃' and '≡' by familiar translations: '$p ⊃ q$' becomes '$\bar{p}$ v q' and '$p ≡ q$' becomes 'pq v $\bar{p}\bar{q}$'. We can confine negation to single letters by (i)–(iv), or simply by (i)–(ii) having first got rid of

'⊃' and '≡'. Finally we can confine conjunction to literals by persistent distribution. The stage (6) can thus be reached in every case. Now the remaining steps, eventuating in a normal schema, are deletion of all patently inconsistent components of alternation and deletion of duplications from conjunctions. These steps go through uneventfully in all cases *except where every one of the components of alternation is patently inconsistent*. This exception needs separate attention because the deletion of patently inconsistent components would in this case annihilate the whole schema.

Let us see then how the exception fares. In general, deletion of the patently inconsistent components of alternation was explained as consisting in their replacement by '⊥', followed by resolution. In the extreme case where every one of the components of alternation is patently inconsistent, this procedure reduces the whole simply to '⊥'. Afterward, if we are interested in being left with a genuine schema, we may translate '⊥' back arbitrarily as '$p\bar{p}$'; for, the reduction of our schema to '⊥' shows its inconsistency, and any inconsistent schema is equivalent to '$p\bar{p}$' by (v) of the preceding section.

So the parting of the ways occurs at the point where we have finished confining negation to letters and conjunction to literals and have set about deleting patently inconsistent components of alternation. If they are all patently inconsistent, we put down '$p\bar{p}$' as our end result; if they are not all patently inconsistent, we delete the inconsistent ones and then delete any duplications from within the surviving conjunctions and so end up with a normal schema. We thus have a general routine for *transforming any truth-functional schema into an equivalent which is either '$p\bar{p}$' or normal*.

Any fundamental schema is consistent; for, it comes out true when the letters which are not negated are interpreted as true and the others as false. E.g., 'pq' comes out true when 'p' and 'q' are interpreted as true; '$\bar{p}\bar{s}$' comes out true when 'p' and 's' are interpreted as false; '$\bar{s}qp$' comes out true when 's' is interpreted as false and 'q' and 'p' as true. It then follows also that every alternation of fundamental schemata is consistent, since whenever even one component of an alternation is made to come out true the alternation comes out true. Therefore *every normal schema is consistent*.

What was previously observed, then, viz., that our routine reduces every truth-functional schema to an equivalent which is either '$p\bar{p}$' or normal, may now be restated more informatively: *Our routine reduces every truth-functional schema to '$p\bar{p}$' if inconsistent and to a normal schema if consistent.*

We have a new technique, then, alternative to that of §6, for testing a schema for consistency: transform it according to the foregoing routine. If the end result is normal, the original was consistent; if '$p\bar{p}$', inconsistent.

But the utility of this procedure of transformation and reduction is more than as a new test of consistency. Normal schemata are generally convenient because their net import is so readily grasped: we can tell at a glance what interpretations will make them true. E.g., an interpretation will make (8) true if and only if it either interprets 'p' and 's' as false (making the first clause of (8) true), or interprets 'p' and 'q' as false (making the second clause true), or interprets 's' as false and 'q' as true, or etc.

This advantage can be enhanced by further simplifications to which a normal schema can commonly be subjected. In passing from (7) to (8) we used one of the seven forms of simplification which were noted in connection with (1) of the preceding section, viz., 'pp' to 'p'. But others of the seven may likewise be used to advantage, e.g., that of '$p \vee pq$' to 'p'. Thus, reducing '$\bar{s}q \vee \bar{s}qp$' to '$\bar{s}q$' in (8), we get:

(9) $\bar{p}\bar{s} \vee \bar{p}\bar{q} \vee \bar{s}q \vee \bar{r}ps.$

Our technique for transforming any truth-functional schema into an equivalent which is either '$p\bar{p}$' or normal has been one of successive transformation into equivalents, and thus bears little resemblance to truth-value analysis. It is interesting to observe, however, that truth-value analysis itself provides an alternative channel whereby any truth-functional schema could be reduced to '$p\bar{p}$' or a normal schema. To see this, let us go back to (1) and perform a truth-value analysis:

$$-\{p \supset \bar{s}q \;.\supset\; -(sq \supset p) : -[-(rp) - (p \supset \bar{s})]\}$$
$$-\{\top \supset \bar{s}q \;.\supset\; -(sq \supset \top) : -\text{etc.}\} \qquad -\{\bot \supset \bar{s}q \;.\supset\; -(sq \supset \bot): -\text{etc.}\}$$
$$-[-(\bar{s}q) - (\bar{r}\bar{s})] \qquad\qquad\qquad ---(sq)$$
$$-[-(\bar{s}q) - (\bar{r}s)] \qquad\qquad\qquad -(sq)$$
$$-[-(\bot q) - (\bar{r}\top)] \;\; -[-(\top q) - (\bar{r}\bot)] \qquad -(\top q) \qquad\qquad -(\bot q)$$
$$\bar{\bar{r}} \qquad\qquad \bar{\bar{q}} \qquad\qquad \bar{q} \qquad\qquad \top$$
$$\bar{r} \qquad\qquad q \qquad\qquad \bot \;\; \top$$
$$\bot \qquad \top \qquad \top \qquad \bot$$

Now '$\top$' occurs as end result just four times here: once as a result of putting '$\top$' for 'p', '$\top$' for 's', and '$\bot$' for 'r', once as a result of putting '$\top$' for 'p', '$\bot$' for 's', and '$\top$' for 'q', once as a result of putting '$\bot$' for 'p', '$\top$' for 's', and '$\bot$' for 'q', and once as a result of putting '$\bot$' for 'p' and 's'. This means that the whole schema, (1), comes out true in just these four cases: where '$ps\bar{r}$' is true, where '$p\bar{s}q$' is true, where '$\bar{p}s\bar{q}$' is true, and where '$\bar{p}\bar{s}$' is true. So (1) amounts to the normal schema:

$$(10) \qquad ps\bar{r} \lor p\bar{s}q \lor \bar{p}s\bar{q} \lor \bar{p}\bar{s}.$$

This does not happen to look like (8) or (9), but it is just as genuinely a normal schema, and its equivalence to (9) may easily be verified by a direct test in the manner of the preceding section.

In general, as seen in the case of (10), we may read off a normal schema directly from a truth-value analysis, so long as there are any '$\top$'s as end results of the analysis. If on the other hand all end results are '$\bot$', so that the given schema is found inconsistent, we may directly set down '$p\bar{p}$' as its equivalent. So two quite different channels are now known to us whereby, for any truth-functional schema, an equivalent may be found which is either '$p\bar{p}$' or normal.

EXERCISES

1. Check the equivalence of (9) to (10) by truth-value analysis. (Mastery of small print unnecessary.)

2. By the method of successive transformation, transform each of these into a normal schema or '$p\bar{p}$':

$$-(p \lor -\{q \lor -[r \lor -(q \lor p)]\}),$$
$$p \supset q \,.\, q \supset r \,.\supset.\, p \supset r,$$
$$p \supset q \,.\supset p \,:\equiv \bar{p}.$$

§11.   DUALITY

All logical computation at the truth-functional level is essentially computation with '$\top$' and '$\bot$'. Hence it is to be expected that two schemata will be quite parallel in their behavior, at least in important structural respects, if they are just alike under truth-value analysis except for a thoroughgoing interchange of '$\top$' and '$\bot$'. Schemata so related are called *duals* of each other. They behave in relation to each other according to laws which, for their theoretical interest and occasional convenience, warrant some notice. This matter seems to have been first treated by Schröder (1877).

Though duals are opposed somewhat in the manner of '⊤' to '⊥', they are not to be confused with mere contradictions or mutual negations. The prime example of duality, rather, is conjunction versus alternation. Conjunction and alternation are alike except for a *thoroughgoing* interchange of '⊤' and '⊥', in the following sense. Conjunction, to begin with, is describable thus:

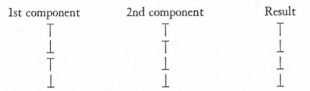

1st component	2nd component	Result
⊤	⊤	⊤
⊥	⊤	⊥
⊤	⊥	⊥
⊥	⊥	⊥

Now to interchange '⊤' and '⊥' merely in the last column would indeed produce a truth function which is the negation of conjunction. Interchange '⊤' and '⊥' throughout all three columns, however, and what you get is precisely a description of alternation:

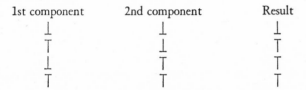

1st component	2nd component	Result
⊥	⊥	⊥
⊤	⊥	⊤
⊥	⊤	⊤
⊤	⊤	⊤

Such is the sense in which '*pq*' and '*p* ∨ *q*' are said to be duals. In general the relationship between dual schemata *S* and *S'* is this: whenever each of '*p*', '*q*', etc. is interpreted oppositely for *S* and *S'*, the truth values of *S* and *S'* turn out oppositely to each other.

Trivially, by this standard, '*p̄*' is dual not to '*p*' but to '*p̄*' itself; for, give opposite values to '*p*' and you get values for '*p̄*' which are opposite to each other.

The duality of '*pq*' to '*p* ∨ *q*' is evident without resort to the above tabulation if we simply compare the original descriptions of conjunction and alternation. A conjunction is true when its components are all true, and otherwise false; whereas an alternation is false when its components are all false, and otherwise true. These two descriptions are alike except for interchange of 'true' and 'false'; hence '*pq*' and '*p* ∨ *q*' are bound to behave alike except for a thoroughgoing interchange of the rôles of '⊤' and '⊥'— which is what duality means. The self-duality of '*p̄*' is evident similarly from the general description of a negation as "true or false according as its component is false or true"; for, switch the words 'true' and 'false' in this description and you simply have the description of negation over again.

More generally now, consider any schema *S* built up of letters by means exclusively of negation, conjunction, and alternation (hence devoid of

'⊃' and '≡'). Suppose a second schema S' is like S except that it has alternation wherever S has conjunction and vice versa. Then truth-value analyses of S and S' are bound to match except for interchange of '⊤' and '⊥' throughout; for, we just saw that the explanations of conjunction and alternation are alike except for switching 'true' with 'false', and that the explanation of negation is unchanged by switching 'true' with 'false'. So S and S' are duals.

What has just been established will be called the *first law of duality*: Where S is any truth-functional schema devoid of '⊃' and '≡', the result of changing alternation to conjunction and vice versa throughout S is dual to S. This law affirms immediately the duality of 'pq' to 'p ∨ q', and the self-duality of '$\bar{p}$' and of 'p'. It affirms also the duality of '$\bar{p}$. q ∨ $\bar{r}$' to '$\bar{p}$ ∨ $q\bar{r}$', the duality of '$p\bar{q}$ ∨ $\bar{p}r$' to 'p ∨ $\bar{q}$. $\bar{p}$ ∨ r', the duality of 'pq ∨ qr ∨ pr' to 'p ∨ q . q ∨ r . p ∨ r', etc.

So we now have a quick and graphic way of forming a dual of a schema: interchange conjunction and alternation. This procedure depends, be it noted, on absence of '⊃' and '≡'; but we can get rid of '⊃' and '≡' in advance, since '$p ⊃ q$' may be rendered as '$\bar{p}$ ∨ q' and '$p ≡ q$' as '$\bar{p}$ ∨ q . $\bar{q}$ ∨ p' or 'pq ∨ $\bar{p}\bar{q}$'.

In interchanging conjunction and alternation to get duals, special care must be taken to preserve grouping. In case of doubt, think of full parentheses as restored in lieu of the dot conventions. Thus 'p . q ∨ r' has as dual not 'p ∨ q . r' but 'p ∨ qr'. For, 'p . q ∨ r' means '$p(q$ ∨ $r)$', and 'p ∨ qr' means 'p ∨ (qr)', in which the same pattern of grouping is preserved; 'p ∨ q . r', on the other hand, means '$(p$ ∨ $q)r$', and is dual rather to 'pq ∨ r'.

Given any schemata S and S', now, we can test whether S' is a dual of S by forming an explicit dual of S according to the above method and then checking it for equivalence to S'. In particular we can thus determine whether a given schema S is a dual of itself; we have merely to form the explicit dual of S by switching conjunction with alternation, as explained, and then to test this result for equivalence to S. Apart from trivial cases, such as '$\bar{p}$', self-duality is rather rare; but it does occur. E.g., 'pq ∨ pr ∨ qr' is dual to itself, since it is equivalent to its own explicit dual 'p ∨ q . p ∨ r . q ∨ r'. (Cf. §9, Exercise 4.)

Switching alternation with conjunction is not the only convenient way of forming a dual. Another way, which does not even require a preparatory elimination of '⊃' and '≡', is provided by the *second law of duality*: If in any schema you negate all letters and also the whole, you get a dual. This law is evident from the original definition of duality; for negating the letters has the same effect as reversing all interpretations of letters, and negating the whole reverses the truth value of the outcome.

DeMorgan's laws themselves (§10) are essentially duality principles, as may be seen by rearguing them in the present context. As dual of '$pq...s$' the first law of duality cites 'p ∨ q ∨ ... ∨ s', whereas the second cites rather

'— $(\bar{p}\bar{q}...\bar{s})$'; these two must then be equivalent to each other, and thus DeMorgan's first law, (i) of §10, holds. (ii) admits of a parallel argument. A *third law of duality* is this: A schema is valid if and only if its dual is inconsistent. For, if two truth-value analyses differ to the extent of a thoroughgoing interchange of '⊤' and '⊥', clearly the one will show validity if and only if the other shows inconsistency.

Fourth law of duality: A schema S_1 implies a schema S_2 if and only if the dual of S_2 implies the dual of S_1 . This is seen as follows. The duals of S_1 and S_2 behave like S_1 and S_2 , under truth-value analysis, except for a switching of 'true' with 'false' throughout. Hence to say that no interpretation of letters makes S_1 true and S_2 false is the same as saying that no interpretation makes the dual of S_1 false and the dual of S_2 true.

Fifth law of duality: Schemata are equivalent if and only if their duals are equivalent. This follows from the fourth law, since equivalence is mutual implication.

The third, fourth, and fifth laws enable us, having established one validity or inconsistency or implication or equivalence by truth-value analysis or otherwise, to infer an additional inconsistency or validity or implication or equivalence without further analysis. E.g., having verified that '$p \lor \bar{q} . q \lor \bar{r} . r \lor s$' implies '$p \lor s$' (as may be done by the method of the fell swoop, §7), we may conclude by the fourth law of duality that 'ps' implies '$p\bar{q} \lor q\bar{r} \lor rs$'. This operation may, in contradistinction to the first, be spoken of as the *full swap*.

Either of DeMorgan's laws, (i)–(ii) of §10, follows from the other by the fifth law of duality. Again, from the law of distributivity of conjunction through alternation (§10) we can, by the fifth law of duality, infer a *law of distributivity of alternation through conjunction*:

'$p \lor qr...t$' is equivalent to '$p \lor q . p \lor r . .... . p \lor t$'.

This law shows that conjunction and alternation are in still more congenial relations to each other than are multiplication and addition. In arithmetic we can multiply out, thus:

$$x(y + z + ... + w) = xy + xz + ... + xw,$$

but we cannot "add out" thus:

$$x + yz...w = (x + y)(x + z)...(x + w).$$

In the case of alternation and conjunction, on the other hand, distribution works both ways.

Indeed, since by the fifth law of duality all equivalences continue to hold when conjunction and alternation are switched, we may conclude at once that the technique of reducing a truth-functional schema to a normal schema (or to '$p\bar{p}$') may be reproduced entire with alternation and conjunction switched. Thus, whereas the procedure of §10 served to reduce inconsistent schemata to '$p\bar{p}$' and consistent ones to normal schemata, this new parallel procedure reduces valid schemata to '$p \vee \bar{p}$' and non-valid ones to "quasi-normal" schemata such as:

$$p \vee \bar{q} \vee r . \bar{p} \vee s . q \vee \bar{r} \vee s$$

—i.e., to schemata which are like normal ones except that the rôles of conjunction and alternation are interchanged. However, whereas the technique of reduction to normal schemata will prove useful on a couple of future occasions (§§19, 32), no use will be made of the corresponding technique of reduction to quasi-normal schemata.

PART TWO

Uniform Quantification

§12. CATEGORICAL STATEMENTS

There are many simple and logically sound inferences for which the foregoing techniques are inadequate. An example is this:

No philosophers are wicked,   *Schematically*: No G are H,
Some Greeks are philosophers;   Some F are G;
Therefore some Greeks are not wicked.   ∴ Some F are not H.

Note that '*F*', '*G*', and '*H*' here stand not for statements, after the manner of '*p*' and '*q*' in Part I, but for common nouns—or, in logical parlance, *terms*.[1] Whether these nouns be thought of as substantive or adjective is an insignificant question of phrasing. '*G*' appears as a substantive in the above example, viz. 'philosophers', and '*H*' as an adjective, 'wicked'; but we could rewrite the adjective as a substantive, 'wicked individuals', if we liked. In the same spirit we can even treat intransitive verbs as terms, in effect, thus reckoning 'Some fishes fly' as a case of 'Some F are G'; for the difference between 'Some fishes fly' and 'Some fishes are flying things' is purely notational. The nouns or verbs which figure as terms may also, of course, be complex phrases such as 'employed for ten years by Sunnyrinse', 'wear brass rings in their noses', etc. Whether terms be thought of as in the singular or the plural is also a logically insignificant question of phrasing; thus there is no need to distinguish between 'No philosopher is wicked' and 'No philosophers are wicked', nor between 'All philosophers are wise' and 'Every philosopher is wise'. There is no

[1]What are spoken of simply as terms in the present pages may, in view of developments in Parts III-IV, be designated more accurately as *general absolute terms*. Actually they will come to be known in Part III, though with a certain shift of emphasis, as *monadic predicates*. But this use of the word 'predicate' is not to be confused, if one can help it, with the mediaeval use explained in the small print of §14.

need even to distinguish between 'Some Greek is a philosopher' and 'Some Greeks are philosophers', provided that, as will be our practice here, we understand 'some' always to mean simply 'at least one'. But, for all the latitude accorded to the concept of term, it remains clear that terms are never statements; and this is why the techniques of Part I are inadequate to the inference exhibited above. Part I dealt with the structures of compound statements relative only to their component statements; statements remained the smallest units of analysis. It is only now, in Part II, that we embark upon the analysis of those component statements in turn into the still smaller parts, not statements at all but terms, of which they are composed. Logically sound inferences depend for their soundness on the structures of the statements concerned, but the relevant structures may be either the broad outward structures studied in Part I or the finer substructures to which we are now turning. The above example is one which depends on structures of the latter kind.

It is the peculiarity of a statement to be true or false. It is the peculiarity of a term, on the other hand, to be *true of* many objects, or one, or none, and false of the rest. The term 'Greek' is true of each Greek, and the term 'wicked' is true of each wicked individual, and nothing else. The term 'satellite of the earth' is true of each satellite of the earth and nothing else, hence true of but one object, the moon. The term 'centaur' is true of each centaur and nothing else, hence true of nothing at all, there being no centaurs.

In place of the clumsy phrase 'is true of' we may also say 'denotes', in the best sense of this rapidly deteriorating word. But I prefer here to resist the temptation of good usage. 'Denotes' is so current in the sense of 'designates', or 'names', that its use in connection, say, with the word 'wicked' would cause readers to look beyond the wicked people to some unique entity, a quality of wickedness or a class of the wicked, as named object. The phrase 'is true of' is less open to misunderstanding; clearly 'wicked' is true not of the quality of wickedness, nor of the class of wicked persons, but of each wicked person individually.

When we are minded to speak of classes, the class of all the objects of which a term is true may, in keeping with a long tradition, be called the *extension* of the term. The extension of 'wicked' is thus the class of wicked persons; the extension of 'satellite of the earth' is the class whose sole member is the moon; and the extension of 'centaur' is the empty class. Terms may be said to *have* extensions, just as statements have truth values; but there is no need to think of a term as somehow a name *of* its extension, any more than there is to think of a statement as a name of its truth value.[1] Far better not, since the use of terms proceeds smoothly on the whole without assumption of any special category of abstract objects called classes. It is ordinarily sufficient to know that a given term is *true of* this and that individual and false of the other, without positing any single collective entity called the term's extension. Reason to appeal to extensions arises only in certain theoretical connections such as the general theory of validity, §§18 ff.

Four ways of joining terms pairwise into statements have been treated as fundamental throughout the logical tradition stemming from Aristotle: 'All *F* are *G*', 'No *F* are *G*', 'Some *F* are *G*', and 'Some *F* are not *G*'. Statements of these four forms were called *categorical*. The four forms were distinguished by special nomenclature and by code letters '**A**', '**E**', '**I**', and '**O**', as follows.

A (Universal affirmative):	All *F* are *G*
E (Universal negative):	No *F* are *G*
I (Particular affirmative):	Some *F* are *G*
O (Particular negative):	Some *F* are not *G*

The form **A**, 'All *F* are *G*', may also be phrased 'If anything is an *F*, it is a *G*'; thus it is recognizable as the "generalized conditional" which was touched on in (1)–(3) of §3. Many other phrasings of **A** also come readily to mind: '*F* are *G*', 'Each (Every, Any) *F* is a *G*', 'Whatever is an *F* is a *G*', '*F* are exclusively *G*', 'Only *G* are *F*'.

E likewise has many phrasings: 'No *F* is (are) *G*', 'Nothing is both an *F* and a *G*', 'Nothing that is an *F* is a *G*', and even 'There is (are) no *FG*' (e.g., 'There is no black swan'), '*FG* do not exist'.

Correspondingly for **I**: 'Some *F* is (are) *G*', 'Something is both an *F* and a *G*', 'Something that is an *F* is a *G*', 'There is an *FG*', 'There are *FG*', '*FG* exist'. **O**, of course, has similar variants.

Often the terms properly answering to '*F*' and '*G*' are not directly visible at all in ordinary phrasing of statements. They may be partially

---

[1]Cf. Carnap, *Meaning and Necessity*, pp. 23–32, 96–111.

covered up by such usages as 'nowhere', 'anywhere', 'always', 'every-one', 'whoever', 'whenever', etc. Thus the statement 'I go nowhere by train that I can get to by plane' is properly analyzable as of the form **E**, 'No *F* are *G*', but here we must understand '*F*' as representing 'places I go to by train' and '*G*' as representing 'places I can get to by plane'. The statement 'Everyone in the room speaks English' has the form **A**, 'All *F* are *G*', where '*F*' represents 'persons in this room' and '*G*' represents 'speakers of English'.

In this last example the restrictions to persons implicit in 'every-one' is essential, since there will be nonpersons in the room which do not speak English. In such an example as 'Everyone who pays his dues receives the Bulletin', on the other hand, 'everyone' is used instead of 'everything' only because of a habit of language, and not because the speaker feels any need of hedging his statement against such absurd objects as subhuman payers of dues. It would be pedantic to construe '*F*' for this example as 'persons who pay their dues', and quite proper to construe it as 'payers of dues'.

In putting statements of ordinary language over into the forms **A**, **E**, **I**, and **O** we must be on the alert for irregularities of idiom, and look beneath them to the intended sense. One such irregularity is omission of '-ever', as in 'Who hesitates is lost', 'I want to go where you go', 'When it rains it pours', 'She gets what she goes after'. An-other irregularity is the nontemporal use of 'always', 'whenever', 'sometimes', 'never'. E.g., the statement:

The sum of the angles of a triangle is always equal to two right angles

really means:

The sum of the angles of any triangle is equal to two right angles,

and may be rendered 'All *F* are *G*' where '*F*' represents 'sums of angles of triangles' and '*G*' represents 'equal to two right angles'.

Frequently an **I** construction having to do with time is implicit in the inflection of a verb; witness 'We saw Stromboli but it was not erupting', which comes out as 'Some *F* are *G*' with '*F*' construed as 'times we saw Stromboli' and '*G*' as 'times Stromboli was not erupt-ing'. (Cf. §8, (5).) Further examples of temporal idioms which call for a little reflection, if the logical structure is to be properly extracted, are:

I knew him before he lost his fortune,
I knew him while he was with Sunnyrinse.

'Before' and 'while' here appear in the guise of statement connectives, like 'and' or 'or' or '⊃'. But the statements are better analyzed as of the form **I**, 'Some F are G', where 'F' represents 'moments in which I knew him' and 'G' represents in the one case 'moments before he lost his fortune' and in the other case 'moments in which he was with Sunnyrinse'.

Reflection, indeed, should be the rule. Proper interpretation is not generally to be achieved through slavish dependence upon a check-list of idioms. 'Always' usually means 'at all moments', but it would be unjust to construe 'Tai always eats with chopsticks' as 'Tai eats with chopsticks at all moments'. The proper interpretation of this example is 'All F are G' where 'F' represents 'moments at which Tai eats' (not simply 'moments') and 'G' represents 'moments at which Tai eats with chopsticks'.

The importance of reflecting upon context and the common sense of the concrete situation, rather than looking to any mere glossary, is manifest even in so basic a construction as 'An F is G'. 'A lady is present' is surely of the form **I**, but 'A Scout is reverent' is more likely to be intended in the form **A**. Caution is similarly needed in equating 'any' with 'every'; for, whereas the statements:

John can outrun every man on the team,
John can outrun any man on the team

need no distinguishing, a divergence appears as soon as 'not' is applied:

John cannot outrun every man on the team,
John cannot outrun any man on the team.

The first two statements are indistinguishably 'All F are G' (where 'F' is 'man on the team' and 'G' is 'whom John can outrun'); the third, however, is 'Some F are not G', while the fourth is 'No F are G'.

EXERCISE

Classify the following statements as between **A**, **E**, **I**, and **O**, and specify in each case what terms answer to 'F' and 'G'.

Blessed are the meek.   We should all be as happy as kings.
All that glisters is not gold.   A policeman's lot is not an 'appy one.
There is no god but Allah.   There are smiles that make you blue.
Hope springs eternal.   I journeyed hither a Boeotian road.
The rule applies to everyone.   I was stopped by the door of a tomb.

§13. VENN'S DIAGRAMS

In a diagrammatic method due to Venn (1880), overlapping circles are used to represent the two terms of a categorical statement. The region in which the two circles overlap represents the objects which are both *F* and *G*. This region, called a *lens* in geometry, is shaded in Diagram 2. Where '*F*' is taken as 'French' and '*G*' as 'generals', this region represents the French generals. Correspondingly the part of the *F*-circle which lies outside the *G*-circle represents the objects which are *F* but not *G*: the French non-generals, in the example. This region, called a *lune* in geometry, is shaded in Diagram 1. The significance of shading is emptiness; thus Diagram 2 affirms that no *F* are *G*, while Diagram 1 affirms that no *F* are other than *G*, or in other words that all *F* are *G*.

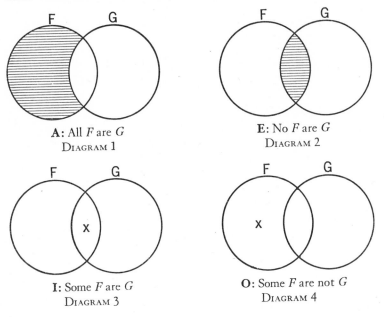

A: All *F* are *G*
DIAGRAM 1

E: No *F* are *G*
DIAGRAM 2

I: Some *F* are *G*
DIAGRAM 3

O: Some *F* are not *G*
DIAGRAM 4

Whiteness of a region in a Venn diagram means nothing but lack of information. In Diagram 2 the two lunes are left unshaded not because we think there are *F* which are not *G* and *G* which are not *F*, but because 'No *F* are *G*' gives us no information on the subject. All that 'No *F* are *G*' says is that the lens is empty, and this is all the information that Diagram 2 records. Similarly the lens and the right-hand lune in Diagram 1 are left unshaded merely because 'All *F* are *G*' gives us no information concerning these further regions.

The great region outside both circles represents the objects, if any, which are neither *F* nor *G*. It is left blank in Diagrams 1 and 2 because 'All *F* are *G*' throws no light on such objects, and neither does 'No *F* are *G*'.

So, whereas shading means emptiness, nonshading does not assure nonemptiness. For nonemptiness another symbol is used, viz., a cross. Thus 'Some *F* are *G*', which affirms nonemptiness of the lens, is expressed by putting a cross in the lens as in Diagram 3. Here again the blankness of the other areas implies neither emptiness nor nonemptiness, but represents mere lack of information.

'Some *F* are not *G*', finally, affirms no more nor less than that the part of the *F*-circle which lies outside the *G*-circle has something in it; so it is represented by putting a cross in that lune as in Diagram 4.

Certain simple laws of categorical statements are graphically reflected in the diagrams. The symmetry of Diagram 2, and of Diagram 3, reflects the fact that in **E** and **I** the order of terms is inessential: 'No *F* are *G*' amounts to 'No *G* are *F*', and 'Some *F* are *G*' to 'Some *G* are *F*'. Such switching of terms was known traditionally as *simple conversion*. The lopsidedness of Diagrams 1 and 4 reflects the fact that simple conversion is not in general applicable to **A** or **O**: 'All Greeks are men' is not to be confused with 'All men are Greeks', nor 'Some men are not Greeks' with 'Some Greeks are not men'.

A and **O** are mutual *contradictories*, or negations: **A** is true if and only if **O** is false. This relationship is reflected in the diagrams by the fact that Diagram 1 shows shading where, and only where, Diagram 4 shows a cross. With respect to blankness, or lack of information, Diagrams 1 and 4 are alike; with respect to information they simply and directly deny each other. Similarly **E** and **I** are mutual contradictories: **E** is true if and only if **I** is false.

A and E, 'All *F* are *G*' and 'No *F* are *G*', may also be felt to be somehow opposite to each other; however, their opposition is no matter of mutual negation, for we cannot say in general that A is true if and only if E is false. On the contrary, examples chosen at random are as likely as not to cause A and E to come out *both* false; this happens in particular when '*F*' is taken as 'French' and '*G*' as 'generals'. Similarly I and O are quite commonly both true, of course, as in this same example. But A and O are never both true nor both false, and similarly for E and I; here are the pairs of contradictories, or mutual negations.

Whereas A and E are very commonly both false and I and O are very commonly both true, it is less common for I and O to come out both false, or for A and E to come out both true; but these things will happen where there are no *F*. Clearly, where there are no *F*, 'Some *F* are *G*' and 'Some *F* are not *G*' will both be false. Also, where there are no *F*, 'No *F* are *G*' will obviously be true; and yet 'All *F* are *G*' will likewise be true, in that there will be no *F* which is not *G*. These points are brought out diagrammatically by shading the *F*-circle in its entirety, as in Diagram 5, to mean that there are no *F*. This diagram verifies both A and E, for it shows both of the areas shaded which are shaded in Diagrams 1 and 2; and it falsifies both I

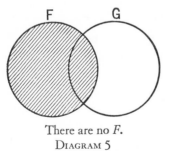

There are no *F*.
DIAGRAM 5

and O, for it shows shading in place of both crosses of Diagrams 3 and 4.

A, 'All *F* are *G*', would seem at first glance to be stronger than I, 'Some *F* are *G*', and to imply it; but it does not, because of the possibility of there being no *F*. Diagram 5 depicts the very situation where, though A holds, I fails. It may happen that all my dimes are shiny (in that I have no dime to the contrary), and yet be false that some of my dimes are shiny, simply because I have no dimes at all. The most we can say is that if all *F* are *G* *and there are F* then some *F* are *G*.

If the reader thinks it odd to say that all of one's dimes are shiny when one has no dimes, he is perhaps interpreting 'All *F* are *G*' to mean, not simply 'There is no *F* that is not *G*', but 'There are *F* and none of them is *G*'. This, however, even if it be one of several defensible interpretations of an ambiguous idiom, is clearly not the interpretation which would make **A** the simple contradictory, or negation, of **O**: 'Some *F* are not *G*'. It is the general logical practice, and a convenient one, to understand 'All *F* are *G*' simply as the contradictory of **O**.

Diagram 5 as it stands was seen to reflect the fact that **I** does not follow from **A**. But Venn diagrams can also be used for constructive ends, as in showing that **I** follows from **A** supplemented with 'There are *F*'. To show this we set down the diagram for **A**, viz. Diagram 1, and then enter 'There are *F*' into the diagram by putting a cross in the *F*-circle. The cross must go in the unshaded part of the *F*-circle, since the shaded part is known to be empty. So the result, showing a cross in the lens as it does, verifies **I**.

What has been said of the relationship between **A** and **I** applies equally to **E** and **O**: from **E**, 'No *F* are *G*', we may infer **O**, 'Some *F* are not *G*', only if we make the further assumption that there are *F*. Diagram 5 shows the situation where, though **E** holds, **O** fails. But we can show that **O** follows from **E** and 'There are *F*', by putting a cross in the *F*-circle of Diagram 2 and observing that we have verified **O**.

Finally let us observe a couple of simple inferences in which a conclusion is drawn from just a single premiss, or assumption, instead of from two:

Some *F* are *G*,   There are no *F*,
∴ There are *G*.   ∴ No *F* are *G*.

These inferences are justified respectively by Diagrams 3 and 5; for Diagram 3 shows a cross in the *G*-circle in support of the conclusion 'There are *G*', and Diagram 5 shows a shaded lens in support of the conclusion 'No *F* are *G*'.

EXERCISES

1. Does **A, E, I** or **O** follow from 'There are no G'? Does **A, E, I**, or **O** conflict with 'There are no G'? Appeal to diagrams.
2. Make a diagram for 'All F are G and all G are F'. Is this compatible with 'No F are G'? Explain.

§14. SYLLOGISMS

What are spoken of traditionally as *syllogisms*[1] are arguments wherein a categorical statement is derived as conclusion from two categorical statements as premisses, the three statements being so related that there are altogether just three terms, each of which appears in two of the statements. Six examples follow; one of them was already noted in §12.

All men are mortal,   All G are H,
All Greeks are men;   All F are G;
∴ All Greeks are mortal.   ∴ All F are H.

No men are perfect,   No G are H,
All Greeks are men;   All F are G;
∴ No Greeks are perfect.   ∴ No F are H.

All philosophers are wise,   All G are H,
Some Greeks are philosophers;   Some F are G;
∴ Some Greeks are wise.   ∴ Some F are H.

No philosophers are wicked,   No G are H,
Some Greeks are philosophers;   Some F are G;
∴ Some Greeks are not wicked.   ∴ Some F are not H.

All Greeks are men,   All H are G,
Some mortals are not men;   Some F are not G;
∴ Some mortals are not Greeks.   ∴ Some F are not H.

Some men are not Greeks,   Some G are not H,
All men are mortal;   All G are F;
∴ Some mortals are not Greeks.   ∴ Some F are not H.

---

[1] *Categorical* syllogisms, more specifically, to distinguish them from *hypothetical* syllogisms, which are certain truth-functional arguments manageable by the methods of Part I.

A "valid" syllogism, ordinarily so-called, is a syllogism of such form as to be incapable of leading from true premisses to a false conclusion. An easy test of validity of syllogisms is afforded by Venn's diagrams. Three overlapping circles are used, as in Diagrams 6–7, to represent the three terms 'F', 'G', and 'H' of the syllogism. We inscribe the

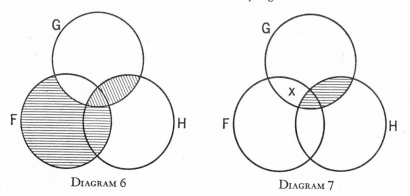

DIAGRAM 6   DIAGRAM 7

content of the two premisses into the diagram by the method explained in connection with Diagrams 1–4, and then we inspect the diagram to see whether the content of the conclusion has automatically appeared in the diagram as a result. Thus, let us test the second syllogism of the above list. We record its first premiss, 'No G are H', by shading the lens common to the G-circle and the H-circle; then we record the second premiss, 'All F are G', by shading the lune which lies in the F-circle outside the G-circle. The result is Diagram 6. It bears out the desired conclusion 'No F are H', since the lens common to the F-circle and the H-circle is fully shaded.

Let us next test the fourth of our six examples. We record the first premiss, 'No G are H', as before, and then we record the second premiss, 'Some F are G', by putting a cross in what remains of the lens common to the F-circle and the G-circle; the result is Diagram 7. It bears out the conclusion 'Some F are not H', there being a cross in the F-circle outside the H-circle.

It is left to the reader to construct diagrams verifying the remaining four of the above six syllogisms. (In the last of them, the second premiss should be handled first; note why.)

The diagrammatic method can be used to determine not merely whether a given conclusion follows from given premisses, but whether any conclusion at all (of a syllogistic kind) is capable of following from given premisses. For, the conclusion—in order to be the conclusion of a so-called syllogism at all—must be 'All *F* are *H*', 'No *F* are *H*', 'Some *F* are *H*', or 'Some *F* are not *H*'; hence, unless the two bottom circles of the finished diagram exhibit one of the four patterns

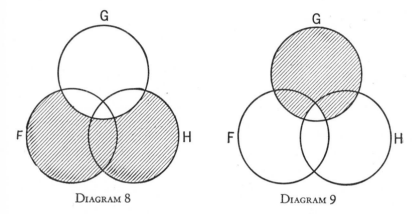

DIAGRAM 8   DIAGRAM 9

shown in Diagrams 1–4, there is no conclusion. In Diagram 8, e.g., the bottom circles exhibit none of the four patterns of Diagrams 1–4; and this shows that the premisses 'All *H* are *G*' and 'All *F* are *G*' cannot be the premisses of any valid syllogism at all.

As a further example consider the premisses 'All *G* are *H*' and 'All *G* are *F*'. These are recorded in Diagram 9; and we see that the diagram justifies no categorical conclusion in '*F*' and '*H*'. But this pair of premisses is interesting in that it *almost* justifies a categorical conclusion in '*F*' and '*H*', viz., 'Some *F* are *H*'. If we add just the further premiss 'There are *G*', to allow us to put a cross in the one part of the *G*-circle that remains unshaded, we then find the conclusion 'Some *F* are *H*' justified by a cross common to the *F*-circle and the *H*-circle. Thus the reinforced syllogism:

All Spartans are brave,	All *G* are *H*,
All Spartans are Greeks,	All *G* are *F*,
There are Spartans;	There are *G*;
∴ Some Greeks are brave	∴ Some *F* are *H*

is valid.

7

In the traditional terminology the term which plays the rôle of '*F*' in 'All *F* are *G*', 'No *F* are *G*', 'Some *F* are *G*', or 'Some *F* are not *G*' is called the *subject* of the statement. The other term, playing the role of '*G*', is called the *predicate*.[1] The predicate of the conclusion is called the *major term* of the syllogism, and the subject of the conclusion is called the *minor term* of the syllogism. The remaining term, occurring in both premisses but not in the conclusion, is called the *middle term* of the syllogism. Thus all the foregoing examples have been lettered in such a way as to make '*F*' the minor term, '*G*' the middle term, and '*H*' the major term.

The premiss which contains the middle and major terms is called the *major premiss* of the syllogism. The other premiss, containing the middle and minor terms, is called the *minor premiss*. Thus all the foregoing examples have been stated with the major premiss first and the minor premiss second.

Medieval logicians had a scheme for coding the various forms of syllogisms. They stipulated the respective forms of the premisses and conclusion (as among **A, E, I**, and **O**) by a triple of letters; thus '**EAO**' meant that the major premiss was of form **E**, the minor premiss **A**, and the conclusion **O**. This much was said to indicate the *mood* of a syllogism. But, even given the mood of a syllogism, there remains the question whether the major premiss has the major term as subject and the middle term as predicate, or vice versa; and correspondingly for the minor premiss. The four possibilities of arrangement which thus arise are called *figures*, and referred to by number as follows:

	1st	2nd	3rd	4th
Major premiss:	*GH*	*HG*	*GH*	*HG*
Minor premiss:	*FG*	*FG*	*GF*	*GF*
Conclusion:	*FH*	*FH*	*FH*	*FH*

Specification of mood and figure determines the form of a syllogism completely. Thus the six examples at the beginning of the present section are respectively **AAA** in the first figure, **EAE** in the first figure, **AII** in the first figure, **EIO** in the first figure, **AOO** in the second figure, and **OAO** in the third figure.

The fourth of the above six, viz. **EIO** in the first figure, can be given variant forms by simple conversion (cf. preceding section) of one or both premisses. We thus get:

No *H* are *G*,	No *G* are *H*,	No *H* are *G*,
Some *F* are *G*;	Some *G* are *F*;	Some *G* are *F*;
∴ Some *F* are not *H*.	∴ Some *F* are not *H*.	∴ Some *F* are not *H*.

These are **EIO** in the second, third, and fourth figures. Similarly **EAE** and **AII** in the first figure (the second and third of the examples at the begin-

---

[1] The word 'predicate' will receive a different and more important meaning in §23.

ning of the section) are carried by simple conversion into **EAE** in the second figure and **AII** in the third.

The four syllogisms last mentioned, viz. **EAE** in the first and second figures and **AII** in the first and third, can be carried over into four further syllogisms by simple conversion of each of their conclusions. If we do this, though, we must afterward reletter '*F*' as '*H*' and '*H*' as '*F*' throughout the results in order that '*F*' may continue to represent the minor term and '*H*' the major term; also we must switch the order of the premisses, so that the major premiss may continue to appear first. The results, which the reader will do well to reproduce, are **AEE** in the fourth and second figures and **IAI** in the fourth and third.

Altogether, then, we have found fifteen valid forms:

First Figure	*Second Figure*
AAA, EAE, AII, EIO	**EAE, AEE, EIO, AOO**

Third Figure	*Fourth Figure*
IAI, AII, OAO, EIO	**AEE, IAI, EIO**

Note that no two of these fifteen have the same premisses, when differences of figure are taken into account. We have here fifteen different pairs of premisses, each with its appropriate conclusion. And it is readily verified by inspection of diagrams that none of these fifteen pairs of premisses justifies any further syllogistic conclusion in addition to the one here indicated for it.

Viewed in terms merely of combinations and without regard to the existence of a valid conclusion, there are sixty-four possibilities for the premisses of a syllogism. They may be **AA**, or **AE**, or **AI**, or **AO**, or **EA**, or **EE**, etc., to sixteen possibilities, and each of these sixteen may occur in any of four figures. In addition to the fifteen pairs of premisses which have been found to yield valid syllogisms, therefore, there are forty-nine further pairs to consider. Now we saw in connection with Diagrams 8–9 how to check whether a given pair of premisses justifies any syllogistic conclusion at all. If the reader so tests these forty-nine pairs (an hour's pastime), he will find that none of them justifies a syllogistic conclusion. The fifteen forms of syllogism listed above are the only valid ones.

In addition, however, nine forms come in for honorable mention. These nine are forms which, like the above example of the Spartans, need a small reinforcing premiss. 'There are *F*' fills the bill for five of them, 'There are *G*' for three, and 'There are *H*' for one. Let me simply record the nine in tabular fashion:

1st Figure	*2nd Figure*	*3rd Figure*	*4th Figure*	*Added Premiss*
AAI, EAO	**AEO, EAO**		**AEO**	There are *F*
		AAI, EAO	**EAO**	There are *G*
			AAI	There are *H*

Inferences involving so-called singular statements such as 'Socrates is a man', e.g.:

All men are mortal,   Socrates is a man;   ∴ Socrates is mortal,

were traditionally fitted into the syllogistic mold by treating the singular statements as of the form **A**. This procedure is artificial but not incorrect; we can construe 'Socrates is a man' as 'All *G* are *H*' where '*G*' represents 'things identical with Socrates'. The above inference thus was classified as **AAA** in the first figure. But we shall end up, in Part IV, with a different treatment of singular inference.

In traditional logic it was customary to propound various rules whereby to test the validity of a syllogism. Examples: every valid syllogism has a universal premiss (**A** or **E**); every valid syllogism has an affirmative premiss (**A** or **I**); every valid syllogism with a particular premiss (**I** or **O**) has a particular conclusion; every valid syllogism with a negative premiss (**E** or **O**) has a negative conclusion. There are further rules whose formulation depends on a concept of "distribution" which has been omitted from the present exposition. As a practical method of appraising syllogisms, rules are less convenient than the method of diagrams. Indeed, the very notions of syllogism and mood and figure need never have been touched on in these pages, except out of consideration for their prominence in logic during two thousand years; for we can apply the diagram test to a given argument out of hand, without pausing to consider where the argument may fit in the taxonomy of syllogisms. The diagram test is equally available for many arguments which do not fit any of the arbitrary delimited set of forms known as syllogisms.

EXERCISES

1. Construct diagrams verifying the remaining four of the six syllogisms at the beginning of the section.

2. Determine by diagrams what syllogistic conclusion, if any, follows from each of the following pairs of premisses.

All who blaspheme are wicked; No saint blasphemes.

No snakes fly; Some snakes lay eggs.

Nothing that lays eggs has feathers; Some fishes have feathers.

Whatever interests me bores George; Whatever interests Mabel bores George.

Whatever interests me bores George; Whatever interests George bores Mabel.

3. For each of the pairs in Exercise 2 which failed to yield a syllogistic conclusion, determine by diagram whether a supplementary

premiss of the form 'There are F', or 'There are G', or 'There are H', would suffice to bring forth a syllogistic conclusion.

§15.   LIMITS OF THESE METHODS

The inferences to which we have thus far been applying Venn's diagrams have all been made up of categoricals **A**, **E**, **I**, or **O** plus an occasional auxiliary of the type 'There are F'. Actually the diagrams can be used somewhat more widely; e.g., in arguing from the

Premisses: Everyone east of the tracks is either slovenly or poor,
            Not everyone east of the tracks is poor,
to the

Conclusion: Some slovenly persons are not poor.

We set up a three circle diagram as usual, wherein 'F' means 'slovenly persons', 'G' means 'persons east of the tracks', and 'H' means 'poor persons'. Then the first premiss is entered in the diagram by shading as empty just that compartment of the circle G which lies outside

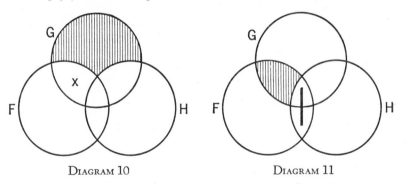

DIAGRAM 10   DIAGRAM 11

both F and H; see Diagram 10. The compartment thus shaded is neither a lune nor a lens, but a third shape. It represents persons east of the tracks who are neither slovenly nor poor; and just such persons are denied existence by the first premiss. Now the second premiss, which says in effect 'Some G are not H', is recorded as usual by putting a cross in what remains of G outside H. The result is seen to substantiate the conclusion 'Some F are not H', since there is a cross in F outside H.

An innovation due to C. I. Lewis (1918) is the use of a long bar instead of the cross in Venn's diagrams. The advantage of the bar is that it can be made to lie across a boundary and thus indicate non-emptiness of a compound region. This innovation is useful in reasoning, e.g., from the

> Premisses: All of the witnesses who hold stock in the firm are
> employees,
> Some of the witnesses are employees or hold stock in
> the firm

to the

> Conclusion: Some of the witnesses are employees.

We set up a three-circle diagram in which '*F*' means 'witnesses', '*G*' means 'stockholders in the firm', and '*H*' means 'employees'. The lens common to *F* and *G*, then, stands for the witnesses who hold stock in the firm; so, on the basis of the first premiss, we shade the part of that lens which lies outside *H*. (See Diagram 11.) Next, on the basis of the other premiss, we run a bar through as much of the unshaded *F* as lies within *H* or *G*. The meaning of the bar is that one or another part of the total region marked by the bar has something in it. But the bar lies wholly within *F* and *H*; so the conclusion is sustained.

The utility and versatility of Venn's diagrams are particularly evident from these last two examples. A shortcoming of the diagrams, however, is that they lend themselves less readily to arguments involving four or more terms. A diagram of overlapping ellipses can be constructed for four-term arguments, but it calls for careful drawing; and there is no way whatever of constructing a diagram which will exhibit *five* or more ellipses or other simple regions in all combinations of overlapping. Where many terms are involved we may, however, try to break the argument down into parts involving manageably few terms. The following example is from Lewis Carroll:

> Premisses: "(1) The only animals in this house are cats;
> "(2) Every animal is suitable for a pet, that loves to
> gaze at the moon;
> "(3) When I detest an animal, I avoid it;
> "(4) No animals are carnivorous, unless they prowl
> at night;

"(5) No cat fails to kill mice;
"(6) No animals ever take to me, except what are in
      this house;
"(7) Kangaroos are not suitable for pets;
"(8) None but carnivora kill mice;
"(9) I detest animals that do not take to me;
"(10) Animals that prowl at night always love to
      gaze at the moon."
Conclusion: "I always avoid a kangaroo."

This argument can be broken down as follows. From (1) and (5) we get the *lemma* or intermediate conclusion:

(11)   All animals in this house kill mice;

this is the sort of step to which a simple three-term diagram is adequate. From (8) and (11), similarly, we get:

(12)   All animals in this house are carnivora.

From (4) and (12) we get:

(13)   All animals in this house prowl at night.

From (6) and (13) we get:

(14)   All animals that take to me prowl at night.

Step by step in this fashion we can proceed to our desired conclusion, never using more than a three-term diagram for any one step. (If the reader cares to carry this through in detail, he should think of the universe as limited for purposes of the argument to animals—thus never bothering with 'animals' itself as a term.)

So we see that the purely mechanical method of diagrams proves inadequate when an argument turns on a *large number of terms*; a supplementary technique has to be invoked, such as that of resolving the argument into parts. Now another place where the unaided method of diagrams bogs down is where there is an *admixture of truth functions*, as in the following example:

Premisses: If all applicants who received the second announcement are of the class of '00, then some applicants did not receive the second announcement.

Either all applicants received the second announcement or all applicants are of the class of '00.

Conclusion: If all applicants of the class of '00 received the second announcement then some applicants not of the class of '00 received the second announcement.

If we assign 'F', 'G', and 'H' in obvious fashion, the inference takes on the form:

All F who are G are $H \supset$ some F are not G,
All F are G v all F are H,
$\therefore$ All F who are H are $G \supset$ some F who are not H are G.

Diagrams are suited to handling the components 'All F who are G are H', 'Some F are not G', etc., and the methods of Part I are suited to '$\supset$' and 'v'; but just how may we splice the two techniques in order to handle a combined inference of the above kind?

So it is time to address ourselves to a more comprehensive theory. The three formulas last set forth, containing 'F', 'G', and 'H', are *schemata* of a sort, but differ from the schemata of Part I in containing 'F', 'G', etc. and such words as 'all', 'some', 'who are', etc., to the exclusion of 'p', 'q', etc. In the ensuing sections such schemata will be reduced to a logical notation subject to a "decision procedure"— i.e., a mechanical routine for deciding validity, implication, consistency, etc. Such a decision procedure exists for truth-functional schemata in truth-value analysis; for the new class of schemata, however, the procedure will have to be more elaborate. Once it is at hand, all inferences of the sort we have been considering in the present Part—including the stubborn last example—can be adjudged mechanically by an implication test on premises and conclusion.

EXERCISES

1. Check the soundness of this inference by diagram:

All of the witnesses who hold stock in the firm are employees,
All of the witnesses are employees or hold stock in the firm;
$\therefore$ All of the witnesses are employees.

2. Check the soundness of this inference by diagram:

Everyone who knows both George and Mabel admires Mabel,
Some who know Mabel do not admire her;
∴ Some who know Mabel do not know George.

3. Check the soundness of this inference by diagram:

Everything is either a substance or an attribute,
Modes are not substances;
∴ Modes are attributes.

Hint: Be prepared to shade the limitless region outside all circles.

4. Finish the kangaroo argument, and supply a three-term diagram to justify each step.

§16.   QUANTIFICATION

The so-called *existential quantifier* '(∃x)' corresponds to the words 'there is something x such that'. Application of '(∃x)' to the expression:

(1)   x is a book . x is boring

in the fashion:

(2)   (∃x)(x is a book . x is boring)

is called *existential quantification* of (1). Also the result, (2), is spoken of as the existential quantification of (1). To say that (2) is true is to say that there is at least one object in the universe such that, when 'x' in (1) is thought of as naming it, (1) becomes true. Thus (2) goes into words fairly literally as:

(3)   There is something such that it is a book and it is boring;

more briefly as:

(4)   Something is a book and is boring;

more briefly still as:

Some books are boring.

Version (4) suggests that instead of adopting the queer and elaborate notation (2) we might have invented a simpler symbolism:

(5)   s is a book . s is boring,

where 's' is short for 'something'. However, this suggestion is wrong; for, given (5), we would have no way of deciding whether to interpret it in the manner of (4) or in the quite different manner:

(6)   Something is a book and something is boring.

The particular statements (4) and (6) are by chance both true, but we get contrasting truth values if we shift our example from 'book' and 'boring' to 'square' and 'round':

(7)   Something is a square and is round,   (false)

(8)   Something is a square and something is round.   (true)

   One of the misleading things about ordinary language is that the word 'something' masquerades as a name but deviates in its behavior at crucial points. When a genuine name is used, the distinction noted between (7) and (8) and between (4) and (6) evaporates; the state-ments:

> Maud is a book and is boring,
> Maud is a book and Maud is boring,

e.g., are quite interchangeable. When 'something' is used, on the other hand, *scope* becomes important: we must distinguish visibly in one way or another between the case where the scope of 'something' is 'is a book and is boring', as in (4), and the case where 'something' recurs with two scopes, 'is a book' and 'is boring', as in (6). Ordinary language effects this distinction, in the case of (4) and (6), by using a compound predicate in (4) and not in (6). In more complex cases, ordinary language has to resort to various circumlocutions to maintain the distinction. In a notation adapted to purposes of logical analysis, however, uniformity is wanted. Thus it is that the notation of quan-tification exemplified in (2) is adopted, wherein the scope of 'some-thing' is indicated explicitly by parentheses. The difference between (4) and (6) is maintained by writing (2) for (4) and, for (6), the fol-lowing:

(9) $(\exists x)(x$ is a book$)$. $(\exists x)(x$ is boring$)$.

What (2) says is that at least one thing x fulfills the simultaneous conditions 'x is a book' and 'x is boring'; what (9) says, on the other hand, is that at least one thing fulfills 'x is a book' and at least one thing, same or different, fulfills 'x is boring'.

The existential quantifier has a companion-piece in the *universal quantifier* '(x)', which corresponds to the words 'each thing x (in the universe) is such that'. Application of '(x)' to the expression:

(10)   x is identical with x

in the fashion:

(11)   (x)(x is identical with x)

is called *universal quantification* of (10); and the result (11) is also spoken of as the universal quantification of (10). To say that (11) is true is to say that, no matter what object in the universe be imagined named by 'x' in (10), (10) becomes true. Thus (11) goes into words fairly literally as:

(12)   Each thing is such that it is identical with itself,

or more briefly:

Everything is identical with itself.

Similarly the quantification:

(13)   (x)(x is a man ⊃ x is mortal)

goes into words fairly literally as:

Each thing is such that if it is a man then it is mortal,

or more briefly:

All men are mortal.

The notation of universal quantification is prompted by a structural consideration like that observed for existential quantification: the necessity of indicating scope. We saw in (7)–(8) the necessity of indicating just how large a portion of a statement is to be comprised within the scope of a given occurrence of the word 'something'. The corresponding necessity in the case of 'everything' can be seen by contrasting the truth:

(14)   Everything is red or not red

with the falsehood:

(15)   Everything is red or everything is not-red.

In the notation of quantification, (14) becomes:

(16) $(x)[x$ is red $\mathbf{v} -(x$ is red$)]$

while (15) becomes:

(17) $(x)(x$ is red$) \mathbf{v} (x) -(x$ is red$)$.

Statements of ordinary language which at first glance seem to be conjunctions or conditionals often demand interpretation as quantifications of conjunctions or conditionals. Examples are:

(18) Sadie stole something at the Emporium and exchanged it for a blouse,

(19) If Sadie wants anything she manages to get it.

These must be interpretated as quantifications:

(20) $(\exists x)$(Sadie stole x at the Emporium . Sadie exchanged x for a blouse),

(21) (x)(Sadie wants $x \supset$ Sadie manages to get x),

rather than as a conjunction and conditional:

(22) $(\exists x)$(Sadie stole x at the Emporium) . Sadie exchanged it for a blouse,

(23) $(\exists x)$(Sadie wants $x) \supset$ Sadie manages to get it.

For, the 'it' of (18) clearly refers back across 'and' to 'something', and correspondingly the 'it' of (19) refers back to 'anything'. The quantifiers must be made to cover the whole compound as in (20) and (21), rather than just the first clause as in (22) and (23), so as to reach out to a lagging recurrence of 'x' in the position of 'it'.

Universal and existential quantification are intimately connected in meaning, through negation. If we write 'Fx' to mean 'x is an F', then '$(\exists x)Fx$' may be read:

There are F,   Some things are F, F exist;

hence its negation '$-(\exists x)Fx$' means

There are no F,   Nothing is an F, F do not exist.

But to say that there are no F is the same as saying that everything is non-F: '$(x) -Fx$'. We thus have two ways of saying that there are no F: '$-(\exists x)Fx$' and '$(x) -Fx$'.

Again, since '$(x)Fx$' may be read:

All is F,   Everything is an F,

Each thing is an F,   There is nothing but F,

its negation '$-(x)Fx$' means:

Not everything is an F,   There are non-F,

which may equally well be rendered '$(\exists x) -Fx$'. Thus the combination of signs '$-(\exists x)$' has the same effect as '$(x) -$', and the combination '$-(x)$' has the same effect as '$(\exists x) -$'. It follows that we could get along without universal quantifiers altogether, adhering to existential ones; for, instead of writing '$(x)Fx$' we could always write the negation '$-(\exists x) -Fx$'. Equally we could get along without existential quantifiers, adhering to universal ones; for, instead of writing '$(\exists x)Fx$' we could always write '$-(x) -Fx$'. Retention of the two kinds of quantifiers is dictated only by convenience.

Next let us survey the categorical forms **A**, **E**, **I**, and **O** (§12) in terms of quantification. **A**, to begin with, is expressed as '$(x)(Fx \supset Gx)$', as already seen in the example (13) above. (This formulation, by the way, follows precisely the lines of what was called a "generalized conditional" in §3; cf. especially (2) of §3.) This being the case, beginners commonly make the mistake of concluding that **I** must become '$(\exists x)(Fx \supset Gx)$'. Since 'All F are G' and 'Some F are G' are alike verbally except for 'All' and 'Some', it is expected that their formulations in terms of quantification will be alike except for '(x)' and '$(\exists x)$'. Actually the proper formulation of **I** is rather '$(\exists x)(Fx \,.\, Gx)$'—as seen in (2) above. The words 'Some F are G' and 'All F are G', insofar as they suggest parallelism of structure, are misleading; the proper contrast of structure is better brought out by the expanded phrasings 'Some things are *both F and G*', 'Everything is, *if* an F, a G'.

To discourage the erroneous rendering '$(\exists x)(Fx \supset Gx)$' of **I** once and for all, let us stop to see what '$(\exists x)(Fx \supset Gx)$' really says. '$Fx \supset Gx$', to begin with, holds for any object x for which '$Fx \,.\, -Gx$'

fails; thus it holds for every object x which is non-F, and it holds also for every object x which is G. Hence '$(\exists x)(Fx \supset Gx)$' says only that there is at least one object which is non-F or G; and this is bound to be true, regardless of how 'F' and 'G' are interpreted, except in the one extreme case where 'F' is true of everything in the universe and 'G' is true of nothing. The form '$(\exists x)(Fx \supset Gx)$' is so trivial, so rarely false, as to be seldom worth affirming.

Correct versions of **E** and **O** are straightway discoverable from those of **A** and **I**. **E**, 'No F are G', amounts to 'All F are non-G' and thus becomes '$(x)(Fx \supset -Gx)$'; whereas **O**, paralleling **I**, becomes '$(\exists x)(Fx . -Gx)$'. Thus, to sum up:

A: All F are G	**E**: No F are G
$(x)(Fx \supset Gx)$	$(x)(Fx \supset -Gx)$
I: Some F are G	**O**: Some F are not G
$(\exists x)(Fx . Gx)$	$(\exists x)(Fx . -Gx)$

If we think of the universe as limited to a finite set of objects a, b, ... , h, we can expand existential quantifications into alternations and universal quantifications into conjunctions; '$(\exists x)Fx$' and '$(x)Fx$' become respectively:

$$Fa \vee Fb \vee \ldots \vee Fh, \qquad Fa . Fb . \ldots . Fh.$$

The distinction between (2) and (9) then comes out quite clearly; '$(\exists x)(Fx . Gx)$' becomes:

$$Fa . Ga .\vee. Fb . Gb .\vee. \ldots .\vee. Fh . Gh,$$

whereas '$(\exists x)Fx . (\exists x)Gx$' becomes:

$$Fa \vee Fb \vee \ldots \vee Fh . Ga \vee Gb \vee \ldots \vee Gh.$$

The distinction between (16) and (17) comes out equally clearly. Furthermore the interchangeability of '$-(x)$' with '$(\exists x) -$' and of '$-(\exists x)$' with '$(x) -$' turns out to be a mere application of DeMorgan's laws (§10); for, '$-(x)Fx$' and '$(\exists x) -Fx$' become respectively:

$$-(Fa . Fb . \ldots . Fh), \qquad -Fa \vee -Fb \vee \ldots \vee -Fh,$$

and '$-(\exists x)Fx$' and '$(x) -Fx$' become respectively:

$$-(Fa \vee Fb \vee \ldots \vee Fh), \qquad -Fa . -Fb . \ldots . -Fh.$$

It thus appears that quantification could be dispensed with altogether in favor of truth-functions if we were willing to agree for all purposes on a fixed and finite and listed universe $a, b, \ldots, h$. However, we are unwilling; it is convenient to allow with some explicitness for variations in the choice of universe. This is convenient not only because philosophers disagree regarding the limits of reality, but also because—as already noted in the preceding section in connection with the kangaroo problem—some logical arguments can be simplified by deliberately limiting the "universe of discourse" to animals, say, or to persons, or to the employees of a given firm, for the space of the problem in hand.[1] For most problems, moreover, the relevant universe comprises objects which we are in no position to list in the manner of $a, b, \ldots, h$. For many problems the relevant universe even comprises infinitely many objects; e.g., the integers. Thus it is that quantification is here to stay.

EXERCISES

1. Rewrite these with help of quantifiers:

John cannot outrun any man on the team,
John cannot outrun every man on the team.

2. Rewrite the premises and conclusion about the slovenly and the poor (§15) with help of quantifiers. Similarly for the other examples in §15 and in the exercises to §15.

3. Supposing the universe to comprise just $a, b, \ldots, h$, express these truth-functionally:

$(\exists x)(Fx \vee Gx),$	$(x)(Fx \vee Gx),$	$(x)(Fx . Gx),$
$(\exists x)Fx \vee (\exists x)Gx,$	$(x)Fx \vee (x)Gx,$	$(x)Fx . (x)Gx.$

Which come out equivalent to one another?

§17. UNIFORM QUANTIFICATIONAL SCHEMATA

The letter 'x' as used in quantification is merely a mark for cross-reference to a quantifier; no deeper significance is to be sought for it. In general quantification theory, as we shall see in Part III, further

---

[1] The notion of universe of discourse goes back to DeMorgan (1847).

letters 'y', 'z', etc. will be needed to the same purpose. Meanwhile, however, we can do a good deal of logic without such further inroads on the alphabet.

Expressions such as:

(1) x is a book, $x = x$, x is a man $\supset$ x is mortal,

which are like statements except for containing 'x' without a quantifier, are called *open sentences*.[1] They are fragmentary clauses, neither true nor false as they stand, and of interest only as potential parts of *closed sentences* such as:

$(\exists x)(x$ is a book$)$, $(x)(x = x)$, $(x)(x$ is a man $\supset$ x is mortal$)$.

Closed sentences are what have hitherto been called statements; it is just these that have truth values. Open sentences are not statements. The analogue of an unquantified 'x' in ordinary language is a pronoun for which no grammatical antecedent is expressed or understood; and the analogue of an open sentence is a clause containing such a dangling pronoun. E.g., the open sentences (1) correspond to 'it is a book', 'it is identical with itself', and 'if it is a man then it is mortal'. Open sentences may, as notational forms, be described as differing from various closed sentences only in lacking a quantifier; or they may be described equally well as differing from various other closed sentences only in containing 'x' in place of a name of a specific object.

Open sentences are neither true nor false, but they may, like terms (cf. §12), be said to be *true of* and *false of* various objects. The open sentence 'x is a book' may, like the term 'book' itself, be said to be true of each book and false of everything else; and 'x is a book . x is boring' may be said to be true of each boring book and false of everything else. '$x = x$' and 'x is a man $\supset$ x is mortal' are true of everything. In general, to say that an open sentence is true of a given object is to say that the open sentence becomes a true statement when 'x' is

---

[1]I follow Carnap in this terminology. In previous writings I have called them *matrices*, using this word in a sense unrelated to the mathematical sense of the word. But "matrices" in the mathematical sense have proved to have more relevance to certain researches in the field of logic itself than I had counted on, so that my use of the word to refer to open sentences proves unfortunate. Logicians having for the most part wisely eschewed my use of the word, my switching to Carnap's phrase involves a minimum of betrayal. The older term for the purpose is 'propositional function', or 'statement function'; but this is to be avoided because, in the more basic mathematical sense of the word, a function is a certain type of relation rather than a notation.

reinterpreted as a name of that object. The notion of the *extension* of a term (§12) likewise carries over to open sentences: the extension of an open sentence is the class of all the objects of which the open sentence is true.

The schematic letters '*p*', '*q*', etc. of Part I, and '*F*', '*G*', etc. of the present part, differ basically in function from '*x*'. Whereas '*x*' can appear in sentences—even in closed sentences, with help of a quantifier—on the other hand '*p*', '*q*', etc. and '*F*', '*G*', etc., cannot appear in sentences at all;[1] they are merely dummy sentences and dummy terms, used in schemata which depict outward forms of sentences.

The schemata with which we were occupied in Part I were truth-functional schemata: truth functions of just the schematic letters '*p*', '*q*', etc. But the notation now at hand engenders schemata of further kinds. The schematic letters '*F*', '*G*', etc., standing in place of terms, combine with '*x*' to form '*Fx*', '*Gx*', etc. ('*x* is an *F*', '*x* is a *G*', etc.). These expressions and all truth functions of them, e.g.:

$$-Fx, \qquad Fx \mathbin{.} Gx \mathbin{\vee} Fx, \qquad -Fx \equiv \mathbin{.} Gx \supset Hx,$$

will be called *uniform open quantificational schemata* or briefly *open schemata*. Finally the quantifications of open schemata, and all truth functions of such quantifications, are *uniform closed quantificational schemata*. Examples are:

$$(x)Fx, \quad (\exists x)Fx, \quad (x)(Fx \supset Gx), \quad (x)Fx \supset (\exists x)(Fx \mathbin{.} -Gx).$$

These will usually be spoken of briefly as *closed schemata*. The truth-functional schemata are indeed likewise closed (through lacking '*x*' altogether), but the phrase "truth-functional schemata" will serve to segregate them such times as they continue to come into consideration. The reason for the qualifier 'uniform', as applied above to open and closed quantificational schemata, is that the category of quantificational schemata both open and closed is due to be vastly extended in Part III. But the qualifier will often be omitted in the present pages.

Schemata are the medium of our technical work, but it is in sen-

---

[1]Exception, for the record: they may appear within quotation marks in sentences. But any meaningless mark may appear within quotation marks in a sentence. The quotation as a whole is a meaningful name of the meaningless mark.

rences that the results of such work find their application. Hence, if the technical developments are not to lose meaning for us, we must keep the relationship of correspondence between sentences and schemata clearly in mind. Roughly the relation is that '*F*', '*G*', etc., represent terms; but more needs to be said.

A term may, as remarked in §12, be thought of indifferently as singular or plural and as substantive, adjective, or verb. Thus, though a tendency to think of terms mainly as substantives has no doubt persisted, grammatical distinctions irrelevant to logic have been overcome to some degree. But there is another linguistic limitation, of a less purely grammatical kind, which must likewise be overcome in thinking of terms; viz., the limitation to conveniently unified phrases. *Every* open sentence, no matter how complex, must admit of being treated as of the form '*Fx*'. When the sentence is '*x* is red', the term represented by '*F*' is not far to seek: 'is red', or 'red', or 'red things'. When the sentence is:

(2) *x* used to work for the man who murdered the second husband of *x*'s youngest sister,

however, we come out after some effort with:

(3) former employee of own youngest sister's second husband's murderer.

Such linguistic gymnastics are inappropriate as an adjunct of logical analysis, and are also unnecessary. Since under our present notation '*F*', '*G*', etc. never occur except in the fashion '*Fx*', '*Gx*', etc., we may dismiss all thought of terms and simply think of '*Fx*', '*Gx*', etc., as representing open sentences. Instead of speaking of interpretation of '*F*' as (3), we may speak directly of interpretation of '*Fx*' as (2). So the sentences which a uniform quantificational schema depicts are those which are obtainable by putting open sentences for '*Fx*', '*Gx*', etc. E.g., the premisses and conclusion of the inference about the class of '00 in §15 are depicted by the respective closed schemata:

(4) $(x)(Fx . Gx . \supset Hx) \supset (\exists x)(Fx . -Gx),$

(5) $(x)(Fx \supset Gx) \lor (x)(Fx \supset Hx),$

(6) $(x)(Fx . Hx . \supset Gx) \supset (\exists x)(Fx . -Hx . Gx).$

Here 'Fx', 'Gx', and 'Hx' are interpreted as the respective open sentences 'x is an applicant', 'x received the second announcement', and 'x is of the class of '00'.

If statements are compounded by truth functions to form a longer statement, the truth value of the compound will depend, we know, on no features of the component statements beyond their truth values. Now a parallel law holds also at the quantificational level of logic, as follows: if open sentences are compounded by truth functions and quantification into a statement, the truth value of the compound will depend on no features of the component open sentences beyond their extensions. For, it is evident from the meaning of quantification that the truth value of a quantification depends on no more than the extension of the open sentence under the quantifier: a universal quantification is true or false according as that extension exhausts the universe or not, and an existential quantification is false or true according as that extension is empty or not.

Thus, just as in a truth-functional schema two interpretations of 'p' are indifferent to the truth value of the whole if they have the same truth value, so in a quantificational schema two interpretations of 'Fx' are indifferent to the truth value of the whole f they have the same extension. Whether we interpret 'Fx' as 'x has a backbone' or as 'x has a heart' will matter none to the resulting truth value of any quantificational schema in which 'Fx' occurs, unless there be in fact some vertebrates without hearts or some hearted creatures without backbones.

Because interpretations of 'p', 'q', etc., are indifferent when alike in truth value, in Part I we commonly interpreted such letters by specifying mere truth values rather than actual statements. At the present stage of logic, correspondingly, we might with equal justice interpret 'Fx', 'Fy', etc., by specifying appropriate extensions rather than actual open sentences. Interpretation may be viewed either way. But whereas in the case of truth values it was quicker to cite '⊤' or '⊥' than to supply an actual statement, on the other hand in the case of extensions no difference is perceptible; for there is no easier way to specify a class as extension of 'Fx' than to supply an actual open sentence whose extension is that class. Thus 'Fx', 'Gx', and 'Hx' in (4)–(6) may be said to have been interpreted by specifying as their respective extensions the class of applicants, the class of receivers of the second announcement, and the class of '00; but nothing is gained over simply supplying the open sentences 'x is an applicant', etc.

The sundry matters which have been touched upon in this section and the preceding one are contributory or incidental to the main business of developing a test of soundness for all inferences at the present level of logic: all inferences of the sorts exemplified in §§12–15, including the one about the class of '00. The task in each case is to test for implication; to justify the inference concerning the class of '00, e.g., what we have to do is show that the conjunction of (4) and (5) implies (6). So the general problem before us is twofold: to define implication, validity, etc., appropriately for uniform closed quantificational schemata, and then to devise a decision procedure—a routine whereby implication, validity, etc., can be mechanically decided.

EXERCISES

1. Complete this observation: An open sentence is true of everything if and only if its universal quantification is . . . , and an open sentence is . . . if and only if its existential quantification is false.

2. Compose schemata depicting the forms of the various statements obtained in Exercise 2 of the preceding section.

§18. VALIDITY

A truth-functional schema was defined to be valid when true under all interpretations of 'p', 'q', etc. (§6). Similarly a uniform closed quantificational schema may be defined to be valid when true under every interpretation of 'Fx', 'Gx', etc. But we must look more closely into this phrase 'every interpretation'.

It is immaterial, we have seen, whether we think of the actual specifying of an interpretation of 'Fx' as consisting in specifying an open sentence as substitute for 'Fx' or a class as extension of 'Fx'. But a subtle difference can arise when, rather than specifying some particular interpretation of 'Fx', we speak in a general theoretical way of *every* interpretation of 'Fx'. Here it might matter whether we mean "every available open sentence as substitute for 'Fx' " or "every class as extension of '*Fx*'. " For, there is no assurance that each class of objects in our universe corresponds as extension to some open sentence constructible from the words of our language. This question depends on our choice of universe, and also on how rich a vocabulary we assume there to be at our disposal over and above our logical notations of truth functions and quantification.[1] The situation here contrasts with that of truth values, for whereas our classes may outrun our open sentences, our truth values do not outrun our statements; even the poorest language has a true statement and a false one.

So in the foregoing definition of validity for closed quantificational schemata let us understand 'for every interpretation' in the strong sense: for every class as extension.[2] In this way the concept of validity becomes independent of the limits of any particular vocabulary. When we are engaged actually in giving interpretations, on the other hand, e.g. so as to illustrate a schema or so as to show its non-validity by producing a counter-example, we still may quite well interpret simply by citing open sentences; for any open sentence cited determines a class as its extension.

It is convenient, as remarked earlier, to allow the choice of universe of discourse to vary from problem to problem. Now the concept of validity, though just now rendered independent of the limits of any particular vocabulary, has been left dependent upon the choice of universe of discourse. For, clearly for each choice of universe we shall

[1] By reasoning based on work of Cantor (1890) it can be shown that no vocabulary can be rich enough to yield an open sentence for every class of objects of an infinite universe. The point is not that we are limited to finitely many expressions; on the contrary, a notation is available e.g. for every one of the integers, infinitely numerous though the integers be. But Cantor's work shows that, given any vocabulary, there must be some unspecifiable infinite *classes of* integers. See my *Mathematical Logic*, page 273, footnote.

[2] It is sound policy to confine the assumption of philosophically contested entities, in particular of abstract entities such as classes, to those portions of theory which need them. The theory of validity of quantificational schemata is, at the stage of exposition represented by the next few sections, such a theory. In §21, however, we shall arrive at a mechanical test of validity of uniform quantificational schemata, comparable to that already at hand for truth-functional schemata in §6. Our preliminary standard of validity which appeals to classes could thereupon be viewed as superseded by an equivalent criterion which makes no such appeal. Note that the practice in Part I of talking as if there were two unitary objects called truth values, to correspond respectively to the true statements and to the false ones, was an insignificant matter of convenience of phrasing and could always be eliminated by dint of some awkward sentence structure. The assumption of a realm of classes, unlisted and unlimited in variety, is philosophically of a very different order.

want to admit as extensions for '*Fx*', '*Gx*', etc., only *subclasses of* that universe, i.e., only classes whose members belong to the universe. Let us then refine our definition of validity so as to take cognizance of possible variations of universe: A uniform closed quantificational schema is *valid* if and only if, no matter what nonempty universe *U* be chosen, the schema comes out true under all interpretations of '*Fx*', '*Gx*', etc. within *U*; i.e., true for all subclasses of *U* as extensions of '*Fx*', '*Gx*', etc.

Some schemata which are valid in the above sense fail when the universe is construed as empty; others continue to hold. One which fails is:

(1) $(x)Fx \supset (\exists x)Fx.$

Though true under all interpretations of '*Fx*' in nonempty universes, (1) turns false when the universe is empty. For, '$(x)Fx$' is bound to come out true for the empty universe (there being no objects for '*Fx*' to be false of), whereas '$(\exists x)Fx$' is bound to come out false.

An obviously valid schema which, unlike (1), suffers no exception on the score of the empty universe, is:

(2) $(\exists x)(Fx \cdot Gx) \supset (\exists x)Fx.$

It is in order not to withhold the status of validity from such schemata as (1) that the qualifier 'nonempty' was inserted into the above definition of validity. Usually the universe relative to which an argument is being carried out is already known or confidently believed not to be empty, so that the failure of a schema in the sole case of the empty universe is usually nothing against the schema from a practical point of view.

Usually, indeed, the universe wanted in arguments worthy of quantification theory is known or believed to have not merely some members, but many. In the definition of validity, then, instead of saying 'every nonempty choice of universe' why not say 'every choice of universe of more than eleven members'? The reason for not doing so is that *no* new schemata would be added to the category of valid schemata by such a liberalization of the definition. If a schema comes true under all interpretations of '*Fx*', '*Gx*', etc. in a large universe, it also comes true under all interpretations of '*Fx*', '*Gx*', etc.

in every smaller nonempty universe.[1] So, happily, the only exception which there is any occasion to make in defining validity is that of the empty universe.

We must not underestimate this exception, for occasionally an argument may most conveniently be carried through under a choice of universe whose nonemptiness is open to question. Still there is no need to cover the empty universe in our general theory of validity, because the question whether a schema holds for the empty universe is easily handled as a separate question. To decide whether a schema comes out true for the empty universe we have merely to put 'T' for all universal quantifications and '⊥' for all existential ones and resolve.

The above definition of validity of closed schemata does not admit of simple extension to open schemata, for we cannot speak of an open schema as coming out true under interpretations of 'Fx', 'Gx', etc. When we interpret an open schema we get an open sentence, and open sentences have no truth values. However, we can define an open schema as valid when, under every nonempty choice of universe U and all interpretations of 'Fx', 'Gx', etc. within U, the schema comes out true *of* every object in U. Clearly this is the same as stipulating that

(i) *Validity of an open schema is validity of its universal quantification.*

An example of a valid open schema is '$Fx \supset Fx$'; for, since it exhibits the form of a valid truth-functional schema '$p \supset p$', it will come out true of any object x no matter whether 'Fx' be interpreted as true or as false of that object. By the same reasoning,

(ii) *Any schema which has the form of a valid truth-functional schema is valid.*

Law (ii) has been stated without restriction to open schemata, because clearly it holds also for closed ones. E.g., since we can obtain:

[1]Why this is so may warrant brief indication here for curious readers. Suppose, in interpreting 'Fx', 'Gx', etc., in a large universe, we cause a large group of objects of the universe to march always together: all or none of those objects are accorded to the extension of 'Fx', all or none to the extension of 'Gx', and so on. The truth value which will accrue to any quantificational schema through such interpretation is the same as if the grouped objects were one. Thus it is that whenever a schema is falsifiable by an interpretation in a small non-empty universe, an interpretation to the same purpose can be devised in any larger universe. Cf. Hilbert and Ackermann, p. 92.

(3) $(x)Fx \ . \ (\exists x)Gx \ . \supset \ (x)Fx$

by putting '$(x)Fx$' for 'p' and '$(\exists x)Gx$' for 'q' in the valid truth-functional schema '$pq \supset p$', we may rest assured that (3) is valid. For, since '$pq \supset p$' comes out true under every interpretation of 'p' and 'q', it follows that (3) must come out true no matter what truth values accrue to its components '$(x)Fx$' and '$(\exists x)Gx$' through interpretation of 'Fx' and 'Gx'. Closed schemata such as (3) and open ones such as '$Fx \supset Fx$' may be said to be valid by truth-functions alone, or truth-functionally valid; they are valid by virtue simply of their external truth-functional structures and independently of the meaning of quantification.

The earlier examples (1) and (2) are of quite another kind. The best we can do toward depicting the general truth-functional structure of (1) or (2) is '$p \supset q$', which of course is not valid; yet (1) and (2) are nevertheless valid. We can falsify '$p \supset q$' by putting a truth for 'p' and a falsehood for 'q', but the corresponding falsification of (1) or (2) is obstructed by properties of the clauses '$(x)Fx$', '$(\exists x)Fx$', and '$(\exists x)(Fx \ . \ Gx)$' themselves which prevent our so interpreting 'Fx' and 'Gx' as to make '$(x)Fx$' or '$(\exists x)(Fx \ . \ Gx)$' true and '$(\exists x)Fx$' simultaneously false. Thus it is that though (1)–(3) are alike valid, they are unlike in that (3) is valid by truth functions alone while (1) and (2) are valid by higher considerations having to do with quantifiers and the interiors of quantifications.

With open schemata the situation is simpler: those which are not truth-functionally valid are not valid at all. E.g., consider '$Fx \supset Gx$'. If we so interpret 'Fx' and 'Gx' that 'Fx' becomes true of a certain object a and 'Gx' does not, clearly '$Fx \supset Gx$' will be false of a; for, '$\top \supset \bot$' resolves to '$\bot$'. But such interpretation of 'Fx' and 'Gx' is easy: interpret 'Fx' as true of everything in the universe and 'Gx' as true of nothing. So it is not the case that every interpretation of 'Fx' and 'Gx' makes '$Fx \supset Gx$' come out true of every object in the universe; in a word, '$Fx \supset Gx$' is not valid. Similar reasoning applies to any open schema, as long as some way of putting '$\top$' and '$\bot$' for 'Fx', 'Gx', etc., in the schema resolves it to '$\bot$'; as long, in other words, as the schema is not truth-functionally valid.

So the treatment of validity of open schemata is now complete, even to a mechanical test: treat 'Fx', 'Gx', etc., as if they were 'p', '*q*', etc., and test for validity by truth-value analysis. Open schemata behave just like truth-functional schemata so far as validity is concerned. It is a sad fact that validity of closed schemata, which is what we are really interested in, cannot be handled thus briefly.

Law (ii) above is one of two laws of substitution useful in generating valid quantificational schemata. It says that the quantificational schemata resulting from substitution for '*p*' and '*q*' in valid truth-functional schema are valid. Now the other law allows for substitution rather in quantificational schemata:

(iii) *Substitution of open schemata for* '*Fx*', '*Gx*', *etc. in valid schemata yields valid results.*

Substituting '*Hx* ∨ *Kx*' for '*Fx*' in the valid schema (2), e.g., we may infer the validity of:

(4) $(\exists x)(Hx \vee Kx \, . \, Gx) \supset (\exists x)(Hx \vee Kx).$

For, given any interpretation of '*Gx*', '*Hx*', and '*Kx*' in (4), we can so interpret '*Fx*' and '*Gx*' in (2) as to make (2) say the same thing as (4). We have merely to give '*Fx*' in (2) the extension which has accrued to the substituted '*Hx* ∨ *Kx*' in (4), and give '*Gx*' in (2) the same interpretation as in (4). Since (2) comes out true under all interpretations, so must (4).

We shall be interested in (iii) only for purposes of substitution in closed schemata, since the validity of open schemata is already so well taken care of. But it is obvious enough that (iii) holds also for open schemata, since open schemata have been seen to behave just like truth-functional schemata so far as validity is concerned.

Appropriate definitions of consistency, implication, and equivalence are evident now that the definition of validity is at hand. Just as a closed schema is valid when it comes out true under *all* interpretations in *every* nonempty universe, so a closed schema is *consistent* when it comes out true under *some* interpretations in *some* nonempty universe. One closed schema *implies* another if, in every nonempty universe, whatever interpretations make the one schema come out true make the other come out true. Two closed schemata are *equivalent* if, in every nonempty universe, all interpretations make the two schemata come out alike in truth value. Parallel definitions hold for open schemata, except that here instead of saying "true" we say "true of all objects in the universe."

Or, what comes to the same thing, inconsistency is validity of the negation, implication is validity of the conditional, and equivalence is validity of the biconditional. Thus (1)–(3) already afford examples of implication: '$(x)Fx$' implies '$(\exists x)Fx$', '$(\exists x)(Fx \; . \; Gx)$' implies '$(\exists x)Fx$', and '$(x)Fx \; . \; (\exists x)Gx$' implies '$(x)Fx$'.

Open schemata were seen to behave exactly like truth-functional ones so far as validity is concerned. It follows that they behave just like truth-functional schemata also as regards consistency, implication, and equivalence. All such matters can be decided for open schemata by truth-value analysis as in Part I, treating 'Fx', 'Gx', etc. simply as 'p', 'q', etc. Likewise the fell-swoop tests of implication in §7 carry over to open schemata; they will in fact prove useful in §20.

Various laws of implication and equivalence were noted in (i)–(iv) of §7 and (i)–(v) of §9: that equivalence is mutual implication, that valid schemata imply only valid ones, etc. We were concerned at that time with truth-functional schemata; but obviously any such laws must carry over to open quantificational schemata, since open schemate behave just like truth-functional ones in matters of validity and the rest. Moreover, the laws can easily be seen to hold also for closed schemata. E.g., take the law that valid schemata imply only valid ones. Let us think of ' - - - ' as representing a valid closed schema which implies a closed schema ' · · · · '. This implication means that ' - - - ⊃ · · · · ' is valid. Therefore any interpretations of 'Fx', 'Gx', etc. make both ' - - - ' and ' - - - ⊃ · · · · ' come out true, and hence also ' · · · · ', since a true conditional with true antecedent has a true consequent.

The other laws may be seen with equal readiness to carry over to closed quantificational schemata. Accordingly one or another of them will be used occasionally in subsequent reasoning without special notice. Also one more related law, not mentioned before, will prove important soon: *One schema implies another if and only if the one in conjunction with the other's negation is inconsistent.* I.e., again imagining ' - - - ' and ' · · · · ' to be schemata, to say that ' - - - ' implies ' · · · · ' is to say that the conjunction:

$$- - - \; . \; -(\cdot \cdot \cdot \cdot)$$

is inconsistent. For, inconsistency of this conjunction is validity of its negation:

$$-[---.-(\cdots)],$$

i.e., validity of the conditional '--- ⊃ ·····'. In Part I the main way of establishing implication was by establishing validity of the conditional; but in §21 we shall find it convenient to establish implications rather by way of inconsistencies, in conformity with the above law.

EXERCISE

Appealing only to (i)–(iii), (2), and validity tests of truth-functional schemata, show that each of the following schemata is valid for all universes. Describe any substitutions in full.

$$(x)(Fx \supset Gx . Gx \supset Hx . \supset . Fx \supset Hx),$$

$$(x)Fx \supset (x)Gx . (x)Gx \supset (x)Hx . \supset . (x)Fx \supset (x)Hx,$$

$$(\exists x)(Fx \supset Gx . Gx \supset Hx) \supset (\exists x)(Fx \supset Gx).$$

§19. EQUIVALENCE. CANONICAL SCHEMATA

This section will carry us half way to a decision procedure. We shall see how to put any closed schema through a series of transformations which are bound to eventuate in a result of one of three kinds: '⊤', '⊥', or a schema of a special kind called *canonical*. The result '⊤' will mean that the schema with which we started was valid, and the result '⊥' will mean that it was inconsistent. If the result is rather a canonical schema, we shall see in the next section how to test it for consistency. Since validity is inconsistency of the negation, and implication is inconsistency of a certain conjunction (as lately remarked), and equivalence is mutual implication, we shall then have arrived at a full decision procedure.

The transformations which are the main business of the present section turn upon equivalence, so let us begin with a closer examination of equivalence.

Simple examples of equivalence have already been anticipated in §16:

(i) '$(\exists x) -Fx$' *to* '$-(x)Fx$',   '$-(\exists x)Fx$' *to* '$(x) -Fx$',

'$(\exists x)Fx$' *to* '$-(x) -Fx$',   '$-(\exists x) -Fx$' *to* '$(x)Fx$'.

Another example, equally obvious, is:

(ii)   '$(\exists x)(Fx \vee Gx)$'   to   '$(\exists x)Fx \vee (\exists x)Gx$'.

'There are things which are either F or G' is equivalent to 'There are F or there are G'. This neat distribution law of existence and alternation is particularly noteworthy in view of the fact, stressed in connection with (2)–(9) of §16, that the corresponding law for conjunction fails: '$(\exists x)(Fx \cdot Gx)$' is not equivalent to '$(\exists x)Fx \cdot (\exists x)Gx$'. On the other hand, just as '$(\exists x)$' may be distributed through alternation, so '(x)' may be distributed through conjunction; the equivalence of

(iii)   '$(x)(Fx \cdot Gx)$'   to   '$(x)Fx \cdot (x)Gx$'

is evident. To say that each thing has mass and takes up space is the same as saying that each thing has mass and each thing takes up space. But '(x)' cannot in general be distributed through alternation, as was seen in contrasting (16) and (17) of §16.

Substitution of two kinds was seen in (ii)–(iii) of the preceding section to transmit validity: substitution for 'p', 'q', etc. in valid truth-functional schemata and substitution for 'Fx', 'Gx', etc., in valid quantificational schemata. We can make use of both kinds of substitution now also in the assurance that they will transmit equivalence; for, equivalence is merely validity of the biconditional. Thus substitution of '$Fx \vee Gx$' for 'Fx' and 'Hx' for 'Gx' leads from the above equivalence (ii) to the equivalence of

'$(\exists x)(Fx \vee Gx \vee Hx)$'   to   '$(\exists x)(Fx \vee Gx) \vee (\exists x)Hx$'.

The interchangeability of equivalents was established, for purposes of the logic of truth functions, under the name of the "second law of interchange" in §9. The law carries over to uniform quantificational schemata:

(iv) *If S_1 and S_2 are equivalent and S_2' is like S_1' except for containing S_2 in place of one or more occurrences of S_1, then S_1' and S_2' are equivalent.*

Case 1: S_1 and S_2 are closed. Then S_1' is a truth function of S_1 and perhaps other components. Put 'p' for the occurrences of S_1 in question, and 'r', 's', etc. (excluding 'q') for the other components, and represent the result as '...p...'. Form '...q...' similarly using 'q' instead of 'p'. By the first law of interchange in §9, '$p \equiv q$' implies '...p... .$\equiv$.

...q...'. By substitution for 'p', 'q', 'r', etc., then, we conclude that the biconditional of S_1 and S_2 implies the biconditional of S_1' and S_2' ("truth-functionally"; see preceding section). Hence if the former biconditional is valid, so is the latter. I.e., if S_1 and S_2 are equivalent so are S_1' and S_2' .

Case 2: S_1 and S_2 are open. Let us represent them as '- - -' and '· · · ·', and let us represent their contexts S_1' and S_2' as '——— - - - ———' and '——— · · · · ———'. Next choose any two capital letters not appearing in these expressions. Suppose they are 'H' and 'K'. Clearly

$$'(x)(Hx \equiv Kx)' \quad \text{implies} \quad '——— Hx ——— . \equiv . ——— Kx ———';$$

for, no classes as extensions of 'Hx' and 'Kx' will make '$(x)(Hx \equiv Kx)$' true unless they are one and the same class, one and the same interpretation. Hence, by substitution,

$$'(x)(- - - \equiv · · · ·)' \quad \text{implies} \quad '——— - - - ——— . \equiv . ——— · · · · ———'.$$

But, since S_1 and S_2 are equivalent, '- - - $\equiv$ · · · ·' is valid. Hence, by (i) of the preceding section, so is '$(x)(- - - \equiv · · · ·)$'. Hence, by the above implication, so is:

$$——— - - - ——— . \equiv . ——— · · · · ———.$$

I.e., S_1' and S_2' are equivalent.

How the laws now at hand combine to yield further equivalences may be illustrated by proving the equivalence, for all universes, of:

(v)   '$(\exists x)(Fx \lor Gx \lor Hx)$' to '$(\exists x)Fx \lor (\exists x)Gx \lor (\exists x)Hx$'.

Substitution in (ii) shows '$(\exists x)(Fx \lor Gx \lor Hx)$' to be equivalent to:

$$(\exists x)(Fx \lor Gx) \lor (\exists x)Hx,$$

which in turn is found equivalent to:

$$(\exists x)Fx \lor (\exists x)Gx \lor (\exists x)Hx$$

by putting the one side of (ii) for the other according to the law of interchange (iv).

Clearly the series of distribution laws begun by (ii) and (v) can be continued indefinitely by continuation of the reasoning which led from (ii) to (v). Corresponding extensions of (iii), for distribution of the universal quantifier through continued conjunctions, can be derived by parallel reasoning.

Preparatory to the next developments we must remind ourselves of what were called "fundamental" and "normal" schemata in §10. A fundamental schema was any literal ('p', '$\bar{p}$', 'q', etc.) or any conjunction of literals in which no letter appeared twice; and a normal schema was any fundamental schema or alternation of such. These are better referred to now as fundamental truth-functional schemata and normal truth-functional schemata, for in analogy to them it will be convenient to speak also of *fundamental open schemata* and *normal open schemata*. These are like the fundamental and normal truth-functional schemata except for having 'Fx', 'Gx', etc., instead of 'p', 'q', etc. The following, e.g., are fundamental open schemata:

$$Fx, \qquad -Fx, \qquad -Gx \, . \, Hx, \qquad Fx \, . -Gx \, . \, Hx.$$

Examples of normal open schemata are the above and also the alternation:

$$-Fx \text{ v.} -Gx \, . \, Hx \text{ .v. } Fx \, . \, Gx.$$

We saw in §10 how any truth-functional schema could be transformed into an equivalent which was either normal or '$p\bar{p}$'. Simply copying that procedure, we can now transform any open schema into an equivalent which is either normal or '$Fx \, . -Fx$'. Equivalence is bound to hold, for we know that substitution of 'Fx', 'Gx', etc. for 'p', 'q', etc., in equivalents yields equivalents.

Now the scheme of transformations which was promised at the beginning of the section can be presented. The steps of the routine will be explained and simultaneously applied to a running example. Consider, then, any closed schema S_0 . Example:

(1) $(\exists x)(Fx \, . \, Gx \, . -Hx) \equiv (x)(Hx \supset . Fx \, . \, Gx) \text{ .v}$
$(\exists x)[Gx \, . -(Gx \text{ v } Hx)].$

First step: Get rid of universal quantifiers by translating any universal quantifications into terms of existential quantification and negation, according to (i). Also, for brevity, we may as well suppress 'x' everywhere; no ambiguity can result, for we have merely to understand an 'x' after each capital letter and each '$\exists$'.[1] Also we may

[1]The joy which this short notation brings is short-lived, for in Part III we shall need to quantify with respect to distinctive letters 'x', 'y', etc., and so shall not be able unambiguously to omit such letters. It is only for the sake of engendering habits of thought useful for Part III that 'x' has been carried in the schemata of Part II at all.

as well drop parentheses from '∃'. Call the result S_1 . Example:

$$\exists(FG\bar{H}) \equiv -\exists -(H \supset FG) \,.\textbf{v}\, \exists[G -(G \textbf{ v } H)].$$

Second step: Within each quantification, transform the entire open schema into an equivalent which is normal or '$F\bar{F}$' (i.e., 'Fx . $-Fx$'). This is the operation remarked upon a couple of paragraphs back. Call the result S_2 . Example, showing stages:

$$\exists(FG\bar{H}) \equiv -\exists[H -(FG)] \,.\textbf{v}\, \exists(G\bar{G}\bar{H})$$

$$\exists(FG\bar{H}) \equiv -\exists(H . \bar{F} \textbf{ v } \bar{G}) \,.\textbf{v}\, \exists(F\bar{F})$$

$$\exists(FG\bar{H}) \equiv -\exists(H\bar{F} \textbf{ v } H\bar{G}) \,.\textbf{v}\, \exists(F\bar{F})$$

Third step: Put '⊥' for any occurrence of '$\exists(F\bar{F})$' and resolve. Result: '⊤' or '⊥' or a schema S_3 which is a truth function of existential quantifications of normal open schemata. Example:

$$\exists(FG\bar{H}) \equiv -\exists(H\bar{F} \textbf{ v } H\bar{G}).$$

Clearly '$\exists(F\bar{F})$', or '$(\exists x)(Fx$. $-Fx)$', comes out false under any interpretation of 'F' within any universe. Therefore S_2 is bound to take on the same truth value as S_3 , under any interpretation of 'Fx', 'Gx', etc. within any universe; in short, S_3 is equivalent to S_2 . Or, if the result of the third step is '⊤' rather than a schema S_3 , it shows that S_2 is bound to come out true under any interpretation within any universe; i.e., S_2 is valid. If the result is '⊥', S_2 is inconsistent.

Now if the third step has issued in a schema S_3 rather than bringing the whole process to an abrupt end in '⊤' or '⊥', we proceed to the

Fourth step: Distribute existential quantifiers through alternations, as illustrated in (ii) and (v). Result: a schema S_4 which is a truth function of existential quantifications of fundamental open schemata. Example:

(2) $$\exists(FG\bar{H}) \equiv -[\exists(H\bar{F}) \textbf{ v } \exists(H\bar{G})].$$

A schema will be called *canonical* if it is like a normal truth-functional schema, as of §10, except that in place of each sentence letter it has an existential quantification of a fundamental open schema. A canonical schema is the usual outcome of the

Fifth step: Handling the whole quantifications in S_4 as if they were

'p', 'q', etc., transform S_4 by the method of §10. Result: '$\bot$' or a canonical schema S_5. Example:

$$\exists(FG\bar{H}) \, . -[\exists(H\bar{F}) \textbf{ v } \exists(H\bar{G})] \textbf{ .v. } -\exists(FG\bar{H}) \, . \, \exists(H\bar{F}) \textbf{ v } \exists(H\bar{G}),$$

$$(3) \; \exists(FG\bar{H}) \, . -\exists(H\bar{F}) \, . -\exists(H\bar{G}) \textbf{ .v. } -\exists(FG\bar{H}) \, . \, \exists(H\bar{F}) \textbf{ .v.}$$
$$-\exists(FG\bar{H}) \, . \, \exists(H\bar{G}).$$

Such, then, is the general method whereby any closed schema S_0 can be transformed until it collapses to '$\top$' or '$\bot$', indicating validity or inconsistency, or else gives way to a canonical schema. In the next section we shall arrive at a consistency test for canonical schemata, and therewith a method of deciding not only consistency but implication, equivalence, and validity for closed schemata generally.

For reduction of work, the routine of transformation set forth above should in practice be varied in several ways. The second step should be interrupted in favor of the third step the moment '$\exists(F\bar{F})$' appears; for the third step may bring great simplifications, or even put an end to the work altogether. Furthermore any observed opportunities for simplification of a truth-functional kind should be exploited promptly on sight; e.g., reduction of 'GG' to 'G' or of '$\exists(FG) \textbf{ v } \exists(FG)$' to '$\exists(FG)$'.

The fifth step can often be facilitated by temporarily putting 'p', 'q', etc., for the quantifications. Thus we might have abstracted the outward truth-functional structure of (2) as '$p \equiv -(q \textbf{ v } r)$' and then transformed this into a normal schema through the stages:

$$p -(q \textbf{ v } r) \textbf{ v. } \bar{p} \, . \, q \textbf{ v } r, \qquad\qquad p\bar{q}\bar{r} \textbf{ v } \bar{p}q \textbf{ v } \bar{p}r,$$

afterward restoring quantifications so as to get (3). In cases more complex than this one, such a detour through sentence letters is helpful.

Sometimes considerable saving of labor and simplification of results can be brought about by rearranging the contents of quantifications so as to put the capital letters of each in alphabetical order. This step should be performed with the fourth. Quantifications which were alike except for internal permutations thus come to be alike, and so the way is opened for incidental simplifications of truth-functional kind in the course of the fifth step. E.g., if S_4 contains '$\exists(H\bar{F}) \, . \, \exists(\bar{F}H)$' as a part, alphabetization will turn the part into '$\exists(\bar{F}H) \, .$

$\exists(\bar{F}H)$'; and this in turn will boil down to '$\exists(\bar{F}H)$' when the fifth step is begun. Or, to take a more striking case, suppose S_4 contains '$\exists(H\bar{F})$. $-\exists(\bar{F}H)$' as a part; alphabetization will turn this part into something of the form '$p\bar{p}$', thereby perhaps facilitating the fifth step to the point of trivialization.

The concept of duality explained in §11 carries over to quantification theory. The extension is accomplished by treating universal and existential quantification as dual to each other, as is suggested by the close relationship of universal and existential quantification respectively to conjunction and alternation; cf. end of §16. Where S is any quantificational schema devoid of '$\supset$' and '$\equiv$', the result of interchanging alternation with conjunction and '$(\exists x)$' with '(x)' throughout S is construed as dual to S. The third, fourth, and fifth laws of duality can be re-established for this broader domain. The equivalences (ii) and (iii) above, e.g., are related by the extended fifth law of duality.

EXERCISES

1. On the basis of (i) and (ii) of the preceding section and (i) and (iv) of this, establish the equivalence of '$(x)(Fx \supset Gx)$' to '$-(\exists x)$ $(Fx$. $-Gx)$'. Make use of the fact that the validity of '$-(Fx \supset Gx)$ $\equiv$. Fx . $-Gx$' means the equivalence of '$-(Fx \supset Gx)$' to 'Fx . $-Gx$'.

2. Reduce each of these to a canonical schema or '$\top$' or '$\perp$', adhering to the described routine.

$(x)(Fx \supset -Gx$. $Gx \supset -Hx$. $Hx \supset -Jx$. $Jx \supset -Fx)$,

$-[(\exists x)(-Fx$. $Gx) \lor (\exists x)(-Fx$. $Hx)$. $\supset (x)(Fx \supset$. Gx . $Hx)]$,

$(\exists x)[-Fx$. $-(Fx \supset Gx)] \supset (x)(Fx \lor Gx)$.

§20. TESTING FOR CONSISTENCY

Our task in the present section is to devise a test of consistency for canonical schemata. Let us begin by classifying the possible forms of canonical schemata into six, as follows.

Form (i): An existential quantification of a fundamental open schema. Example: $(\exists x)(Fx$. $-Gx$. $Hx)$.

Form (ii): A negation of a schema of form (i).

Form (iii): A conjunction of schemata of form (i).

Form (iv): A conjunction of schemata of form (ii).

9

Form (v): A conjunction of schemata of forms (i) and (ii).

Form (vi): An alternation of schemata of any one or more of the forms (i)–(v).

A fundamental open schema, it will be recalled, is any of 'Fx', '$-Fx$', 'Gx', '$-Gx$', etc., or a conjunction of such without repetitions of capital letters. Given any fundamental open schema S_0 and any object a, we can easily so interpret 'Fx', 'Gx', etc., as to make S_0 come out true of a; we have merely to interpret those of 'Fx', 'Gx', etc., as true of a which occur affirmatively in S_0, and the others as false of a. E.g., we make '$Fx \cdot -Gx \cdot Hx$' true of a by interpreting 'Fx' and 'Hx' as true of a and 'Gx' as false of a.

Since any fundamental open schema S_0 can thus be made true *of* any desired object by suitable interpretations, it follows that the existential quantification of S_0 can be made *true* (in a nonempty universe) by suitable interpretations. In other words, any schema of form (i) is bound to be consistent.

It is equally easy to see that any schema of form (ii) is bound to be consistent. E.g., consider:

(1) $-(\exists x)(Fx \cdot -Gx \cdot Hx)$.

We can make this come out true, in any desired universe, by interpreting 'Fx' as true of nothing (and interpreting 'Gx' and 'Hx' as we please). For, '$Fx \cdot -Gx \cdot Hx$' then becomes true of nothing, and so (1) becomes true. In general, similarly, given any schema S of form (ii), pick out a capital letter—say 'F'. If, in the fundamental open schema which follows the quantifier, 'Fx' appears affirmatively, then interpret 'Fx' as true of nothing; the schema S as a whole will thereupon come out true, as seen in the above example. If on the other hand 'Fx' appears negatively, then interpret 'Fx' rather as true of everything in the universe, so that '$-Fx$' becomes true of nothing; then again, clearly, S as a whole will come out true.

So far as forms (i) and (ii) are concerned, therefore, there is no problem of testing for consistency; a schema of either of these forms is *ipso facto* consistent. Now the same is true also of form (iii). This is seen as follows. A schema S of form (iii) is a conjunction of existential quantifications of fundamental open schemata S_1, ... , S_m. We have seen how, by interpreting 'Fx', 'Gx', etc., we can make

S_1 true of a chosen object a_1 ; also how we can make S_2 true of a chosen object a_2 ; and so on. By keeping a_1 , a_2 , ... , a_m distinct so as to avoid conflict, we can so interpret 'Fx', 'Gx', etc., as to make S_1 , S_2 , ... , S_m simultaneously true respectively of a_1 , a_2 , ... , a_m ; and then the conjunction S of existential quantifications comes out true.

E.g., consider:

(2) $(\exists x) -Fx \, . \, (\exists x)(Fx \, . \, -Gx) \, . \, (\exists x)(Fx \, . \, Gx \, . \, -Hx).$

We pick three distinct objects a_1 , a_2 , a_3 . Then we make '$-Fx$' true of a_1 by interpreting 'Fx' as false of a_1 ; we make '$Fx \, . \, -Gx$' true of a_2 by further interpreting 'Fx' as true of a_2 and 'Gx' as false of a_2 ; and we make '$Fx \, . \, Gx \, . \, -Hx$' true of a_3 by further interpreting 'Fx' and 'Gx' as true of a_3 and 'Hx' as false of a_3 . This much suffices to make (2) come out true, however the interpretations of 'Fx', 'Gx', and 'Hx' be fixed in relation to the rest of the objects of the universe.

So a schema of any of the forms (i)–(iii) is consistent. Now let us examine form (iv), beginning with the example:

(3) $-(\exists x)(-Fx \, . \, Gx) \, . \, -(\exists x)(Fx \, . \, -Gx) \, . \, -(\exists x)(Fx \, . \, Gx \, . \, Hx).$

To make this come out true we must so interpret 'Fx', 'Gx', and 'Hx' as to make each of the open schemata '$-Fx \, . \, Gx$', '$Fx \, . \, -Gx$', and '$Fx \, . \, Gx \, . \, Hx$' true of nothing. This can of course be done by taking the universe as empty; but our problem, in establishing consistency, is to achieve the same effect in some nonempty universe. Our problem is to find an interpretation of 'Fx', 'Gx', and 'Hx' which will cause '$-Fx \, . \, Gx$', '$Fx \, . \, -Gx$', and '$Fx \, . \, Gx \, . \, Hx$' all to be false of all the objects of a nonempty universe. In other words, our problem is to find an interpretation of 'Fx', 'Gx', and 'Hx' which will cause the conjunction:

(4) $-(-Fx \, . \, Gx) \, . \, -(Fx \, . \, -Gx) \, . \, -(Fx \, . \, Gx \, . \, Hx)$

to be *true* of everything in a nonempty universe. Note that (4) is just (3) with quantifiers deleted. More generally, suppose that S is any schema of form (iv), and that S' is what remains of S when quantifiers are deleted; then, as in the above example, the problem of showing S consistent reduces to the problem of so interpreting 'Fx', 'Gx', etc., as to make S' true of everything in a nonempty universe.

Let us then address ourselves to the reduced problem: interpretation of 'Fx', 'Gx', etc., such as will make S' true of everything in a nonempty universe. A convenient first step is truth-value analysis of S'; or, in the example, truth-value analysis of (4):

$$-(-Fx \,.\, Gx) \,.\, -(Fx \,.\, -Gx) \,.\, -(Fx \,.\, Gx \,.\, Hx)$$
$$-(\bot.Gx).-(\top.-Gx).-(\top.Gx.Hx) \qquad -(\top.Gx).-(\bot.-Gx).-(\bot.Gx.Hx)$$
$$Gx \,.\, -(Gx \,.\, Hx) \qquad\qquad\qquad -Gx$$
$$\top \,.\, -(\top \,.\, Hx) \quad \bot \,.\, -(\bot \,.\, Hx) \qquad\qquad \bot \qquad \top$$
$$-Hx \qquad\qquad \bot$$
$$\bot \qquad \top$$

Next we fix our attention upon an arbitrary one of the cases which led to '$\top$'; one such, in the above example, is the case of 'Fx' and 'Gx' true and 'Hx' false. (4), the analysis has shown, is true of anything x of which 'Fx' and 'Gx' are true and 'Hx' false. Therefore we can make (4) true of everything, in any universe, by interpreting 'Fx' and 'Gx' as true of everything and 'Hx' as true of nothing. So (3) has been found consistent.

Clearly what we have done with (4) can be done with any example S' unless S', unlike (4), yields no '$\top$' at all under truth-value analysis. In this event (viz., *inconsistency* of S'), naturally there is no hope of so interpreting 'Fx', 'Gx', etc., as to make S' true of everything in a nonempty universe; and in this event, consequently, S is inconsistent.

We have therefore arrived at a simple decision procedure for consistency of schemata of form (iv); viz., *delete all quantifiers and test the remaining open schema for consistency*. The test of consistency for open schemata, we know, is mere truth-value analysis.

Next let us take up form (v), beginning with the example:

$$(5) \quad (\exists x)(Fx \,.\, Gx) \,.\, (\exists x)(Fx \,.\, Hx) \,.\, -(\exists x)(Fx \,.\, Gx \,.\, Hx) \,.$$
$$-(\exists x)(Fx \,.\, -Gx \,.\, Hx).$$

To make this come out true we must so interpret 'Fx', 'Gx', and 'Hx' as to make '$Fx \,.\, Gx$' come out true of something a, and make '$Fx \,.\, Hx$' come out true of something b, and make '$Fx \,.\, Gx \,.\, Hx$' and '$Fx \,.$'

$-Gx$. Hx' come out true of nothing. But this is impossible; for, if 'Fx . Hx' is to be true of b, clearly 'Fx . Gx . Hx' or 'Fx . $-Gx$. Hx' will be true of b. So (5) is inconsistent.

Consider now a second example of form (v):

(6) $(\exists x)(Fx . Gx) . (\exists x)(Fx . -Hx) .$
                $-(\exists x)(Fx . Gx . -Hx) . -(\exists x)(Fx . -Gx . Hx).$

We can make this come out true by interpreting 'Fx' as true of two objects, a and b, and interpreting 'Gx' and 'Hx' as true of just a. Then 'Fx . Gx' becomes true of a; 'Fx . $-Hx$' becomes true of b; and 'Fx . Gx . $-Hx$' and 'Fx . $-Gx$. Hx' become true of nothing. (6) comes out true under these interpretations, and is therefore consistent.

A general criterion of consistency of schemata of form (v) may, subject to justification in the next paragraph, be formulated as follows. Let S be a schema of form (v); let S_1 , . . . , S_m be the open schemata which are affirmatively quantified in S; and let S'_1 , . . . , S'_n be the open schemata which are negatively quantified in S. Then *S is consistent if and only if no one of S_1 , . . . , S_m implies the alternation of S'_1 , . . . , S'_n* (or implies S'_1 , if n is 1). E.g., the source of the inconsistency of (5) is that 'Fx . Hx' implies:

$$Fx . Gx . Hx .\mathbf{v}. Fx . -Gx . Hx.$$

(6) is consistent because neither 'Fx . Gx' nor 'Fx . $-Hx$' implies:

$$Fx . Gx . -Hx .\mathbf{v}. Fx . -Gx . Hx.$$

For testing implication between any such open schemata, truth-functional methods are known to suffice.

In general the justification of the above consistency criterion is as follows. If one of S_1 , . . . , S_m , say S_i , implies the alternation of S'_1 , . . . , S'_n , then we cannot make S_i true of an object without making at least one of S'_1 , . . . , S'_n true of that object. In this case, therefore, we cannot make all the quantifications affirmed in S come out true without also making some of the quantifications denied in S come out true; so S is inconsistent. If on the other hand none of S_1 , . . . , S_m implies the alternation of S'_1 , . . . , S'_n , then we can find interpretations of 'Fx', 'Gx', etc., which will make S come out true, as follows.

We take a universe of just m objects, $a_1, \ldots, a_m$. Now since S_1 does not imply the alternation of $S'_1, \ldots, S'_n$, there is some way of assigning '⊤' and '⊥' to 'Fx', 'Gx', etc., which causes S_1 to resolve to '⊤' and yet causes $S'_1, \ldots, S'_n$ all to resolve to '⊥'. Let us interpret each of 'Fx', 'Gx', etc., as true of a_1 or false of a_1 in conformity with that particular way of assigning '⊤' and '⊥'; then S_1 comes out true of a_1, while all of $S'_1, \ldots, S'_n$ come out false of a_1. Similarly, since S_2 does not imply the alternation of $S'_1, \ldots, S'_n$, we can further interpret 'Fx', 'Gx', etc. in relation to a_2 so as to make S_2 come out true of a_2 while $S'_1, \ldots, S'_n$ all come out false of a_2. Continuing thus to S_m and a_m, we end up with interpretations of 'Fx', 'Gx', etc., which make $S_1, \ldots, S_m$ come out true of $a_1, \ldots, a_m$ respectively, while $S'_1, \ldots, S'_n$ come out false of all these objects—hence false of all objects in the universe. Then the existential quantifications affirmed in S all come out true while those denied in S all come out false; and thus S comes out true.

We can now make short work of form (vi). An alternation of given components is consistent if and only if at least one of those components is consistent; for, any interpretation which verifies even one of those components verifies the alternation. To test a schema of form (vi) for consistency, therefore, we examine each of the components of forms (i)–(v) until we find a consistent one; failing such, we adjudge the whole inconsistent.

A full decision procedure for consistency of canonical schemata is now at hand. Let us sum it up.

Form (i): An existential quantification of a fundamental open schema. *Always consistent.*

Form (ii): A negation of a schema of form (i). *Always consistent.*

Form (iii): A conjunction of schemata of form (i). *Always consistent.*

Form (iv): A conjunction of schemata of form (ii). *Consistent if and only if the result of deleting its quantifiers is consistent.*

Form (v): A conjunction of schemata of forms (i) and (ii). *Consistent if and only if none of $S_1, \ldots, S_m$ implies the alternation of $S'_1, \ldots, S'_n$ (or implies S'_1, if n is 1).*

Form (vi): An alternation of schemata of one or more of the forms (i)–(v). *Consistent if and only if at least one of those components is consistent.*

Let us test the canonical schema (3) of the preceding section for consistency. It is of form (vi), so we begin by testing the part:

(7) $\exists(FG\bar{H}) \: . -\exists(H\bar{F}) \: . -\exists(H\bar{G})$,

which is of form (v). We have to decide whether '$FG\bar{H}$' implies '$H\bar{F} \lor H\bar{G}$'. A negative answer is reached in a fell swoop:

$$\underset{\perp}{\underline{\perp} \lor \underline{\perp}}$$

So (7) is consistent. Hence (3) of the preceding section is consistent. Hence so is (1) of that section.

Note that amenability to the fell swoop is no peculiarity of the above example. Questions of implication on the part of fundamental schemata can always be settled thus.

We now have a consistency test not merely for any canonical schema, but for any closed schema whatever: transform it by the method of the preceding section, and if it does not thereby reduce to '⊤' or '⊥', thus showing its validity or inconsistency, then test the resulting canonical schema for consistency.

EXERCISES

1. Test each of the following two schemata for consistency.

$-\exists(F\bar{G}) \: . -\exists(JG) \: . \: \exists(JF) \: . -\exists(GH)$,

$-\exists(FGH) \: . \: \exists(GJ) \: . \: \exists(GK) \: . -\exists(\bar{F}J) \: . -\exists(\bar{H}K)$.

2. Do likewise for the canonical schemata obtained in Exercise 2 of the preceding section.

3. Schematize the following statement, then transform the schema as in the preceding section, and finally test for consistency.

Some who take logic and Latin take neither physics nor Greek, but all who take either Latin or chemistry take both logic and Greek.

§21.   TESTING FOR IMPLICATION

The test of consistency at which we have arrived affords, as a by-product, a test of validity: we can test a schema for validity by testing its negation for inconsistency. But the most useful consequence is an implication test: *to decide whether a premiss or conjunction of premisses implies a conclusion we put the premisses into conjunction with the negation of the conclusion and test for inconsistency.* (Cf. §18, end.) To test for equivalence, finally, we may test forwards and backwards for implication.

For a simple illustration of the implication test, let us take the syllogism:

$$(x)(Gx \supset -Hx), \qquad (\exists x)(Fx . Gx); \qquad \therefore (\exists x)(Fx . -Hx).$$

We have to test the conjunction:

$$(x)(Gx \supset -Hx) . (\exists x)(Fx . Gx) . -(\exists x)(Fx . -Hx)$$

for inconsistency. By the technique of §19 we turn it into a canonical schema.

$$-\exists -(G \supset \bar{H}) . \exists(FG) . -\exists(F\bar{H}) \qquad \text{(1st step)}$$

$$-\exists(GH) . \exists(FG) . -\exists(F\bar{H}) \qquad \text{(2d step; 3d–5th not needed)}$$

Finally we test this for inconsistency in conformity with the preceding section.

$$\begin{array}{ccc} \text{'}FG\text{'} & \text{implies} & \text{'}GH \text{ v } F\bar{H}\text{'?} \\ & & \daleth H \text{ v } \daleth\bar{H} \\ & & H \text{ v } \bar{H} \qquad \text{Yes.} \end{array}$$

But we could use Venn diagrams for such problems. Let us turn now to a more serious example: that of the class of '00. The schemata to be tested for implication here are (4)–(6) of §17. To test them for implication we test the conjunction:

$$(x)(Fx . Gx . \supset Hx) \supset (\exists x)(Fx . -Gx) . (x)(Fx \supset Gx) \text{ v } (x)(Fx \supset Hx)$$
$$. -[(x)(Fx . Hx . \supset Gx) \supset (\exists x)(Fx . -Hx . Gx)]$$

for consistency. We begin by transforming it successively in conformity with §19. First step:

$$-\exists -(FG \supset H) \supset \exists(F\bar{G}) . -\exists -(F \supset G) \text{ v } -\exists -(F \supset H) .$$
$$-[-\exists -(FH \supset G) \supset \exists(F\bar{H}G)].$$

Second step, accompanied by alphabetical rearrangements:

$$-\exists(FG\bar{H}) \supset \exists(F\bar{G}) . -\exists(F\bar{G}) \text{ v } -\exists(F\bar{H}) . -[-\exists(F\bar{G}H) \supset$$
$$\exists(FG\bar{H})].$$

Third and fourth steps: none. Fifth step:

$$\bar{p} \supset q \,.\, \bar{q} \vee \bar{r} \,.\, -(\bar{s} \supset p),$$
$$p \vee q \,.\, \bar{q} \vee \bar{r} \,.\, \bar{s}\bar{p},$$
$$p\bar{q} \vee p\bar{r} \vee q\bar{q} \vee q\bar{r} \,.\, \bar{s}\bar{p},$$
$$p\bar{q} \vee p\bar{r} \vee q\bar{r} \,.\, \bar{s}\bar{p},$$
$$p\bar{q}\bar{s}\bar{p} \vee p\bar{r}\bar{s}\bar{p} \vee q\bar{r}\bar{s}\bar{p},$$
$$q\bar{r}\bar{s}\bar{p}.$$
$$\exists(F\bar{G}) \,.\, -\exists(F\bar{H}) \,.\, -\exists(F\bar{G}H) \,.\, -\exists(FG\bar{H}).$$

Finally we test this according to the preceding section.

'$F\bar{G}$'   implies   '$F\bar{H} \vee F\bar{G}H \vee FG\bar{H}$'?
$$\top\bar{H} \vee \top\top H \vee \top\bot\bar{H}$$
$$\bar{H} \vee H \qquad\qquad \text{Yes.}$$

The existence of such a test for implication, validity, and the rest is philosophically significant in relation to the question of admitting classes as entities. For, validity and the related concepts were defined in §18 in a way which appealed to an unlimited realm of classes. But what we now have is an equivalent criterion consisting in a mechanical test, which can be described from beginning to end without assumption of classes. However necessary it may be for other purposes to assume classes, this is one place where the assumption has proved eliminable.

In Part III (§§27 ff.) we shall come upon another technique of proving implication, validity, and the rest, which will apply not only to all the problems to which our present method applies but also to others which are beyond the reach of uniform quantificational schemata. Some of the problems within the reach of our present method can be handled more briefly by the later method, others less so. In any case the present method has a great virtue which that of Part III will lack: it is mechanical. Under the method of Part III the process of discovering a proof for a given purpose may, as in mathematics fairly generally, turn on factors of luck and ingenuity not reducible to prescribable routine. One may, in hopes of quick success, try that method on a problem which could be done by the present mechanical method; in case of failure to find the desired proof, however, the present unfailing method stands in reserve. Unfortunately, no similarly unfailing routine of mechanical test is possible for the whole generality of problems covered in Part III.

Löwenheim (1915) was the first to present a mechanical test of validity for what I have called uniform quantificational schemata. Various alternative techniques to the same purpose have since appeared.[1] Some of these alternative methods cover a territory which is broader in several respects than the realm of uniform quantificational schemata. Our present method will now be extended in one of those respects. Extension in another respect, which is essentially notational, will take place in §32.

A sharp division has been preserved between the schemata of Part I and those of Part II, those of Part I being truth functions of sentence letters while those of Part II are truth functions of quantifications. By mixing these ingredients, however, we get a new class of schemata which allow for the handling of additional problems. One such problem is this:

Premises: If the Bissagos report is to be trusted then the *chargé d'affaires* is a mere tool of the sisal interests and none of the natives really favored the coupon plan.

If the *chargé d'affaires* is a mere tool of the sisal interests then some of the natives either really favored the coupon plan or were actuated by a personal animosity against the deputy resident.

Conclusion: If the Bissagos report is to be trusted then some who were actuated by a personal animosity against the deputy resident did not really favor the coupon plan.

Putting 'p' for 'the Bissagos report is to be trusted', 'q' for 'the *chargé d'affaires* is a mere tool of the sisal interests', 'Fx' for 'x is a native', 'Gx' for 'x really favored the coupon plan', and 'Hx' for 'x was actuated by a personal animosity against the deputy resident', we can represent the premises and conclusion by the mixed schemata:

$$p \supset . q . (x)(Fx \supset -Gx),$$
$$q \supset (\exists x)(Fx . Gx \vee Hx),$$
$$p \supset (\exists x)(Hx . -Gx).$$

Let us translate '(x)' into '$-(\exists x) -$' and then omit 'x' everywhere, also simplifying '$-(F \supset \bar{G})$' to 'FG'; then the conjunction of the premises with the negation of the conclusion runs thus:

[1]See my paper "On the logic of quantification" for one such and for references to others. The method of the present pages derives partly from that paper, and both approaches are reminiscent of procedures developed by Behmann (1922) and Parry (1932). I used a quite different and more intuitive method in *O Sentido* (pp. 126–129), but that method tends in application to run to greater length than the present one. For a lucid exposition using the same principle as *O Sentido* see von Wright (1949).

(1) $p \supset . q . -\exists(FG) : q \supset \exists(F . G \vee H) . -[p \supset \exists(H\bar{G})].$

So this is the conjunction to test for inconsistency.

The appropriate sense of 'inconsistency' for such mixed schemata is evident enough, for we have merely to combine the concepts of inconsistency for truth-functional schemata and for closed quantificational schemata. Thus a mixed schema may be said to be inconsistent if, for every choice of a nonempty universe U, it comes out false under all interpretations of 'Fx', 'Gx', etc. within U and all interpretations (truth values) of 'p', 'q', etc.

Clearly then a mixed schema will be inconsistent if and only if, whenever we put '$\underline{\bot}$'s and '$\top$'s for 'p', 'q', etc., and make all possible reductions by resolution (§5), we end up either with '$\underline{\bot}$' or with an inconsistent quantificational schema. So, to test a mixed schema for inconsistency we may begin by constructing a preliminary truth-value analysis under it as it stands. This analysis proceeds just as in Part I: the most frequent sentence letter is replaced first by '$\top$' and then by '$\underline{\bot}$', and resolutions are made; then each result is treated similarly; and so on, until either '$\top$' is obtained (in which case we stop work, with a verdict of consistency) or each case has yielded '$\underline{\bot}$' or an unmixed quantificational schema. (Note that in the course of this process the substitutions of '$\top$' and '$\underline{\bot}$' are made only for sentence letters 'p', 'q', etc., not for quantifications or capital letters.) Finally each of the resulting quantificational schemata may be tested separately for inconsistency, by the method lately developed. As soon as one of them is found consistent we may stop, knowing that the original mixed schema is consistent.

In the case of (1) the preliminary truth-value analysis, which will be omitted here, issues in '$\underline{\bot}$' in each case but one; and in this case it issues in the schema:

(2) $-\exists(FG) . \exists(F . G \vee H) . -\exists(H\bar{G}).$

What then remains to be done is to transform (2) into a canonical schema and check for inconsistency.

EXERCISES

1. Test (2) for inconsistency. (Mastery of small print unnecessary.)

2. Check various inferences of §15, as has been done above for the one about the class of '00. Also, for quick drill, those of §§13–14.

3. Check the following argument.

> Premises: The persons responsible for the recent kidnappings
> are experimental psychologists.
>   If no experimental psychologists are known to the police,

then none of the former bosses of the bootleg ring are experimental psychologists.

Conclusion: If any of the former bosses of the bootleg ring are responsible for the recent kidnappings then some experimental psychologists are known to the police.

Hint: Represent the conclusion as '$(\exists x)(Fx . Gx) \supset (\exists x)(Hx . Jx)$'.

4. Test each of these pairs for equivalence, by an implication test in each direction.

$(x)Fx,$ $(x)(Fx \lor Gx) . (x)(Fx \lor -Gx);$

$(x)Fx,$ $(x)(Fx . Gx) \lor (x)(Fx . -Gx);$

$(\exists x)Fx,$ $(\exists x)(Fx \lor Gx) . (\exists x)(Fx \lor -Gx);$

$(\exists x)Fx,$ $(\exists x)(Fx . Gx) \lor (\exists x)(Fx . -Gx).$

PART THREE

General Theory of Quantification

§22. QUANTIFICATION EXTENDED

In the logical tradition terms are distinguished into two kinds, *relative* and *absolute*. The characteristic of a relative term is that it describes things only relatively to further things which have afterward to be specified in turn. Thus 'father' as in 'father of Isaac', and 'north' as in 'north of Boston', are relative terms. What were spoken of as terms in §12, on the other hand, are absolute terms. Words capable of behaving as relative terms can regularly be used *also* as absolute terms, through what amounts to a tacit existential quantification in the context; thus we may say absolutely that Abraham is a father, meaning that there is something of which Abraham is a father.

In English a convenient earmark of the relative use of a term is the adjoining of an 'of'-phrase or possessive modifier whose sense is not that of ownership. Thus 'father of Isaac', or 'Isaac's father', has nothing to do with proprietorship on Isaac's part, but means merely 'that which bears the father-relation to Isaac'. Aristotle brought out the distinction between the possessive 'my' and the relative 'my' by citing the fallacy:

This dog is mine,   This dog is a father;   ∴ This dog is my father.

A relative term, like an absolute one, may occur indifferently as substantive, adjective, or verb. In 'x is a helper of y' we use the substantive, in 'x is helpful toward y' the adjective, and in 'x helps y' the verb; but logically there is no need to distinguish the three. Logically the important thing about relative terms is that they are true of objects pairwise. Whereas 'man', 'walks', etc., are true of Caesar, Socrates, etc., one by one, on the other hand the relative term 'helps' is true of Jesus and Lazarus as a pair (or, true of Jesus with respect to Lazarus), and true of Farley and Roosevelt as a pair (or, true of Farley with respect to Roosevelt), and so on. If as in the foregoing pages we write '*Fx*' for '*x* is an *F*', then the analogous notation in connection with relative terms should be '*Fxy*', '*x* is *F* to *y*'. The order of '*x*' and '*y*' in '*x* helps *y*' is in one respect accidental: '*x* helps *y*' can as well be phrased '*y* is helped by *x*'. But in another respect the order is essential: '*x* helps *y*', e.g., 'Jesus helps Lazarus', is not equivalent to '*y* helps *x*'. So the sentence '*x* helps *y*' may be described equally as of the form '*Fxy*' and as of the form '*Fyx*', but the interpretations thus successively imposed on '*F*' are then distinct from each other—as distinct as 'helps' and 'is helped by'. '*Fxy*' cannot in general be equated with '*Fyx*'.

Besides relative terms in the sense just now touched upon, which are *dyadic*, we may recognize also *triadic* ones, *tetradic* ones, and so on; e.g., '*Gxyz*' may mean '*x* gives *y* to *z*', and '*Hxyzw*' may mean '*x* pays *y* to *z* for *w*'.

There are forms of inference, logically no less sound than those dealt with in Part II, which are insusceptible to the methods of Part II simply because their analysis calls for recognition of relative terms. An example, of medieval vintage, is:

All circles are figures;   ∴ All who draw circles draw figures.

The premiss can be represented in our previous notation as '$(x)(Fx \supset Gx)$', but the conclusion presents difficulties. We can indeed represent the conclusion as '$(x)(Hx \supset Jx)$', interpreting '*Hx*' as '*x* draws a circle' and '*Jx*' as '*x* draws a figure', but then the schemata '$(x)(Fx \supset Gx)$' and '$(x)(Hx \supset Jx)$' bear no visible interconnection which could justify inference of the one from the other. What we must do is extend our category of quantificational schemata to admit such forms as '*Hyx*' for '*y* draws *x*'. Then '*y* draws a circle' can be represented as '$(\exists x)(Fx \,.\, Hyx)$', and '*y* draws a figure' as '$(\exists x)(Gx \,.\, Hyx)$'; thereupon our conclusion as a whole, 'All who draw circles draw figures', becomes:

(1) $(y)[(\exists x)(Fx \,.\, Hyx) \supset (\exists x)(Gx \,.\, Hyx)]$

and thus exhibits an unaccustomed '*y*' in its universal quantifier. Quantification theory needs to be extended in such a way as to enable us to show, among other things, that '$(x)(Fx \supset Gx)$' implies (1).

Another example of the need of thus extending quantification theory is this:

Premiss: There is a painting that all critics admire;
Conclusion: Every critic admires some painting or other.

With 'Gx' interpreted as 'x is a critic', and 'Hxy' as 'x admires y', we may represent 'all critics admire y' as '$(x)(Gx \supset Hxy)$'. So, interpreting 'Fy' as 'y is a painting', we may represent the above premiss as:

(2) $(\exists y)[Fy . (x)(Gx \supset Hxy)]$.

Further, since 'x admires some painting or other' becomes '$(\exists y)(Fy . Hxy)$', the conclusion as a whole takes on the form:

(3) $(x)[Gx \supset (\exists y)(Fy . Hxy)]$.

One more example:

Premiss: There is a philosopher whom all philosophers contradict,
Conclusion: There is a philosopher who contradicts himself.

The premiss here has a form closely similar to (2).

(4) $(\exists y)[Fy . (x)(Fx \supset Gxy)]$.

The conclusion is simply '$(\exists x)(Fx . Gxx)$'.

We saw in §16 and §19 how differences in grouping could affect the meaning of a quantification; '$(x)(Fx \vee Gx)$' had to be distinguished from '$(x)Fx \vee (x)Gx$', and '$(\exists x)(Fx . Gx)$' from '$(\exists x)Fx . (\exists x)Gx$'. Considerations of this kind come to loom larger now that we allow quantifications within quantifications. Thus, let us reflect next on the expression:

(5) $(x)[Fx \supset (\exists y)(Fy . Gxy)]$.

If we interpret 'Fx' as 'x is a number' and 'Gxy' as 'x is less than y', then (5) comes to mean:

Every number is such that some number exceeds it,

or briefly 'Every number is exceeded by some number'. This might carelessly be rephrased 'Some number exceeds every number' and then be put back into symbols as:

$(\exists y)(y$ is a number . y exceeds every number),

i.e., (4). But actually there is all the difference between (5) and (4) that there is between truth and falsity. (5) says that for every number there is a larger, which is true, whereas (4) says there is some great number which, at once, exceeds every number. This last is false on two counts: for there is no greatest number, and even if there were it would not exceed itself.

The distinction in form between (3) and (2) is the same as just now stressed between (5) and (4). The wording of the premiss and conclusion about paintings illustrates again the awkwardness of ordinary language in keeping the distinction clear. The notation of quantification is handier in this respect.

The mathematical concept of limit provides, for readers familiar with it, an apt further illustration of the above distinction. A function $f(x)$ is said to approach a limit h, as x approaches k, if for every positive number ϵ there is a positive number δ such that $f(x)$ is within ϵ of h for every x within δ of k. In terms of quantifiers this condition appears as follows:

$$(\epsilon)\{\epsilon > 0 . \supset (\exists \delta)[\delta > 0 . (x)(|x - k| < \delta . \supset . |f(x) - h| < \epsilon)]\}.$$

As textbooks rightly emphasize, we must think of ϵ as chosen first; for each choice of ϵ a suitable δ can be chosen. This warning is, in effect, a warning against confusing the above formula with the essentially different one:

$$(\exists \delta)\{\delta > 0 . (\epsilon)[\epsilon > 0 . \supset (x)(|x - k| < \delta . \supset . |f(x) - h| < \epsilon)]\}.$$

The distinction between these two formulas will be recognized as identical with that between (5) and (4), and between (3) and (2).

The essential contrast between (5) and (4), and between (3) and (2), becomes simpler and more striking when we compare:

(6) $(x)(\exists y)Fxy,$ $(\exists y)(x)Fxy.$

Suppose we interpret 'Fxy' as 'x and y are the same thing', so that the schemata (6) become:

(7) $(x)(\exists y)(x$ and y are the same thing),

(8) $(\exists y)(x)(x$ and y are the same thing).

For each chosen object x, clearly there will be an object which is the same (viz., the chosen object x itself). Of each object x, therefore, the sentence:

$$(\exists y)(x \text{ and } y \text{ are the same thing})$$

is true. So (7) is true. On the other hand, as long as there are more objects than one in the universe, no one object can be the same as each; i.e., no one object y can be such that

$$(x)(x \text{ and } y \text{ are the same thing}).$$

So (8) is false.

In general '$(x)(\exists y)Fxy$' says that once any object whatever x is fixed upon, an object y is forthcoming such that Fxy. Different choices of x may bring forth different choices of y. On the other hand '$(\exists y)(x)Fxy$' says that some object y can be fixed upon such that, for this same fixed y, 'Fxy' will hold for all comers x.

Supposing a limited universe of objects $a, b, \cdots, h$, let us see how '$(x)(\exists y)Fxy$' and '$(\exists y)(x)Fxy$' compare when the quantifications are expanded into conjunctions and alternations (cf. end of §16). '$(x)(\exists y)Fxy$' becomes first:

$$(\exists y)Fay \,.\, (\exists y)Fby \,.\, \cdots \,.\, (\exists y)Fhy$$

and then:

$$Faa \lor Fab \lor \cdots \lor Fah \,.\, Fba \lor Fbb \lor \cdots \lor Fbh \,.\, \cdots \,.$$
$$Fha \lor Fhb \lor \cdots \lor Fhh.$$

On the other hand '$(\exists y)(x)Fxy$' becomes first:

$$(x)Fxa \lor (x)Fxb \lor \cdots \lor (x)Fxh$$

and then:

$$Faa \,.\, Fba \,.\, \cdots \,.\, Fha \,.v.\, Fab \,.\, Fbb \,.\, \cdots \,.\, Fhb \,.v.\, \cdots \,.v.$$
$$Fah \,.\, Fbh \,.\, \cdots \,.\, Fhh.$$

It was remarked in §16 that though in ordinary language the words 'something' and 'everything' masquerade as substantives, their behavior deviates from that of genuine substantives. Further examples of such deviation are provided by (7) and (8). For, (7) might be put into words as 'Everything is identical with something', and (8) as 'Something is identical with everything'. If 'everything' and 'something' really behaved like names, we should expect these two statements to be equivalent—and in fact we should expect both to be false. But actually, as seen, (7) is true and (8) false. Further, if 'nothing' and 'everything' were genuine names we should certainly expect 'Nothing is identical with everything' to be false; actually, however, this statement simply denies (8) and hence is true. Also we might expect 'Everything is identical with everything' to be equivalent to the truth 'Everything is identical with itself', whereas actually it expresses the falsehood:

$$(9) \qquad\qquad (x)(y)(x \text{ is identical with } y).$$

One reason why quantificational analysis aids clear thinking is simply that the spurious substantives 'something', 'everything', and 'nothing' (and their variants 'somebody', 'nobody', 'everybody') give way to a less deceptive idiom.

The combination '$(x)(y)$' in (9) is not to be thought of as somehow a double quantifier; '$(x)(y)Fxy$' is simply a quantification of '$(y)Fxy$' as a whole. Whereas (1)–(8) show existential quantifications within universal ones and vice versa, (9) shows universal within universal. For another example of the latter kind, consider the statement:

Whoever bets on every horse in the race loses little.

This becomes:

$(x)(x$ bets on every horse in the race $\supset x$ loses little),

wherein 'x bets on every horse in the race' gives way in turn to:

$(y)(y$ is a horse in the race $\supset x$ bets on y).

So the whole has the form:

$$(x)[(y)(Fy \supset Gxy) \supset Hx].$$

The following example, on the other hand, leads to existential quantification within existential:

Sadie stole something at the Emporium and exchanged it for something.

It becomes first:

$(\exists x)$(Sadie stole x at the Emporium . Sadie exchanged x for something) (cf. (20) of §16); then 'Sadie exchanged x for something' gives way in turn to:

$$(\exists y)(\text{Sadie exchanged } x \text{ for } y).$$

So the whole has the form:

$$(\exists x)[Fx \, . \, (\exists y)Gxy].$$

Clearly we must extend a quantification over a whole compound, in representing the logical structure of a verbal statement, when the statement contains a pronoun in the farther component which must be construed as referring back to the quantifier. This point was illustrated in §16, (18)–(23). The point is brought out again by the statements:

> If you own any houses then you should sell them,
> If you own any houses then your taxes will be high,

which become respectively:

(10) $(x)(\text{you own } x \, . \, x \text{ is a house } . \supset \text{ you should sell } x)$,

(11) $(\exists x)(\text{you own } x \, . \, x \text{ is a house}) \supset \text{your taxes will be high}$.

These have the respective forms '$(x)(Fx \supset Gx)$' and '$(\exists x)Fx \supset p$'.

But let it not be concluded that a quantification may cover a compound *only* if both components refer back to the quantifier. On the contrary, clauses lacking reference to the quantifier will also be permitted hereafter within quantifications. Thus the statement:

(12) $(\exists x)(\text{you own } x \, . \, x \text{ is a house } . \supset \text{ your taxes will be high})$

is to be admitted as legitimate along with (11), but must be distinguished from it; it has the form '$(\exists x)(Fx \supset p)$' rather than '$(\exists x)Fx \supset p$'. (12), unlike (11), comes out trivially true regardless of taxes as long as there are things at all in the universe besides your houses. For, the conditional:

> you own x . x is a house . $\supset$ your taxes will be high

which appears within (12) is true of all things other than your houses simply because its antecedent is false of such things. (12) expresses an unnatural but straightforward enough thought, and goes into unnatural words as:

There is something such that if it is a house of yours then your taxes will be high.

Quantifiers are subject, in point of grouping, to the same convention which governs the negation sign (§4): a quantifier applies to the shortest possible ensuing sentence or schema. In '$(\exists x)(Fx \supset p)$', or (12), the quantifier is required by the parentheses to apply to the whole conditional; in '$(\exists x)Fx \supset p$' or (11), on the other hand, the quantifier is understood as lying within the antecedent and applying only to it. The distinction between '$(\exists x)(Fx \supset p)$' and '$(\exists x)Fx \supset p$' can be reproduced generally in words thus:

> There is something x such that if Fx then p,
> If there is something x such that Fx then p.

It is just as essential to distinguish between '$(x)Fx \supset p$' and '$(x)(Fx \supset p)$' as between '$(\exists x)Fx \supset p$' and '$(\exists x)(Fx \supset p)$'. In due course we shall find, indeed, that '$(x)Fx \supset p$' is equivalent to '$(\exists x)(Fx \supset p)$', whereas '$(x)(Fx \supset p)$' is equivalent to '$(\exists x)Fx \supset p$.' However, this is a good point at which to stop anticipating formal developments. The moral to be carried away from the present comments is merely that parentheses are not to be lightly dismissed.

EXERCISES

1. Supposing the universe limited to a, b, $\cdots$, h, expand the quantifications into alternation and conjunction in each of the following examples:

$$(x)(y)Fxy, \quad (\exists x)(\exists y)Fxy, \quad (\exists x)(Fx \supset p), \quad (\exists x)Fx \supset p.$$

Do each of the first two in two stages.

2. Rewrite these with help of quantification:

> Every solid is soluble in some liquid or other,
> There is a liquid in which every solid is soluble.

3. Rewrite this example (DeMorgan's) with help of quantification:

If all horses are animals then all heads of horses are heads of animals.

4. Express, with help of quantification, the likeliest interpretation of the statement:

She had a ring on every finger.

5. Where 'F' means 'harms', and the universe is mankind, put this unambiguously and idiomatically into words:

$$(x)[(y)(Fyx \supset Fxy) \supset Fxx].$$

Hint: As a first step put just the inside quantification into words, retaining 'x'.

6. Supposing the universe to comprise just the points on an endless line, judge each of these three statements as to truth value and explain your reasoning.

$$(\exists x)(y)(\exists z)(x \text{ is between } y \text{ and } z),$$
$$(y)(\exists x)(\exists z)(x \text{ is between } y \text{ and } z),$$
$$(\exists x)(\exists z)(y)(x \text{ is between } y \text{ and } z).$$

7. Express each of these statements with help of quantification, and indicate its truth value:

Nothing is identical with nothing,
Something is identical with something,
Everything is identical with nothing,
Nothing is identical with anything.

§23. QUANTIFICATIONAL SCHEMATA AND PREDICATES

Throughout Part II the one letter used in quantification was 'x'. It served as a pronoun, for cross-reference to quantifiers. No letters beyond 'x' were needed because, in Part II, quantifications never occurred within quantifications. Since each occurrence of 'x' stood thus in a unique quantification, there could be no doubt as to which occurrence of '(x)' or '$(\exists x)$' a given occurrence of 'x' referred back to. With the advent of quantifications within quantifications, however, it has become necessary to use distinctive letters 'x' and 'y' to keep cross-references straight. Quantifications can pile up in such a way as to demand recourse also to 'z' and further letters.

Such letters are called *variables*. Care must be taken, however, to divorce this traditional word of mathematics from its archaic connotations. The variable is not best thought of as somehow varying through time, and causing the sentence in which it occurs to vary with it. Neither is it to be thought of as an unknown quantity, discoverable by solving equations. The variables remain mere pronouns for cross-reference to quantifiers; just as 'x' in its recurrences can usually be rendered 'it' in verbal translations, so the distinctive variables 'x', 'y', 'z', etc., correspond to the distinctive pronouns 'former' and 'latter', or 'first', 'second', and 'third', etc. The statement:

($\exists x$)[Sadie stole x at the Emporium . ($\exists y$)(Sadie exchanged x for y)]

corresponds fairly literally to the words:

There is something such that Sadie stole it at the Emporium and such that there is something such that Sadie exchanged the former for the latter.

An occurrence of a variable in a sentence is called *free* in that sentence when it is unquantified; i.e., when it neither stands in, nor refers back to, any quantifier within the limits of the given sentence. Thus the occurrences of 'x' in:

(1) x is a man $\supset$ x is mortal, x is a book . x is boring

are free therein, but the occurrences of 'x' in:

(x)(x is a man $\supset$ x is mortal),   ($\exists x$)(x is a book . x is boring)

are *bound*, i.e. not free, in these sentences. In the sentence:

(2)   ($\exists x$)(y is uncle of x)

the occurrence of 'y' is free, there being no '(y)' or '($\exists y$)' present; but the occurrences of 'x' are bound, because of '($\exists x$)'. One and the same occurrence of 'x' may be bound in a whole sentence and free in a part; the final occurrence of 'x' in (2), e.g., is bound in (2) but free in the part 'y is uncle of x'. In one and the same sentence, moreover, one occurrence of 'x' may be free and others bound; this happens in the conjunction:

(3) x is red . (x)(x has mass),

in which the quantifier has to do only with the second clause. (3)

means 'x is red and everything has mass', and could just as well be written with distinct variables:

(4) x is red . $(y)(y$ has mass$)$.

The sentences (1)–(4), in which one or more variables are free (i.e., have free occurrences), are called *open* sentences; others are *closed*. The notion of open sentence is broader now than in Part II, but only in the ways necessitated by the broadening of quantification: there are now other variables than 'x' to consider, and there is now the phenomenon of quantification within quantification. A sentence S can now contain a quantification and still have a free variable, this variable being preparatory to the eventual imposition of another quantifier covering S as a whole. Thus it is that we have open sentences (2)–(4) containing quantifiers, whereas in Part II only closed sentences were thought of as containing quantifiers.

By starting with 'p', 'q', 'Fx', 'Gx', 'Fy', 'Gxy', etc., and applying quantifiers and the truth-functional notations, we obtain a category of schemata which will be called *quantificational schemata*. These include all the "uniform" quantificational schemata, i.e. the quantificational schemata of Part II, and they also include a wide variety of further forms such as (1)–(6) of the preceding section. They also include such mixtures as '$(\exists x)Fx \supset p$' and '$(\exists x)(Fx \supset p)$'; and, continuing to the extreme, they even include as a special case the purely truth-functional schemata of Part I. Just this restriction is to be imposed: no one capital letter is to be allowed to recur in a schema with different numbers of occurrences of variables attached, as in '$(x)(Fx \supset Fxx)$' or '$(x)(Fx \supset (\exists y)Fxy)$'. Such combinations are excluded because they would raise special questions of interpretation, and there is no need of them.

Quantificational schemata, like sentences, will be called *open* if they contain one or more free variables, and otherwise *closed*. Thus the schema:

$$(x)[Fx \supset (\exists y)(Gy . Hyx)]$$

is closed, but its parts:

$Fx \supset (\exists y)(Gy . Hyx)$, $(\exists y)(Gy . Hyx)$, $Gy . Hyx$

are all open. What were called open and closed schemata in Part II are clearly still open and closed schemata, respectively, in the present sense. Truth-functional schemata, e.g., '$p \supset q$', count as closed. In interpreting uniform quantificational schemata we found it convenient in §17 to dismiss all thought of 'F', 'G', etc. as representative of terms, and to think of 'Fx', 'Gx', etc., rather in their entirety as representing any open sentences. But this easy course is now at an end, because of such examples as the one in the preceding section about the philosopher:

(5) $(\exists y)[Fy \cdot (x)(Fx \supset Gxy)] \supset (\exists x)(Fx \cdot Gxx)$.

We cannot view 'Fx' and 'Fy' here as representing simply any pair of open sentences having the respective free variables 'x' and 'y'. Rather, if we construe 'Fx' as 'x is a philosopher' we must construe 'Fy' as 'y is a philosopher'; if we construe 'Fx' as 'x is a number' we must construe 'Fy' as 'y is a number'. The admissible interpretations of 'Gxy' and 'Gxx' in (5) are similarly tied together: if we interpret 'Gxy' as 'x contradicts y' we must construe 'Gxx' as 'x contradicts x'.

A retreat to the view of capital letters as representing terms, absolute and relative (cf. preceding section), thus seems indicated. When a capital letter occurs monadically, i.e., with variables attached singly (cf. 'F' in (5)), we may interpret it as representing an absolute term; when it occurs *dyadically*, i.e., with variables attached pairwise (cf. 'G' in (5)), we may interpret it as representing a dyadic relative term; and so on. Thus 'F' and 'G' in (5) may be explained for purposes of the example of the philosopher as representing respectively the absolute term 'philosopher' and the dyadic relative term 'contradicts'.

But, as stressed in §17, every open sentence having 'x' as sole free variable must admit of being treated as of the form 'Fx'. Likewise every open sentence having 'x' and 'y' as sole free variables must admit of being treated as of the form 'Gxy'; and so on. Thus, while the terms appropriate to the philosopher example happened to be readily specifiable in a word apiece, 'philosopher' and 'contradicts', we find some awkwardness in fashioning a term which as interpretation of 'F' will cause 'Fx' to represent:

(6) x used to work for the man who murdered the second husband of x's youngest sister

(to recur to the example of §17); and the awkwardness involved verges on genuine difficulty when we try to devise a relative term which as interpretation of 'G' will cause 'Gxy' to represent:

(7) x used to work for the man who murdered y and y was the second husband of x's youngest sister.

The best course now seems to be rather this third one: to supplant the notion of term by that of *predicate*,[1] conceiving predicates artificially in the image of sentences as follows: a predicate is like a sentence except that it contains the arbitrary sign '①', or '①' and '②', or '①', '②', and '③', etc., in some places appropriate to free variables. Then, where 'Fx' is to mean 'x is red', we explain 'F' not as the term 'red' but as the predicate '① is red'; where 'Fx' is to mean (6) we explain 'F' as the predicate:

(8) ① used to work for the man who murdered the second husband of ①'s youngest sister;

and where 'Gxy' is to mean (7) we explain 'G' as the predicate:

(9) ① used to work for the man who murdered ② and ② was the second husband of ①'s youngest sister.

The circled numerals are merely numbered blanks showing where the variables are to be put in passing from 'F' to 'Fx', or 'Fxy', etc.: the leftmost of the variables is to be put for '①', the next for '②', and so on.

If a meaning for these strange expressions called predicates be demanded, e.g., for (8), an answer is 'former employee of own youngest sister's second husband's murderer'; for circled numerals may be viewed simply as a supplementary device, more convenient and systematic than those existing in ordinary language, for abstracting complex terms out of complex sentences. Thus the shift which we have made from terms to predicates can be viewed as a case merely of improving and renaming the idea of term.

So far as our work is concerned, however, we can as well view these predicates merely as auxiliary diagrams useful in specifying what

---

[1] If the reader has not yet forgotten the medieval sense of 'predicate' explained in the small print of §14, let him do so now.

open sentences are to be put for 'Fx', 'Fy', etc., or for 'Fxy', 'Fyz', etc., in a schema. We shall not use predicates themselves as actual parts of sentences, since the variables to which the predicates are applied take the place of the circled numerals. Where 'F' is interpreted, e.g., as:

(10)   ② amuses ① more than y amuses ②,

the schema:

(11) $(\exists x)Fxy \lor (\exists x)Fyx . \supset (\exists x)Fxx$

becomes:

(12) $(\exists x)(y$ amuses x more than y amuses $y) \lor$
    $(\exists x)(x$ amuses y more than y amuses $x) . \supset$
                    $(\exists x)(x$ amuses x more than y amuses $x).$

The importance of the predicate (10) is as an intermediary diagram, or so to speak a template or stencil, helpful in determining just what combinations of sentences *can* legitimately be put, e.g., for 'Fxy', 'Fyx', and 'Fxx' in (11). It would be harder, without appeal to (10), to detect the essential relationship between the arrangement of variables in (12) and that in (11).[1]

[1] The use of "predicates" in the form here described, as well as the notion of "introduction" taken up in the next paragraph, come from my *Elementary Logic* (pp. 119 ff.), where they figured as devices for simplifying the formulation of substitution in quantification theory. I used the word 'stencil' there instead of 'predicate'; but I find the latter word apter and more instructive, both because of its linguistic connotations and because of its currency in modern logical writings to mean, in a vague way, that which a statement says about something.—There is a use of circumflexed variables '$\hat{x}$', '$\hat{y}$', etc., as old as Whitehead and Russell's *Principia Mathematica* (I refer to the internal use as of Part I, Section B, not to the circumflexed prefixes of Section C) which is surely best construed as amounting to this present use of circled numerals; the formulas of *Principia* which contain such circumflexed variables might likewise, therefore, be spoken of as predicates. Whitehead and Russell called such formulas "propositional functions," in one of several ill-distinguished senses of this phrase. At points they view those formulas as names of attributes, but identification of them with predicates in my sense need not affect this debatable point of philosophical attitude. Accordingly, preferring old symbols to new, I should like to use '$\hat{w}$', '$\hat{x}$', '$\hat{y}$', etc., instead of '①', '②', '③', etc., and am deterred only by the fact that the circumflexed variables are harder to work with. Consider, e.g., the transformation of (11) into (12): at each occurrence of 'F' the *positionally* first variable following 'F' supplanted the '①' of (10) and the positionally second supplanted '②'. Using '$\hat{w}$' and '$\hat{x}$' instead of '①' and '②' in (10), we should have had to say that the positionally first variable after 'F' is to supplant the *alphabetically* earliest circumflexed variable and the positionally second is to supplant the alphabetically second; and this, though straightforward enough, would in practice invite confusion.

The complex operation of supplanting an occurrence of a predicate letter[1] and its attached variables by a predicate, and then putting those successive variables for '①', '②', etc., in the predicate, will be called *introduction* of the predicate *at* that occurrence of the predicate letter. Such, then, is the operation whereby an interpretation of a predicate letter in a schema is put into effect; not by just putting the chosen predicate for all occurrences of the predicate letter, but by *introducing* it at all occurrences of the letter.

But "introduction" is still imperfectly formulated. Consider, e.g., the predicate of being a mother, viz. '① is a mother', or more fully '$(\exists x)$(① is mother of x)'. When this is introduced at an occurrence of 'F', we want the effect to be that simply of interpreting 'F' as the predicate of being a mother. Thus we want introduction of the predicate to turn 'Fx', 'Fy', etc., into 'x is a mother', 'y is a mother', etc. In the case of 'Fy' the result is indeed as planned; introduction of '$(\exists x)$(① is mother of x)' gives '$(\exists x)(y$ is mother of $x)$', meaning 'y is a mother'. But in the case of 'Fx' the result is not as planned; introduction of '$(\exists x)$(① is mother of x)' turns 'Fx' into the quite irrelevant falsehood '$(\exists x)(x$ is mother of $x)$', devoid of free 'x' and remote in meaning from the intended 'x is a mother'. So the notion of introduction must be subjected to this *first restriction*: Variables entering the predicate in place of the circled numerals must not be such as to be captured by quantifiers within the predicate.

Predicates, like sentences, will be called *open* when they contain free variables, and otherwise *closed*. Thus (10) is open, because of the free 'y', whereas (8), (9), and '$(\exists x)$(① is mother of x)' are closed. Now introduction of an open predicate, say '① caused y', at an occurrence of 'F' is intended to turn 'Fx', 'Fy', etc., into 'x caused y', 'y caused y', etc., the indeterminancy of 'y' being retained. Correspondingly it is intended to turn '$(\exists x)Fx$' (or 'F something') into '$(\exists x)(x$ caused $y)$' (or 'Something caused y'). All these things turn out, certainly, as planned. But difficulty arises when in place of '$(\exists x)Fx$' we have '$(\exists y)Fy$'; for though this has quite the same meaning as '$(\exists x)Fx$' (viz. 'F something'), the effect of introducing '① caused y' here is the quite irrelevant statement '$(\exists y)(y$ caused $y)$',

---

[1] In the past dozen sections, care has been taken to favor 'F', 'G', etc., with no better name than 'capital letters'. Hereafter we may call them predicate letters.

devoid of free 'y' and remote in meaning from the intended 'Something caused y'. So the notion of introduction must be subjected still to this *second restriction*: Variables free in the predicate must not be such as to be captured by quantifiers in the schema into which the predicate is introduced.

We may sum up the two restrictions symmetrically thus: Quantifiers of the introduced predicate must not capture variables of the schema in which the introduction takes place, and variables of the introduced predicate must not be captured by quantifiers of the schema in which the introduction takes place. These restrictions simply ward off confusions of variables which, if allowed, would cause "introduction" to deviate from its intended purpose of interpreting predicate letters.

In turning quantificational schemata into sentences we have not only predicate letters but also sentence letters to reckon with. For sentences the appropriate operation of "introduction" is simpler, there being no question of putting variables for circled numerals. *Introduction of a sentence* at an occurrence of a sentence letter consists merely in putting the sentence for the occurrence of the letter. The first of the two restrictions set forth above, moreover, no longer has a place, there being no circled numerals. But the *second restriction carries over*: Variables free in the introduced sentence must not be such as to be captured by quantifiers in the schema into which the sentence is introduced. This restriction merely makes explicit the understanding which governed the discussion of '$(x)(Fx \supset p)$' and '$(\exists x)(Fx \supset p)$' at the end of the preceding section; viz., that 'p' represents a sentence devoid of free 'x'.

EXERCISES

1. Introduce each of the predicates:

① is ashamed of x, x is ashamed of ①,   ① is ashamed of ①

at the occurrence of 'F' in 'Fx'. Compatibly with the restrictions on introduction, which of these predicates can be introduced at the occurrence of 'F' in '$(\exists x)Fx$'? What does the resulting statement mean?

2. Find a predicate which, introduced at the occurrences of '*F*' in '*Fxy ⊃ Fyx*', will yield:

$$y^z = xy + y . \supset . x^z = yy + x.$$

3. Decide which of the following predicates may, compatibly with the restrictions on substitution, be introduced at the occurrence of '*F*' in '(∃*x*)*Fxy*':

② praised ② to ①,	② praised *y* to ①,
② praised ① to ①,	(∃*y*)(② praised *y* to ①),
② praised *x* to ①,	(∃*z*)(② praised *z* to ①).

Put the results of those legitimate introductions into words, supposing the universe limited to mankind.

§24. VALIDITY OF QUANTIFICATIONAL SCHEMATA

The phrases 'true of' and 'false of' were adopted in §12, to begin with, in connection with absolute terms. In §17 they were carried over to open sentences, insofar as open sentences were there recognized: sentences with '*x*' as sole free variable. Henceforward, however, the useful application of those phrases is rather to predicates; for it is predicates henceforward that the letters '*F*', '*G*', etc., are thought of as representing.

A predicate is called a *one-place* predicate if it contains '①', to any number of recurrences, but no further circled numerals; a *two-place* predicate if it contains '①' and '②' but no higher; and so on.[1] Now a one-place predicate which is closed (devoid of free variables) may be said to be *true of* or *false of* a given object according as the predicate becomes a true or a false statement when '①' is imagined to name that object. Likewise the phrases 'true of' and 'false of' may be used

---

[1]Predicate letters are said to occur monadically when followed by variables singly, dyadically when followed by variables in pairs, and so on. The words 'dyadic', 'triadic', etc., have been applied also to relative terms. But it is through no caprice that the words 'monadic', 'dyadic', etc., are being withheld from predicates in favor of 'one-place', 'two-place', etc. In the next section we shall have occasion to speak of one-place "predicate-schemata," two-place predicate-schemata, etc., referring thereby (as in the present usage in connection with predicates) to the number of circled numerals present; but we *also* have occasion to speak of monadic and polyadic schemata, referring thereby rather to the absence or presence of polyadically occurring predicate letters.

of closed two-place predicates substantially as they were used of dyadic relative terms (§22): a closed two-place predicate is true or false of a given pair of objects according as the predicate becomes true or false when '①' and '②' are imagined to name those respective objects. Correspondingly for three-place predicates and higher. On the other hand an open predicate cannot be said to be true or false of an object, any more than an open sentence can be said to be true or false.

Likewise we may speak of *extensions* (cf. §§12, 17) of closed predicates. The extension of a closed one-place predicate is the class of all the things of which the predicate is true; the extension of a closed two-place predicate is the class of all the pairs of which the predicate is true; and so on. Open predicates have no extensions, just as open sentences have no truth values.

When we speak of "all interpretations" it can make a difference, we saw in §18, whether we mean all interpretative expressions or all possible extensions, all classes. This matter is not changed by our having switched to predicates. The point is relevant primarily, here as in §18, to the definition of validity; and indeed the definition of validity in §18 may, as far as it goes, be carried over directly to present purposes. A schema is valid if and only if, for every choice of a nonempty universe U, it comes out true under all interpretations within U of its predicate letters; i.e., true for all subclasses of U as extensions of its predicate letters. This definition does not yet cover quantificational schemata in which predicate letters occur polyadically (i.e., followed by more than single variables), nor does it cover quantificational schemata in which there are sentence letters or free variables: first, however, let us pause for examples devoid of those features. The ones devoid of those features are mostly just the ones covered in §§18–21 under the head of uniform quantificational schemata, but not entirely so. Here are four valid quantificational schemata which, though devoid of polyadic letters and sentence letters and free variables, still fall outside the category of uniform quantificational schemata. As a group they show an interesting symmetry. All four will prove of basic importance to the next two sections.

$$(1) \quad (y)[(x)Fx \supset Fy],$$
$$(2) \quad (y)[Fy \supset (\exists x)Fx],$$
$$(3) \quad (\exists y)[Fy \supset (x)Fx],$$
$$(4) \quad (\exists y)[(\exists x)Fx \supset Fy].$$

Suppose 'F' means 'has mass'. (I.e., suppose 'F' interpreted as the predicate '① has mass', or as having the class of objects with mass as its extension.) Then '$(x)Fx$' in (1) means 'everything has mass'; and accordingly (1) as a whole says that each object, no matter how selected, is bound to be such that if everything has mass then *it* (the selected object) has mass. Again '$(\exists x)Fx$' in (2) says that something has mass; accordingly (2) as a whole says that each thing is such that if it has mass then something has mass.

(3) is less evident. It says there is something such that, if it has mass, everything has mass. To see the truth of this statement clearly, we must keep the meaning of the material conditional in mind. Now if there is anything y lacking mass, the conditional '$Fy \supset (x)Fx$' becomes true for such y (simply because of falsity of antecedent); hence, if there is anything lacking mass, (3) becomes true. If on the other hand everything has mass, '$Fy \supset (x)Fx$' becomes true (by truth of consequent) regardless of y; so again (3) becomes true (provided merely that there is anything y in the universe at all).

(4), finally, says there is something such that, if there are any objects at all that have mass, it has. Now if no objects have mass, '$(\exists x)Fx \supset Fy$' becomes true (by falsity of antecedent) regardless of y; so (4) then becomes true (provided merely that there is anything y in the universe at all). If on the other hand some object y does have mass, '$(\exists x)Fx \supset Fy$' becomes true for such y (by truth of consequent), and accordingly (4) again becomes true.

Next let us examine (1)–(4) in terms directly of the definition of validity which preceded them. Actually the reasoning will be largely a repetition of that which we have just now been through. To see that (1) is valid, consider any universe and any interpretation, within that universe, of 'F'. *Case* 1: 'F' is interpreted as true of everything in the universe. Then, for each object y in the universe, '$(x)Fx \supset Fy$' becomes true because of true consequent; so (1) comes out true. *Case* 2: 'F' is interpreted otherwise. Then, for each object y in the universe, '$(x)Fx \supset Fy$' becomes true because of false antecedent; so (1) comes out true.

To see that (2) is valid, consider again any universe and any interpretation of 'F'. *Case* 1: 'F' is interpreted as true of nothing. Then, for each object y, '$Fy \supset (\exists x)Fx$' becomes true because of false antecedent; so (2) comes out true. *Case* 2: 'F' is interpreted otherwise.

Then, for each object y, '$Fy \supset (\exists x)Fx$' becomes true because of true consequent; so (2) comes out true.

To see that (3) is valid, consider any nonempty universe and any interpretation of 'F'. *Case* 1: 'F' is interpreted as true of everything. Then, for each object y in the universe, '$Fy \supset (x)Fx$' becomes true because of true consequent; therefore (3) comes out true, there being objects in the universe. *Case* 2: 'F' is not so interpreted. Then there is an object y in the universe for which 'Fy' becomes false, and hence '$Fy \supset (x)Fx$' true; so (3) comes out true.

The argument for (4) is left to the reader.

The broadening of our definition of validity to allow for polyadically occurring predicate letters offers no difficulty. Just as any class of members of a universe U counts as an interpretation within U of a monadically occurring predicate letter, so any class of pairs of members of U counts as an interpretation within U of a dyadically occurring predicate letter, and so on. Provision for sentence letters likewise presents no difficulty, these being interpretable as usual by assignment of truth values. So, postponing still a little the question of free variables, we may define validity generally for *closed* quantificational schemata thus: A closed schema is valid if and only if, for every choice of a nonempty universe U, it comes out true under all interpretations within U of its predicate letters and all interpretations, by truth-value, of its sentence letters.

The added clause concerning sentence letters in this definition was irrelevant to the foregoing examples, there being no sentence letters present. Moving now to the opposite extreme, consider any schema which contains sentence letters to the exclusion of predicate letters, and is hence merely a truth-functional schema as of Part I. It is now the other clause, that about predicate letters, that ceases to be relevant; so our definition says merely that the schema counts as valid if and only if it comes out true under every assignment of truth values to its sentence letters. So validity under our new definition is the same as in Part I so far as truth-functional schemata are concerned.

To turn next to an example involving both a predicate letter and a sentence letter, the schema:

(5) $(x)(Fx \supset p) \equiv . (\exists x)Fx \supset p$

is valid. To see this, consider any universe, any interpretation of 'F' therein, and either truth value for 'p'. *Case* 1: 'p' as true. For each object x of the universe, '$Fx \supset p$' comes out true (having true consequent); so '$(x)(Fx \supset p)$' comes out true. But '$(\exists x)Fx \supset p$' also comes out true, having true consequent. *Case* 2: 'p' as false. By resolution, '$(\exists x)Fx \supset p$' becomes '$-(\exists x)Fx$'. Likewise, for each object x of, the universe, '$Fx \supset p$' amounts to '$-Fx$', so that '$(x)(Fx \supset p)$' amounts to '$(x) -Fx$' and hence to '$-(\exists x)Fx$'.

Validity of (5) means equivalence of '$(x)(Fx \supset p)$' to '$(\exists x)Fx \supset p$'. This, it will be recalled, is one of the two equivalences which were promised at the end of §22. Its significance is that a universally quantified conditional, whose consequent lacks the variable in question, can be rewritten with the quantifier confined to the antecedent provided it be changed to existential. Later (§29) we shall come upon a whole set of such laws of confinement of quantifiers.

Our definition of validity still applies only to closed schemata —schemata without free variables. But insertion of one more clause, following the line of our definition of validity for open uniform schemata in §18, yields finally a general definition: A quantificational schema is *valid* if and only if, for every choice of a nonempty universe, the schema comes out true under all interpretations within that universe of its predicate letters, all interpretations of its sentence letters, and all choices of objects of the universe as interpretations of its free variables.

Clearly then an open schema is valid if and only if its *universal closure*, a closed schema formed from it by subjecting the whole to a universal quantifier for each of its free variables, is valid. In particular we may conclude that the open schemata:

$$(x)Fx \supset Fy, \qquad\qquad Fy \supset (\exists x)Fx$$

are valid, since (1) and (2) are their universal closures.

The above observation on universal closures is the extension to general quantification theory of the law (i) of §18, which equated validity of an open uniform schema with validity of its universal quantification. But note that a law yet more closely resembling (i) itself in outward form also holds: *A universal quantification S' of an*

*open schema S, with respect to any one of the free variables of S, is valid
if and only if S is valid.* For, if there are no further free variables then
S' is the universal closure of *S*; if on the other hand there are further
free variables, then some one closed schema is a universal closure both
of *S'* and of *S*.

EXERCISES

1. Show that (4) is valid.

2. Do (1)–(4) go into valid schemata when '(y)' is changed to
'(∃y)' and '(∃y)' to '(y)'? Justify your answers in detail.

§25. SUBSTITUTION IN QUANTIFICATIONAL SCHEMATA

We have known since §18 that substitution of truth-functional or
quantificational schemata for '*p*', '*q*', etc., and of open schemata for
'*Fx*', '*Gx*', etc., in valid schemata can be depended upon to yield
valid schemata. But when these matters were examined, quantificational schemata were being understood exclusively as uniform quantificational schemata.

In quantificational schemata in the general sense now at hand the
letters '*F*', '*G*', etc., may occur followed by other variables than '*x*',
and even by several at a time. For this reason we were led in §23 to
abandon our old integral view of '*Fx*', '*Gx*', etc., in favor of treating
the separate letters '*F*', '*G*', etc. as representative of predicates.
Correspondingly we must now abandon the notion of substituting
schemata for '*Fx*', '*Gx*', etc., as wholes, and speak rather of substitutions for '*F*', '*G*', etc.

But if, instead of speaking, e.g., of substitution of the schema
'*Gx* ∨ (∃z)Hzx*' for '*Fx*', we are to phrase the operation as somehow a
substitution for '*F*', what sort of thing are we to regard as substituted
for '*F*'? Clearly a *predicate-schema*, '*G①* ∨ (∃z)Hz①*'. Predicate-
schemata are doubly artificial expressions conceived in the image of
sentence schemata (or ordinary quantificational schemata) but containing circled numerals. Just as a predicate is like a sentence except
for containing '①', or '①' and '②', etc., in some places appropriate
to free variables, so a predicate-schema is like a sentence schema ex-

cept for containing '①', or '①' and '②', etc., in some places appropriate to free variables.[1]

Substitution of a predicate-schema for a predicate letter is substitution in an indirect sense: the sentence schema resulting from the substitution does not actually contain the predicate-schema with its circled numerals, any more than a sentence contains a predicate with its circled numerals. Substitution of a predicate-schema for a predicate letter in a sentence schema, e.g., '$G① ∨ (∃z)Hz①$' for 'F' in '$(x)Fx ⊃ Fy$', consists in *introducing* the predicate-schema at each occurrence of the predicate letter, thus:

(1) $(x)[Gx ∨ (∃z)Hzx] ⊃ . Gy ∨ (∃z)Hzy.$

The notion of "introduction" involved here corresponds exactly to that in §23, and is subject to corresponding restrictions. Let us transfer those formulations explicitly to our new sphere of activity:

Introducing a predicate-schema at an occurrence of a predicate letter consists in supplanting that occurrence of the letter and its attached variables by the predicate-schema with '①', '②', etc., changed respectively to those successive variables. *Introducing* a sentence schema at an occurrence of a sentence letter consists merely in putting the schema for that occurrence of the letter.

First restriction: Quantifiers of the introduced predicate-schema must not capture variables of the schema in which the introduction takes place.

Second restriction: Variables of the introduced predicate-schema or sentence schema must not be captured by quantifiers of the schema in which the introduction takes place. Finally

Substitution of a predicate-schema or sentence schema for a predi-

[1]There will be little occasion to speak of predicate-schemata beyond the limits of the present section. On the other hand sentence schemata, such as have been known up to now as "quantificational schemata" and commonly just as "schemata," will continue to be the focus of attention for many sections to come. It would be unfortunate if references to these latter had hereafter to be encumbered always with adjectives in order merely to avoid confusion with the present transitory phenomenon of predicate-schemata. In order that this may not be necessary, the double precaution will be taken of never referring to predicate-schemata simply as schemata, but always by full title, and of hyphenating the title as a reminder of its indissolubility. The word 'schema' without modifier will therefore continue to mean sentence schema as heretofore. Such time as predicate-schemata continue to be in the air, however, the contrasting phrase "sentence schema" will be held to for emphasis.

cate letter or sentence letter consists in introducing the schema at all occurrences of the letter. Only one-place predicate-schemata are to be substituted for monadically occurring predicate letters (predicate letters followed by single variables); only two-place predicate-schemata are to be substituted for dyadically occurring predicate letters; and so on.

One example of substitution was seen to lead to (1). Another example, viz., substitution of '$G①$ v $-H①$' for 'F' and 'Gy' for 'p', leads from:

(2) $\qquad\qquad (x)(Fx \supset p) \equiv . (\exists x)Fx \supset p \qquad$ ((5) of §24)

to:

(3) $\qquad (x)(Gx \text{ v } -Hx . \supset Gy) \equiv . (\exists x)(Gx \text{ v } -Hx) \supset Gy.$

In general the utility of substitution, here as in Parts I–II, is as a means of generating valid schemata from valid schemata. E.g., since (1) and (3) were got by substitution in schemata which were seen in §24 to be valid, we conclude that (1) and (3) are valid.

Substitution can be depended upon to transmit validity for essentially the reasons already noted in §6 and §18. But it will be well to review the matter now in the new setting. To begin with let us see why it is that the above substitution in (2) yields a valid result. Validity of the result (3) means truth under all interpretations of 'G' and 'H' and the free variable 'y', within any nonempty universe. Suppose the universe fixed, then, and consider any particular choice $\Im$ of such interpretations; what we want to see is that (3) comes out true under $\Im$. To see this we derive from $\Im$ the following interpretations for the schematic letters of (2): we interpret 'F' as having the extension which '$G①$ v $-H①$' comes to have under $\Im$, and we interpret 'p' as having the truth value which 'Gy' comes to have under $\Im$. Being valid, (2) must come out true under these interpretations; hence (3), which simply repeats (2) under these interpretations, comes out true too.

More generally, suppose a sentence schema S' obtained by substitution in S. Each free variable and each schematic letter in S has a correspondent among the materials of S'; this correspondent is in each case either the same letter over again, or else a substituted sentence schema or predicate-schema. Now given any choice $\mathfrak{J}$ of interpretations for the free variables and schematic letters of S', let us adopt as interpretation of each free variable or schematic letter of S the same object or truth value or extension which has already accrued to its correspondent through $\mathfrak{J}$. S, so interpreted, matches S' as interpreted by $\mathfrak{J}$. Since this works for each choice of $\mathfrak{J}$, we see that S' is valid (or true for all interpretations) if S is.

The function of the two restrictions on introduction is to assure that the correspondents just now spoken of really correspond (cf. §23). Let us now have some examples showing how substitution can fail to transmit validity when the restrictions are violated.

Substitution of '$(\exists y)G①y$' for 'F' in '$(x)Fx \supset Fy$', in violation of the first restriction, would yield:

(4) $(x)(\exists y)Gxy \supset (\exists y)Gyy.$ (invalid)

That this is not valid, despite the validity of '$(x)Fx \supset Fy$', is seen by confining the universe to persons and interpreting 'G' as '② is mother of ①'; thereupon the antecedent of (4) becomes true ('everyone has a mother') and the consequent false.

Substitution of '$Gx①$' for 'F' in '$(x)Fx \supset Fy$', in violation of the second restriction, would yield:

(5) $(x)Gxx \supset Gxy.$ (invalid)

That this is not valid may be seen by taking 'G' as 'identical with'; then (5) says 'If everything is identical with itself then x is identical with y', and this is clearly not true for every choice of x and y. Or, to restate this refutation in more explicit relation to the definition of validity: when we adopt a universe of two or more objects, and take one of these objects as interpretation of the free 'x' of (5) and a different one as interpretation of 'y', and interpret 'G' as having the extension of '① is identical with ②', thereupon (5) becomes false.

In (1), the expressions '$Gx \lor (\exists z)Hzx$' and '$Gy \lor (\exists z)Hzy$' which supplanted the 'Fx' and 'Fy' of '$(x)Fx \supset Fy$' are symmetrical in 'x' and 'y': the one expression has 'x' where, and only where, the other has 'y'. In the invalid substitution which led to (5), on the other hand, the expressions 'Gxx' and 'Gxy' which supplanted 'Fx' and 'Fy' fail to show this symmetry; 'Gxy' does not have 'y' everywhere that 'Gxx' has 'x'. The reader must be warned that this asymmetry has nothing to do with the invalidity of (5). It is unnecessary, in general, for the expression supplanting 'Fx' to have 'x' where and only where the expression supplanting 'Fy' has 'y'. It is quite proper, e.g., to substitute '$G①y$' for 'F' in '$(x)Fx \supset Fy$' and infer the validity of:

(6) $(x)Gxy \supset Gyy$

(e.g., 'If everyone hates y then y hates himself'). Despite the asymmetry of 'Gxy' and 'Gyy' with respect to 'x' and 'y', (6) is a genuine special case of '$(x)Fx \supset Fy$', as a verbal comparison immediately reflects: 'If everything is an F then y is an F'; 'If everything is a G of y then y is a G of y'; 'If everyone is a Herbert-hater then Herbert is a Herbert-hater'.

To be assured of the correctness of a substitution, we need look only to these points: we must be able, on demand, to specify the actual sentence schema or n-place predicate-schema which is substituted for the sentence letter or n-adically occurring predicate letter; we must be sure that the sentence schema or predicate-schema has been "introduced" at each occurrence of the letter; we must be sure that at each point of introducing the predicate-schema the particular variables there appended to the predicate letter have been put for the circled numerals; and finally we must be sure that the substitution has not led to new capturing of variables by quantifiers, in violation of the two restrictions.

Let us now shift from '$(x)Fx \supset Fy$' to another schema whose validity was likewise noted in the preceding section, viz., '$Fy \supset (\exists x)Fx$'. From this we may proceed to:

(7) $Gyy \supset (\exists x)Gxy$

by the legitimate substitution of '$G①y$' for 'F'; but it would be illegitimate to substitute '$Gx①$' for 'F' and thus proceed to:

(8) $Gxy \supset (\exists x)Gxx$.   (invalid)

An example of (7) is 'If Herbert hates himself then someone hates Herbert', which is quite unexceptionable; but an example of (8) is 'If Amos is uncle of Herbert then someone is uncle of himself'.

Note that though the same principles of substitution are operative here as before, the pair (7) and (8) is rather opposite in appearance to (6) and (5). The valid (6) had unlike variables in the antecedent and like variables in the consequent, but in the valid (7) the opposite is the case.

As far as substitution in our particular examples '$(x)Fx \supset Fy$' and '$Fy \supset (\exists x)Fx$' is concerned, note that the net effect of the two restrictions is just this: the respective sentence schemata S_x and S_y which come to supplant 'Fx' and 'Fy' must be alike except that S_y has free 'y' wherever S_x has free 'x'. (S_x and S_y may also have additional free occurrences of 'y', as seen in (6) and (7).) Any such S_x and S_y can be made to supplant 'Fx' and 'Fy', in '$(x)Fx \supset Fy$' and '$Fy \supset (\exists x)Fx$', by substituting for 'F' the predicate-schema which is like S_x except for having '①' in place of all free 'x'. So, insofar as we are concerned merely with substitution in '$(x)Fx \supset Fy$' and '$Fy \supset (\exists x)Fx$', we may omit all thought of predicate-schemata, instead directly supplanting 'Fx' as a whole by any sentence schema S_x containing free 'x', and 'Fy' by a schema S_y which is like S_x except for having free 'y' in place of all free 'x'.

But when we substitute for 'F' in the valid closed schemata:

(9) $(y)[(x)Fx \supset Fy]$,   (11) $(\exists y)[Fy \supset (x)Fx]$,

(10) $(y)[Fy \supset (\exists x)Fx]$,   (12) $(\exists y)[(\exists x)Fx \supset Fy]$

of the preceding section the effect of the two restrictions is more stringent: the sentence schemata S_x and S_y which supplant 'Fx' and 'Fy' here must be alike except that S_y has free occurrences of 'y' in all *and only* the places where S_x has free occurrences of 'x'. For, the second restriction requires that the predicate-schema substituted for 'F' be devoid of free occurrences of 'y', in view of the initial quantifiers in (9)–(12).

Thus, whereas it was allowable to substitute '$G①y$' for 'F' in '$(x)Fx \supset Fy$' and '$Fy \supset (\exists x)Fx$' so as to obtain (6) and (7), it is forbidden to make the same substitution in (9)–(12) so as to obtain:

(13) $(y)[(x)Gxy \supset Gyy]$,   (15) $(\exists y)[Gyy \supset (x)Gxy]$,   (invalid)

(14) $(y)[Gyy \supset (\exists x)Gxy]$,   (16) $(\exists y)[(\exists x)Gxy \supset Gyy]$.   (invalid)

(13) and (14) happen indeed to be valid anyway, but only because they are the universal closures of the valid open schemata (6) and (7). (15) is not valid, as may be seen by adopting a universe of two or more objects and interpreting 'G' as 'is identical with'. ('Gyy' thereupon becomes true and '$(x)Gxy$' false for every object y; hence '$Gyy \supset (x)Gxy$' becomes false for every object y; thus (15) comes out false.) Likewise (16) is not valid, as may be seen by interpreting 'G' as 'is distinct from'.

The line to be followed in ensuing sections happens to be such in the main as to call for no substitution for polyadic predicate letters, and indeed no substitution even for monadic predicate letters elsewhere than in five of the specific schemata in which illustrative substitutions have already been made in the present section; viz., '$(x)Fx \supset Fy$', '$Fy \supset (\exists x)Fx$', (2), (11), and (12). We have already noted short-cut characterizations of the legitimate substitutions in all of these except (2). In '$(x)Fx \supset Fy$' and '$Fy \supset (\exists x)Fx$' we may put S_x and S_y for 'Fx' and 'Fy' provided merely that S_y has free 'y' wherever S_x has free 'x'. In (11) and (12) we may put S_x and S_y for 'Fx' and 'Fy' only in case S_y has free 'y' where *and only* where S_x has free 'x'. The corresponding condition for (2) is evident: we may put any sentence schemata for 'Fx' and 'p' provided that only the former has free 'x'.

EXERCISES

1. List all the schemata whose validity can be shown by legitimate substitution of one or another of the following predicate-schemata for 'F' in '$(x)Fx \supset Fy$' or '$Fy \supset (\exists x)Fx$' or (2) or (11) or (12):

$$Gx① \lor G①y, \quad Gx① \lor G①x, \quad Gy① \lor G①y, \quad (y)(Gy① \lor G①y).$$

Taking the universe as the members of the council and interpreting '$G①②$' as '① denounced ②' and 'p' as 'steps must be taken', put the results into ordinary language.

2. Determine which of the following schemata are legitimately obtainable from '$(x)Fx \supset Fy$' or '$Fy \supset (\exists x)Fx$' or (2) or (11) or (12) by substitution. Identify the substituted predicate-schema in each case.

$(x)Fxx \supset Fyy$, $Gyx \supset (\exists x)Gxy$,

$(\exists x)[Gxx \supset (\exists y)Gyy]$, $(\exists x)[(y)Gy . Hz . \supset . Gx . Hz]$,

$(x)(Gyx \supset Hxz) \supset . Gyy \supset Hyz$, $Gxy . Hyz . \supset (\exists x)(Gxx . Hxz)$,

$Gy . (z)(Gy \supset Gz) . \supset (\exists x)[Gx . (z)(Gx \supset Gz)]$,

$(x)[(y)(Gxy \supset Gyy) \supset Gyy] \equiv . (\exists x)(y)(Gxy \supset Gyy) \supset Gyy.$

§26. LAWS OF IMPLICATION

In general quantification theory as elsewhere, implication may be explained as validity of the conditional. Thus, in view of the validity of '$(x)Fx \supset Fy$',

(i)   '$(x)Fx$' *implies* 'Fy';

and, in view of the validity of '$Fy \supset (\exists x)Fx$',

(ii)   'Fy' *implies* '$(\exists x)Fx$'.

We saw in the preceding section how to generate valid schemata from valid schemata by substitution. Now substitution serves likewise to generate implications from implications, since implication is validity of a conditional schema. E.g., from (i) we conclude by substitution that

'$(x)[Gx \vee (\exists z)Hzx]$' *implies* '$Gy \vee (\exists z)Hzy$'

and   '$(x)Gxy$' *implies* 'Gyy'.

In affirming these implications we merely reaffirm the validity of the conditionals (1) and (6) of the preceding section.

Implications obtained thus by substitution in the particular example (i) are going to be so important for ensuing developments that a special phrase is needed for them; they will be said to hold *by universal instantiation*. Thus '$(x)Fx$' is said to imply 'Fy' by universal instantiation; '$(x)Gxy$' is said to imply 'Gyy' by universal instantiation; and similarly for any other results of substitution in (i), subject of course to the restrictions in the preceding section. As noted, those restrictions boil down in the present instance to the following: the schemata S_x and S_y which supplant 'Fx' and 'Fy' must be alike except that S_y

has free occurrences of 'y' in all places where S_x has free occurrences of 'x'.

But there is no need here to adhere to the particular letters 'x' and 'y'. The same argument which showed '$(x)Fx \supset Fy$' to be valid also shows '$(y)Fy \supset Fw$' to be valid, and '$(z)Fz \supset Fw$', etc.; the choice of letters for variables is immaterial. We may even choose the same letter for both parts, as in '$(y)Fy \supset Fy$'; the last 'y' being beyond the reach of the quantifier, '$(y)Fy \supset Fy$' differs none in meaning from '$(x)Fx \supset Fy$'.

Accordingly, getting away from the particular choice of variables 'x' and 'y', we may phrase our definition thus: Where V and V' are any variables, and S and S' are alike except that S' has free occurrences of V' at all places where S has free occurrences of V, the universal quantification of S with respect to V is said to imply S' *by universal instantiation*. It is to be kept in mind that S and S' may contain free occurrences of V' over and above those which supplant V; this has already been illustrated by the example of '$(x)Gxy$' and 'Gyy'. Also, as noted, V' may even be V, in which case S' is S; thus '$(y)Fy$' implies 'Fy' by universal instantiation.

Implications obtained by substitution in the particular example (ii) will be said to hold *by existential generalization*. Thus 'Fy' itself is said to imply '$(\exists x)Fx$' by existential generalization; also 'Gyy' is said to imply '$(\exists x)Gxy$' by existential generalization (cf. (7) of the preceding section). The phrase will be used also where the variables are other than 'x' and 'y'; in general, thus, whenever V, V', S, and S' are as in the preceding paragraph, S' is said to imply the existential quantification of S with respect to V *by existential generalization*.

Let us not lose sight of the curious contrasts noted in the preceding section among (5), (6), (7), and (8). Thus '$(x)Gxy$' implies 'Gyy' and 'Gyy' implies '$(\exists x)Gxy$', but '$(x)Gxx$' does not imply 'Gxy', nor does 'Gxy' imply '$(\exists x)Gxx$'. Also '$(x)(\exists y)Gxy$' does not imply '$(\exists y)Gyy$'; cf. the discussion of (4) in the preceding section. All such strictures upon universal instantiation and existential generalization are exactly provided for in the above general formulations in terms of 'V', 'V'', 'S', 'S''.

There are of course no end of further implications besides those by universal instantiation and existential generalization. In particular the implications between truth-functional schemata, studied in Part I, qualify still as implications for quantification theory. For implication is simply validity of the conditional, and we have seen (§24) that a truth-functional schema which is valid in the sense of Part I counts also as a valid schema in the sense of quantification theory. Moreover, since substitution generates implications from implications, the implications between truth-functional schemata afford a basis from which to generate implications between other schemata. E.g., since 'pq' implies 'p', we conclude by substitution that 'Gx . $(y)Fy$' implies 'Gx'. Implications thus derivable are said to hold *truth-functionally.*

Given any two quantificational schemata, we can decide mechanically whether the one implies the other truth-functionally. We have only to put 'p', 'q', etc., for the components so as to obtain purely truth-functional schemata, and then test these latter for implication as in §7. E.g., to decide whether the schema:

$$(\exists x)(Fx \,.\, Gx) \supset Gy \,.\supset (\exists x)Fx$$

truth-functionally implies the schema:

$$(\exists x)Fx \,\vee\, (\exists x)(Fx \,.\, Gx)$$

we first abstract the superficial truth-functional structures by putting 'p', 'q', and 'r' for the components, thus: '$p \supset q \,.\supset r$', '$r \vee p$'. Then we test these truth-functional schemata for implication in a fell swoop:

$$\underset{\displaystyle \bot}{\bot \supset q \,.\supset \bot}$$

and find that '$p \supset q \,.\supset r$' implies '$r \vee p$'.

Besides deciding thus mechanically whether one schema implies another truth-functionally, we can of course decide by inspection whether any schema implies another by universal instantiation or by existential generalization. But these three types of implication are very special. A technique has still to be developed, in ensuing sections, for establishing implication in general—and similarly for validity. The three special types of implication just now singled out will, however, contribute in a fundamental way to that general technique.

The development of that technique will depend also upon various broad principles of implication such as have been familiar since §7.

These principles need to be re-established quite explicitly for general quantification theory, in view of the increased complexity of the subject matter. One such principle is this:

(iii) *Any schema implied by a valid schema is valid.*

Let S' and S be any schemata such that S' is valid and implies S. We want to show that S is valid. I.e., we want to show that S comes out true under all interpretations of its schematic letters and free variables, in any nonempty universe. Suppose, then, any nonempty universe, and any choice $\Im$ of interpretations for the schematic letters and free variables of S. We want to show that S comes out true under $\Im$. Now if there are schematic letters or free variables in S' additional to those of S, let us give them arbitrary interpretations supplementary to $\Im$, say as follows: empty extensions for the additional predicate letters, truth for the additional sentence letters, and some one arbitrary object of our nonempty universe for all the additional free variables. Let $\Im$, thus supplemented, be called $\Im'$. Now S' comes out true under $\Im'$, since S' is valid. Also the conditional whose antecedent is S' and whose consequent is S comes out true under $\Im'$, since it is valid (for, S' implies S). Therefore S comes out true under $\Im'$; for, any true conditional with true antecedent has a true consequent. Then, since $\Im'$ differs none from $\Im$ so far as S is concerned, S comes out true under $\Im$.

Illustration of (iii): Since the valid schema '$(x)Fx \supset Fy$' truth-functionally implies '$-Fy \supset -(x)Fx$', we may conclude that '$-Fy \supset -(x)Fx$' is valid (and hence that '$-Fy$' implies '$-(x)Fx$').

Another law of implication, likewise familiar since §7, is this:

(iv) *A valid schema is implied by any schema.*

That this continues to hold for quantification theory is readily seen. Any schema S truth-functionally implies the conditional which has S as consequent and any schema S' as antecedent. By (iii), then, that conditional is valid if S is valid. But validity of the conditional means that S' implies S.

Now to an even more evident law regarding validity:

(v) *Any conjunction of valid schemata is valid.*

For, consider a conjunction of valid schemata S_1, S_2, $\cdots$. If any universe is adopted and any interpretations are fixed upon for the schematic letters and free variables of the conjunction, then each of S_1, S_2, $\cdots$ will come out true (being valid), and hence so will the conjunction.

There follows another law of implication:

(vi) *If a schema implies each of several, it implies their conjunction.*

Suppose S implies each of S_1, S_2, $\cdots$. That is to say, the conditional having S as antecedent and S_1 as consequent is valid; so also is the conditional having S as antecedent and S_2 as consequent; and so on. By (v), then, the conjunction of these conditionals is valid. But this conjunction truth-functionally implies the conditional whose antecedent is S and whose consequent is the conjunction of S_1, S_2, $\cdots$. By (iii), then, this latter conditional is valid. I.e., S implies the conjunction of S_1, S_2, $\cdots$.

Illustration of (vi): Since 'Fy' implies '$Fy \vee Gy$' truth-functionally, and also implies '$(\exists x)Fx$' by existential generalization, we may conclude that 'Fy' implies '$Fy \vee Gy . (\exists x)Fx$'.

Another law, familiar since §7, is this:

(vii) *If S_1 implies S_2 and S_2 implies S_3 then S_1 implies S_3.*

This can be established by an argument similar in its main lines to that of (vi). The details are left to the reader.

Illustration of (vii): Since '$(x)Fx$' implies 'Fy' by universal instantiation, and 'Fy' implies '$(\exists x)Fx$' by existential generalization, we may conclude that '$(x)Fx$' implies '$(\exists x)Fx$'.

A further law which will be convenient is this:

(viii) *If the conjunction of S_1 and S_2 implies S_3, then S_1 implies the conditional whose antecedent is S_2 and whose consequent is S_3.*

Let us represent S_1 as '$\cdots\cdots$', S_2 as '$---$', and S_3 as '$\underline{\qquad}$'. By hypothesis, the conditional:

$$\cdots\cdots \, . \, --- \, . \, \supset \underline{\qquad}$$

is valid. But it truth-functionally implies the conditional:

$$\cdots\cdots \supset \, . \, --- \supset \underline{\qquad},$$

which accordingly is valid by (iii). But this means that '· · · ·', or S_1, implies '- - - $\supset$ ——'.

Illustration of (viii): Since 'Fy . Gy' implies '$(\exists x)(Fx$. $Gx)$' by existential generalization, we may conclude that 'Fy' implies '$Gy \supset (\exists x)(Fx$. $Gx)$'.

Illustration of the illustration: Take 'Fy' as:

> The Platte is a broad river,

and the implied '$Gy \supset (\exists x)(Fx$. $Gx)$' as:

> If the Platte is shallow then some broad rivers are shallow.

In preparation for later work we must still note one more law of implication. This one is less elementary in character than the foregoing ones.

(ix) *If the existential quantification of a schema S with respect to a variable V is valid, then any schema S' is valid which is implied by S and lacks free V.*

Supposing V to be 'x', let us represent S as '· · ·x· · ·' and the implied schema S' as '- - -'. By the definition of implication, the conditional:

(1) · · ·x· · · .$\supset$. - - -

is valid. Therefore so is:

(2) $(x)(\cdots x \cdots .\supset . \text{- - -})$

(cf. §24). But the schema:

(3) $(x)(\cdots x \cdots .\supset . \text{- - -}) \equiv : (\exists x)(\cdots x \cdots) \supset . \text{- - -}$

is valid, being a result of substitution in (2) of the preceding section. Also, by hypothesis, '$(\exists x)(\cdots x \cdots)$' is valid. By (v), then, the conjunction of '$(\exists x)(\cdots x \cdots)$' with (2) and (3) above is valid. But this conjunction implies '- - -' truth-functionally. (For, a test shows that '$pq : q \equiv . p \supset r$' implies '$r$'. The method here is a fell swoop, levelling out into an inconsistency test of 'pq . $q \equiv \bar{p}$' by truth-value analysis.) By (iii), then, '- - -' is valid.

Illustration of (ix): Take V as 'y', S as '$Gy \supset p .\supset (x)(Gx \supset p)$', and S' as '$p \supset (x)(Gx \supset p)$'. The existential quantification:

$$(\exists y)[Gy \supset p .\supset (x)(Gx \supset p)]$$

of S is valid, by substitution in (11) of the preceding section. But S truth-functionally implies S'. (For, it is found in a fell swoop that '$q \supset p . \supset r$' implies '$p \supset r$'.) Moreover, S' lacks free 'y'. So we may conclude, by (ix), that S' is valid. Our conclusion may also be phrased thus: 'p' implies '$(x)(Gx \supset p)$'.

Illustration of the illustration: Take 'p' as:

O'Donohue is incorruptible

and 'Gx' as 'O'Donohue is offered x'. Then the '$(x)(Gx \supset p)$' which 'p' has been found to imply becomes:

No matter what O'Donohue may be offered, O'Donohue is incorruptible.

EXERCISES

1. Establish (vii).

2. Since '$(x)Fx$' implies 'Fy' and also 'Fz' by universal instantiation, what further schema must '$(x)Fx$' imply according to (vi)? Cite a schema which this implied schema implies in turn by existential generalization. Finally, from the two implications thus far obtained in this exercise, infer a further implication by (vii).

3. Starting with the fact that '$Fx \lor Gx . Fx \lor -Gx$' truth-functionally implies 'Fx', deduce by means exclusively of (viii), (vii), and existential generalization that

'$Fx \lor Gx$' implies '$(\exists y)(Fx \lor -Gy . \supset Fx)$'.

4. Starting with an appropriate truth-functional implication and an appropriate implication by existential generalization, show by one appeal to (vii) and one appeal to (viii) that

'Fx' implies '$-Gx \supset (\exists z) -(Fx \supset Gz)$'.

§27. DEDUCTION

Chain reasoning of the sort allowed by (vii) above proves so important as a technique of quantification theory that a special form of notation will be used to indicate it. The example cited in connection with (vii) appears as follows in the new notation.

$$\star(1) \quad (x)Fx$$
$$\star(2) \quad Fy \qquad (1)$$
$$\star(3) \quad (\exists x)Fx \qquad (2)$$

The first star has the sense of 'suppose', and the succeeding stars mark consequences of that initial premiss. The numbers on the left are for reference, and the numbers on the right are references back; thus the '(1)' at the right indicates that the line in which it stands, (2), is got from (1), and the '(2)' at the right indicates that (3) is got from (2). The upshot of the whole is that (1) implies (3). The whole array is called a *deduction*.

Implication of (3) by (1) is validity of a conditional having (1) as antecedent and (3) as consequent. So we may, if we like, supplement the above deduction with a valid last line. thus:

$$\star(1) \quad (x)Fx$$
$$\star(2) \quad Fy \qquad\qquad\qquad (1)$$
$$\star(3) \quad (\exists x)Fx \qquad\qquad (2)$$
$$(4) \quad (x)Fx \supset (\exists x)Fx \quad \star(3)$$

The absence of a star as prefix to (4) means that this line is not, like (2) and (3), merely shown to hold if (1) holds; it is shown to hold absolutely. The star attached to the reference at the right means that a star was left behind with (3). Whereas a starred line in a deduction purports merely to be implied by the premiss at which the column of stars began, an unstarred line claims validity. In general, as in the above example, an unstarred line may be got from a starred one (referred back to by a starred numeral at the right) by incorporating, as antecedent of a conditional, the premiss with which that column of stars began. This way of getting a line is called *conditionalization*.

Unstarred lines which are thus proved valid by conditionalization are limited in form to conditionals. However, further unstarred lines of other forms may be deduced in turn from them, as at the end of the following deduction:

$$\star(1) \quad (x)(Gx \,.\, -Gx)$$
$$\star(2) \quad Gy \,.\, -Gy \qquad\qquad\qquad\qquad (1)$$
$$(3) \quad (x)(Gx \,.\, -Gx) \supset .\, Gy \,.\, -Gy \quad \star(2)$$
$$(4) \quad -(x)(Gx \,.\, -Gx) \qquad\qquad\qquad (3)$$

Here the premiss (1) is taken as starting point and then (2) is put down, with star, as implied by (1). This implication is by universal instantiation. Next (3) is got by conditionalization. Finally (4) is put down as implied by (3). This implication is truth-functional; for, thinking of 'p' in place of '$(x)(Gx . -Gx)$' and 'q' in place of 'Gy', we may verify in a fell swoop that '$p \supset q\bar{q}$' implies '$\bar{p}$'. The result (4) is put down unstarred (hence as valid) because the line (3) which implied it was unstarred; thus the principle of reasoning involved here is (iii) of the preceding section, rather than (vii).

Conditionalization will be used not only to get unstarred conditionals, which are valid, but also to get starred conditionals, which are merely implied by prior premisses. The technique involved here is one of multiple starring, as in the following deduction:

$\star$(1) $Fy \supset p$
$\star\star$(2) $(x)Fx$
$\star\star$(3) Fy (2)
$\star\star$(4) p (1)(3)
$\star$(5) $(x)Fx \supset p$ $\star$(4)

Here we begin with the premiss (1), and what we want to show is that, on this assumption, (5) holds. As an intermediate step toward this end we adopt (2), the antecedent of the desired conditional (5), as a temporary additional premiss, with the intention of getting rid of it before we are through. With (2) we start a second column of stars. Line (3), then, is set down as implied by (2); this implication is by universal instantiation. (3) has, like (2), to bear the additional star; for, (3) has not been justified on the basis merely of the initial premiss (1), but depends on (2). (4), next, is put down as implied by the conjunction of (1) and (3); this implication is truth-functional. (4), like (3), has to bear the extra star; for, in deriving (4) we had to suppose (3) to hold, and (3) had the extra star. In the final step of conditionalization, however, we get rid of the extra star; for the added premiss (2) which started the second column of stars has been incorporated into (5) as antecedent, and so is no longer depended upon as an outside assumption. But (5) still carries the one star, for the derivation of (5) is contingent still on the premiss (1); our deduction does not show (5) valid, but shows only that (1) implies (5). We could, of course, by an additional step of conditionalization, supplement our deduction with an unstarred and valid sixth line, thus:

$$(6) \quad Fy \supset p . \supset . (x)Fx \supset p \quad *(5)$$

The result (6) is uninteresting, for clearly the familiar valid schema '$(x)Fx \supset Fy$' truth-functionally implies (6). Nor can we hope for interesting results until our present technique of deduction has been completed, in the next section, by the addition of two more rules. Meanwhile, however, let us consolidate our position. Our present rules of deduction need to be justified with some care; for it is not immediately evident, particularly when conditionalization is combined with multiple starring, that our deductions can always be depended upon to establish the implications or validities which they purport to establish.

Before undertaking justification of our rules, we must make them explicit; and before making them explicit, we must adopt a little technical terminology.

If a line in a deduction stands alongside one or more columns of stars, the several lines at which those columns of stars begin will be called *premisses of* the line in question. Thus a line has as many premisses as stars. In the example last set forth, lines (1) and (5) have the single premiss (1); lines (2)–(4) have the premisses (1) and (2); and the added line (6) has no premisses.

The word 'subjoin' will hereafter be used in a technical sense, as follows. *Subjoining* a line, numbered (n) say, to one or more lines (i), (j), $\cdots$, (m), consists in writing (n) as a line later than all of (i), (j), $\cdots$, (m), and alongside all the columns of stars (at least) which pass alongside any of the lines (i), (j), $\cdots$, (m), and appending numerals to line (n) referring back to all of (i), (j), $\cdots$, (m). Thus, in the example last set forth, line (3) is subjoined to (2), and line (4) is subjoined to (1) and (3).

It is evident from the above definitions that where (n) is subjoined to (i), (j), $\cdots$, (m), all premisses of any of (i), (j), $\cdots$, (m) are among the premisses of (n).

The next definition introduces a curious extension of the notion of subjunction, preparatory to the formulation of the rule of conditionalization. Let us speak of *subjoining* a line (n) to a *line and star*, $*(m)$, in this sense: such subjunction consists in writing (*n*) as a line later than (*m*) and alongside *all but the innermost* of the columns of stars which pass alongside (*m*), and appending a starred numeral to line (*n*) referring back to (*m*). In the illustrative deduction last set forth, line (5) is subjoined to ⋆(4); and the added line (6) is subjoined to ⋆(5). In general, where (*n*) is subjoined to ⋆(*m*), all but the last of the premisses of (*m*) are premisses of (*n*).

Now we are ready for the rules.

Rule of premisses (P): We may set down any schema as a line at any stage in the course of a deduction, provided that we initiate a new innermost column of stars at that point.

Rule of universal instantiation (UI): To any line we may subjoin, as a new line, any schema which the given line implies by universal instantiation.

Rule of existential generalization (EG): To any line we may subjoin, as a new line, any schema which the given line implies by existential generalization.

Rule of truth-functional inference (TF): To any line or lines we may subjoin, as a new line, any schema which is truth-functionally implied by the given line or by the conjunction of the given lines.

Rule of conditionalization (Cd): To any line and star, ⋆(*m*), we may subjoin the conditional whose consequent is the same as (*m*) and whose antecedent is the same as the last premiss of (*m*).

The reader will do well to identify, for each line in the various illustrative deductions thus far set forth, the rule which authorizes it.

Now what we want to show by way of justifying our rules is that in every deduction constructed by those rules the last line can be depended upon to be implied by its premiss or by the conjunction of its premisses, or, lacking premisses, to be a valid schema. It will be convenient to rephrase the matter by speaking of a deduction as *sound in* any one of its lines if that line is a valid schema, or has a premiss which implies it, or has premisses whose conjunction implies it. In these terms, what we want to show is that every deduction by our rules is sound in its last line. It is just as easy, actually, to establish this more sweeping thesis: Every deduction by our rules is sound in every line.

The proof that deductions are sound in every line will take the following form. It will be shown that *a deduction is sound in any line if sound in all earlier lines*. But any deduction is clearly sound in its first line, since the first line is bound to be a premiss and hence its own premiss. So, once we have proved the law just now italicized, it will follow that all deductions are sound in their first two lines. Thence, by the same law, it will follow in turn that all deductions are sound in their first three lines; and so on. Thus our thesis, that deductions are sound in all lines, is established in its entirety once we have established the law that a deduction is sound in any line if sound in all earlier lines. Let us now proceed to establish that law.

Suppose, then, we are given a deduction which is sound in every line earlier than some particular line, numbered say (n). What we want to show is that the deduction is sound also in (n). There are five cases to consider, according as (n) enters the deduction by P, UI, EG, TF, or Cd.

CASE P: Trivial; (n) is one of its own premisses.

CASES UI and EG: Here (n) is subjoined to a line (m) which implies (n). Being earlier, (m) is a line in which our deduction is sound. Thus (m) is valid or implied by a premiss or conjunction of premisses of (m). But, by the meaning of 'subjoin', any premisses of (m) are premisses of (n). Therefore (m) is valid or implied by a premiss or conjunction of premisses of (n). Then (n), being implied by (m), is likewise valid or implied by a premiss or conjunction of premisses of (n). (Cf. (iii) and (vii) of §26.) In short, the deduction is sound in (n).

CASE TF: Here (n) is subjoined either to a line (m) which implies (n), or to lines (m_1), (m_2), $\cdots$ whose conjunction implies (n). In the former event, the argument of Cases UI and EG may be repeated without modification. So now suppose rather that (n) is subjoined to several lines (m_1), (m_2), $\cdots$. Being earlier, each of (m_1), (m_2), $\cdots$ is a line in which the deduction is sound. Thus each of (m_1), (m_2), $\cdots$ is valid or implied by its premiss or the conjunction of its premisses.

Subcase 1: None of (m_1), (m_2), $\cdots$ have premisses. Then all are valid. Then, by (v) of §26, their conjunction is valid. Then, by (iii) of §26, (n) is valid, being implied by that conjunction. Thus the deduction is sound in (n).

Subcase 2: Some or all of (m_1), (m_2), $\cdots$ have premisses. By the meaning of 'subjoin', all such premisses are premisses also of (n). So each of (m_1), (m_2), $\cdots$ is valid or implied by the premiss or conjunction of premisses of (n). Or, since the valid ones are themselves implied by anything we like (cf. (iv) of §26), we may put the matter more simply: each of (m_1), (m_2), $\cdots$ is implied by the premiss or conjunction of premisses of (n). Therefore the conjunction of (m_1), (m_2), $\cdots$ is so implied (cf. (vi) of §26). But it in turn implies (n). So, by (vii) of §26, (n) is implied by the premiss or conjunction of premisses of (n). Thus the deduction is sound in (n).

CASE Cd: Here (n) is subjoined to $\star(m)$, and is a conditional whose consequent is the same as (m) and whose antecedent is the same as the last premiss (k) of (m). Being earlier than (n), (m) is a line in which the deduction is sound; thus (m) is implied either by (k) alone or by (k) in conjunction with further premisses of (m). But, by the meaning of 'subjoin to $\star(m)$', any premisses of (m) other than (k) are premisses of (n). So (m) is implied either by (k) alone or by (k) in conjunction with premisses of (n). But if (m) is implied by (k) alone, then, by the meaning of 'imply', the conditional having (k) as antecedent and (m) as consequent is valid; i.e., (n) is valid. If on the other hand (m) is implied by (k) in conjunction with premisses of (n), then we know from (viii) of §26 that the conditional (n) is implied simply by those premisses of (n). In either event, the deduction is sound in (n).

EXERCISES

1. For each of the illustrative lines of deduction in the early pages of the section, cite the appropriate rule.

2. Classify each of those lines as to case and subcase of the above argument (including the various untitled subcases).

3. Set up a deduction having this as unstarred last line:

(5) $(x)(Fx \,.\, Gx) \supset (\exists x)(Gx \lor Hx)$ $\star(4)$

§28. COMPLETION OF THE METHOD

Of the five rules of deduction thus far adopted, two are concerned explicitly with quantifiers: UI and EG. UI allows us to drop a universal quantifier, and EG allows us to add an existential quantifier (changing the variable if we like). Now in order to round our method out we need two more rules, fairly symmetrical to UI and EG: those of *universal generalization* (UG) and *existential instantiation* (EI). UG will allow us to add a universal quantifier, and EI will allow us to drop an existential quantifier (changing the variable if we like).

The basis for UI and EG was that '$(x)Fx$' implies 'Fy' and 'Fy' implies '$(\exists x)Fx$'. For UG and EI we cannot plead that 'Fy' implies '$(x)Fx$' nor that '$(\exists x)Fx$' implies 'Fy'. Yet UG and EI can, under certain restrictions, be used as steps in trustworthy deductions.

They are not wholly alien to unformalized thinking. EI occurs when, having shown or assumed that there are objects x such that Fx, we "let y be any one such." UG occurs when, having proved 'Fy' without regard to special conditions on 'y', we conclude: "But y was anything; so $(x)Fx$." Still, these vernacular foreshadowings are indistinct, and need careful restricting if they are to be reduced to justifiable rule. I shall develop a method of UG and EI which, though restricted in necessary ways, so outruns in other ways any vernacular prototype that it may best be studied without thought of informal antecedents. Exact operations will be devised and justified.

Here is an example using EI, UI, EG, and UG:

$$\star(1)\quad (\exists y)(x)Fxy$$
$$\star(2)\quad (x)Fxz \qquad (1)\ z$$
$$\star(3)\quad Fwz \qquad (2)$$
$$\star(4)\quad (\exists y)Fwy \qquad (3)$$
$$\star(5)\quad (x)(\exists y)Fxy \qquad (4)\ w$$

The variable 'z' is *flagged* at the right of line (2), as a signal that only something less than implication can here be claimed. (1) does not imply the flagged line (2); the conditional:

$$(6)\qquad\qquad (\exists y)(x)Fxy \supset (x)Fxz,$$

in other words, is not valid. What is valid is only a weaker schema, the existential quantification of (6) with respect to the flagged 'z':

$$(7)\qquad\qquad (\exists z)[(\exists y)(x)Fxy \supset (x)Fxz].$$

This *is* indeed valid, being a case of (12) of p. 145.

If a line (k) in a deduction is subjoined to another, (h), by EI, UI, EG, or UG, then by the *step-conditional* of (k) let us mean the conditional formed of (*h*) as antecedent and (*k*) as consequent. In the above deduction, the step-conditional of line (2) is (6); that of line (3) is the valid '$(x)Fxz \supset Fwz$'; and so on. If a line is got by UI or EG, its step-conditional is of course valid; and not so in the case of EI and UG. Flagging means that what is claimed valid is not the step-conditional, but its existential quantification with respect to the flagged variable. The flagged '*w*' of line (5) says that what is claimed valid is not the step-conditional:

(8) $(\exists y)Fwy \supset (x)(\exists y)Fxy$

of (5), but only its existential quantification:

(9) $(\exists w)[(\exists y)Fwy \supset (x)(\exists y)Fxy]$.

This *is* valid, being a case of (11) of p. 145.

UG and EI are, despite the weakened claims, useful as links in deductions which as wholes still establish implication. The above is an example. (1) does imply (5) outright, and the deduction is meant to prove it. Intervening use of UG or EI does not impair the implication of conclusion by premiss, as long as no flagged variable retains free occurrences in premiss or conclusion. This general remark has of course still to be proved.

The net claim of the above deduction is that (1) implies (5); in other words, that the "leap-conditional":

(10) $(\exists y)(x)Fxy \supset (x)(\exists y)Fxy$

is valid. Now the step-conditionals of (2), (3), (4), and (5) of course do together imply (10); but the rub, wherein this example differs from normal chain inferences as of §27, is that those step-conditionals are not all valid. The step-conditionals of (3) and (4) are, but those of (2) and (5) (namely, (6) and (8)) are not. To justify deductions like this one we need a theory of chain inference that allows for a weakening of some links by existential quantification.

The problem, in application still to our present example, can be sharpened. Knowing that the four step-conditionals together imply (10), and knowing that just two of those step-conditionals are valid, and that only the weakened quantifications (7) and (9) of the other two step-conditionals are valid, we want to show (10) valid. But we can drop the two valid step-conditionals from the discussion; for, since their validity is given, to speak of (10) as implied by them and others is simply to speak of (10) as implied by the others. Our prob lem is thus sharpened to this: knowing that the two step-conditionals (6) and (8) together imply (10), and that the quantifications (7) and (9) of (6) and (8) are valid, to show (10) valid.

More generally, the form of this problem is as follows: knowing that schemata C_1, $\cdots$, C_n together imply a schema C, and that the existential quantifications of C_1, $\cdots$, C_n (with respect to variables V_1, $\cdots$, V_n respectively) are valid, to show C valid. Now this can indeed be shown if V_i, for each number i, is free in none of C_{i+1}, $\cdots$, C_n nor in C. This special condition is met by our example; 'z' is free in neither (8) nor (10), and 'w' is not free in (10).

So the law to be established is this:

(i) If C_1, $\cdots$, C_n together imply C, and V_i for each i is free in none of C_{i+1}, $\cdots$, C_n nor in C, and for each i the existential quantification of C_i with respect to V_i is valid, then C is valid.

Proof. Since C_1, $\cdots$, C_n together imply C, clearly C_1 implies the conditional comprised of C_2, $\cdots$, C_n as combined antecedent and C as consequent. Then, since V_1 is not free in that conditional, and the existential quantification of C_1 with respect to V_1 is valid, (ix) of p. 152 says the conditional is valid. So C_2, $\cdots$, C_n together imply C; we are rid of C_1. Repeating the argument, we show that C_3, $\cdots$, C_n imply C. After n such rounds we find C valid.

In the above proof we needed the assurance that V_1, $\cdots$, V_n not be free in C (which answers to (10)). Thus it is that we are unwarranted in supposing the last line of a deduction to be implied by its premises unless what we have is a *finished* deduction: one whose flagged variables are not free in the last line nor in premises of the last line. Further, our proof required for each i that V_i be free in none of C_{i+1}, $\cdots$, C_n. This requirement must be provided for in any explicit formulation of the rules UG and EI, so let us see what it comes to. In our initial example, what answered to C_1, C_2, $\cdots$ were (6) and (8); and these were the step-conditionals of lines subjoined by UG and EI. What answered to V_1 and V_2 were 'z' and 'w': the flagged variables. The restriction sought may accordingly be formulated, for deductions generally, as follows:

(A) If there are n (> 1) flagged steps in a deduction, then the flagged variable of some step must be free in the step-conditionals of none of the remaining $n - 1$; the flagged variable of another step must be free in the step-conditionals of none of the remaining $n - 2$; and so on.

This restriction is vital. Observe what happens when we violate it:

$\star$(1) $(x)(\exists y)Fxy$
$\star$(2) $(\exists y)Fwy$ (1)
$\star$(3) Fwz (2) z
$\star$(4) $(x)Fxz$ (3) w (wrong)
$\star$(5) $(\exists y)(x)Fxy$ (4)

The flagged 'z' is free in the step-conditional '$Fwz \supset (x)Fxz$' of the line where 'w' is flagged, and conversely the flagged 'w' is free in the step-conditional '$(\exists y)Fwy \supset Fwz$' of the line where '$z$' is flagged; so (A) is clearly unsatisfiable. Incidentally the purport of this faulty deduction, viz. that (1) implies (5), is false; cf. (7)–(8) of p. 122.

In (i) we have only a hint of the justification of UG and EI. We need a full proof that the last line of any finished deduction, using the rules of §27 plus UG and EI, is valid or implied by its premisses.

First I shall show that if D is any finished deduction with unstarred last line, say line (m), then (m) is valid. The step-conditionals of the flagged lines of D can, by (A), be listed in some order $C_1, \cdots, C_n$ (not necessarily their order *in* D) such that, for each i, the variable V_i (flagged in the line whose step-conditional is C_i) is free in none of $C_{i+1}, \cdots, C_n$. Nor will V_i be free in (m), since D is a finished deduction. Now form a new deduction D' from D by adding an extra premiss at the top, marked '$\star$(0)' so as not to disturb old numbers. It is to be the conjunction of $C_1, \cdots, C_n$. A new outer column of stars, appropriate to this premiss, is to flank the whole old deduction, to and including (m). All use of UG and EI, and therewith all flagging of variables, is dispensed with in D'; for each line that had been subjoined to some prior line by UG or EI can now be reckoned as subjoined to that prior line and (0), by TF. Now since D' is a deduction under the rules of §27, we know that (0) implies (m); i.e., that $C_1, \cdots, C_n$ together imply (m). Moreover, the existential quantification of C_i with respect to V_i is (for each i) a case of (11) or (12) of p. 145 and hence valid. Moreover, we saw that, for each

* Gumin & Hermes   Archiv für Philosophie vol 5 (1956) pp 388-3?
[JSL 24 220]

i, V_i is free in none of $C_{i+1}, \cdots , C_n$ nor in (m). By (i), then, (m) is valid, q.e.d.

It follows that any starred last line of a finished deduction is implied by its premisses. For, we can extend the deduction by Cd until we end up with an unstarred conditional consisting of the old starred line and all its premisses. This conditional, being unstarred, will be valid according to our preceding theorem. But its validity shows that the old starred line was implied by its premisses, q.e.d.

Now that we have established the soundness of our extended method of deduction, let us put (A) into a more convenient form. There is talk in (A) of certain variables not being free in certain step-conditionals. We can simplify this by referring not to step-conditionals $C_1, \cdots , C_n$, but to their consequents, say $L_1, \cdots , L_n$, the actual flagged lines. For it is evident in general that the free variables of C_i for each i are those of L_i plus perhaps the flagged variable V_i itself. Instead of saying of a variable that it is not free in certain step-conditionals $C_{i+1}, \cdots , C_n$, accordingly, we may say that it is distinct from $V_{i+1}, \cdots , V_n$ and not free in $L_{i+1}, \cdots , L_n$. It thus becomes evident that (A) may be rephrased as two restrictions thus:

(B) No variable may be flagged twice in a deduction.

(C) It must be possible to list the flagged variables of a deduction in some order $V_1, \cdots , V_n$ such that, for each number i from 1 to $n - 1$, V_i is free in none of the lines in which $V_{i+1}, \cdots , V_n$ are flagged. ✗

A rule of thumb that assures conformity to requirement (C) is this: pick your letters so that each flagged variable is alphabetically later than all other free variables of the line it flags.

It is well that (B) is singled out for separate attention, for it is simple and urgent. See what can happen when it is ignored:

*(1) $(\exists x)Fx$			*(1) $(\exists x)Fx \cdot (\exists x)Gx$	
*(2) Fy	(1) y		*(2) $(\exists x)Fx$	(1)
*(3) $(x)Fx$	(2) y (wrong)		*(3) Fy	(2) y
			*(4) $(\exists x)Gx$	(1)
*(1) Fz			*(5) Gy	(4) y (wrong)
*(2) $(x)Fx$	(1) z		*(6) $Fy \cdot Gy$	(3)(5)
(3) $Fz \supset (x)Fx$	*(2)		*(7) $(\exists x)(Fx \cdot Gx)$	(6)
(4) $(y)[Fy \supset (x)Fx]$	(3) z (wrong)			

The first of these three faulty deductions purports to show that
'$(\exists x)Fx$' implies '$(x)Fx$', which is obviously wrong. The second
purports to show '$(y)[Fy \supset (x)Fx]$' valid, which again is wrong; for,
where 'F' means 'red', '$Fy \supset (x)Fx$' fails for red y. The third example
purports to show that '$(\exists x)Fx \ . \ (\exists x)Gx$' implies '$(\exists x)(Fx \ . \ Gx)$',
which we know to be wrong in view of (7) and (8) of p. 84.

For final statement of UG and EI, we must define a few terms. If
Q is a quantification of some achema S with respect to some V, and
S' is like S except for having free occurrences of a variable V' where-
ever S has free V, let us call S' an *instance* of Q; and let us call V' the
instantial variable. Thus 'Gxy', 'Gzy', and 'Gyy' are instances of
'$(x)Gxy$' and of '$(\exists x)Gxy$', and the respective instantial variables are
'x', 'z', and 'y'. Further, if S' has free occurrences of V' where and
only where S has free V, let us call S' a *conservative* instance of Q.
Thus the instances 'Gxy' and 'Gzy' were conservative, but 'Gyy' not.

In terms of 'instance' the rules UI and EG of §27 may be restated
thus: to a universal quantification we may subjoin an instance, and
to an instance we may subjoin an existential quantification. We must
not, however, state UG and EI correspondingly. The efficacy of UI UG
and EG rests on the validity of quantifications like (7) and (9) above,
which are cases of (11) and (12) of p. 145; and these latter, as stressed
on pp. 145–146, do not admit all the substitutions that are admitted
by the schema '$(x)Fx \supset Fy$' that underlies UI, or by the schema
'$Fy \supset (\exists x)Fx$' that underlies EG. The upshot is precisely this: in
UI and EG we can talk simply of instances, but in UG and EI we
must talk of conservative instances. So here is the final formulation:

Rule of universal generalization (UG): We may subjoin a universal
quantification to a line which is a conservative instance of it.

Rule of existential instantiation (EI): To a line which is an existential
quantification we may subjoin a conservative instance of it.

Flagging: Off to the right of each line subjoined by UG or EI, we
must flag the instantial variable by writing it in the margin.

Restrictions: (B) and (C) above.

If a deduction has no flagged variables, each line is valid or implied
by its premisses. This was shown in §27. With the advent of flagged
variables, we have had to lower our claims: it is in general only of
the *last* line of a *finished* deduction that we can say that it is valid
or implied by its premisses. That much was proved, p. 164.

But now, incidentally, what of the last line of an unfinished deduction? It is, if unstarred, a schema that becomes valid when existentially quantified with respect to all flagged variables free in it. (For, the deduction can be finished by adding steps of EG to just that effect.) If it is starred, then what becomes valid when thus quantified is rather the conditional comprised of that last line and its premisses.

These observations assign a status not only to the last lines of unfinished deductions, but to all lines of all deductions. For, each line is the last line of the deduction which you get by stopping there.

Historical remarks:

Quantification theory was founded by Frege in 1879. Sharply formulated systems of rules for general quantification theory have existed in the literature from then onward, but mostly such systems have been of radically different type from the system set forth in this and the preceding section, and have resembled more the alternative system which will appear toward the middle of §32. The method set forth in the present pages is of a type known as *natural deduction*, and stems, in its broadest outlines, from Gentzen and Jaśkowski (1934).

The rule of conditionalization, which is the crux of natural deduction, appeared as an explicit formal rule somewhat earlier, having been derived by Herbrand (1930) and also in effect by Tarski (1929) from systems of their own of a type other than natural deduction. The derivation consisted in showing that whenever one statement could be deduced from another in the concerned system, the conditional formed of the two statements could also be proved as a theorem by the original rules of that system. In this status of derived rule relative to one system or another, the rule of conditionalization has come to be known in the literature as the *theorem of deduction*.

Jaśkowski's system of natural deduction is conspicuously unlike that of the present pages; for Jaśkowski dispenses with EG and EI, and gets along with milder restrictions on UG, by the expedient of treating '$(\exists x)$', '$(\exists y)$', etc., as abbreviations of '$-(x)-$', '$-(y)-$', etc. This course is economical in rules, but greatly increases the difficulty and complexity of the deductions themselves; hence I have not adopted it. The crucial difference between Gentzen's system and that of the present pages is in EI; he had a more devious rule in place of EI, with the result that many deductions proved more complicated.

Because of the presence of EI, the present system differs from Gentzen's and Jaśkowski's considerably on the score of restrictions upon the rules.

In particular the device of flagging is a novelty. Gentzen and Jaśkowski had restrictions too, but gave them different forms. Also it might be mentioned that Gentzen and Jaśkowski used, in place of TF, a bundle of more elementary rules; but this difference is trivial. EI itself is not altogether new. Cooley, in pp. 126–140 of his *Primer of Formal Logic* (1942), made use of natural deduction in a form which included substantially EI, but without exact formulation of restrictions. Explicitly formulated rules and restrictions, resembling the present system except for wide variations in the restrictions, have been set forth by Rosser and independently by me in mimeographed lecture notes from 1946 on.

EXERCISES

1. Check each of the following to see whether it is a correct deduction according to the rules, and a finished one.

*(1) Fy
*(2) $(x)Fx$ (1) y
(3) $Fy \supset (x)Fx$ (2)

*(1) $(x)(Fx \supset Gx)$
*(2) $Fy \supset Gy$ (1)
*(3) $(\exists x)(Fy \supset Gx)$ (2)
*(4) $(w)(\exists x)(Fw \supset Gx)$ (3) y

*(1) $(x)(Fx \lor Gy)$
*(2) $Fy \lor Gy$ (1)
*(3) $(x)(Fy \lor Gx)$ (2) y

*(1) $Fx \lor Gy$
*(2) $(y)(Fx \lor Gy)$ (1) y
*(3) $(\exists x)(y)(Fx \lor Gy)$ (2)

*(1) $(x)(Fx \,.\, Gx)$
*(2) $Fy \,.\, Gy$ (1)
*(3) Fy (2)
*(4) $(x)Fx$ (3) y
*(5) Gy (2)
*(6) $(x)Gx$ (5) y
*(7) $(x)Fx \,.\, (x)Gx$ (4)(6)

2. If any of the above deductions is correct but unfinished, append further lines so as to produce a finished deduction. If any is incorrect but can be revised into a correct deduction to the same effect, so revise it.

3. Wherein does page 165 assume that no variable is flagged twice?

§29.   DEDUCTIVE TECHNIQUE

In the preceding section we saw a number of examples of the misuse of two of our rules, UG and EI. Now it is time for some illustrations of the correct use of our rules. For this purpose various *equivalences*, which are incidentally worth knowing on their own account, will be established by deduction. Since equivalence is mutual implication, to establish equivalence of two schemata we have merely to deduce each schema from the other.

The following equivalences are of interest in showing how quantification can be confined to one component of a compound when the other component lacks the variable.

(i)	'$(\exists x)(p \lor Fx)$'	to	'$p \lor (\exists x)Fx$',
(ii)	'$(\exists x)(p \cdot Fx)$'	to	'$p \cdot (\exists x)Fx$',
(iii)	'$(x)(p \lor Fx)$,	to	'$p \lor (x)Fx$',
(iv)	'$(x)(p \cdot Fx)$'	to	'$p \cdot (x)Fx$',
(v)	'$(\exists x)(p \supset Fx)$'	to	'$p \supset (\exists x)Fx$',
(vi)	'$(x)(p \supset Fx)$'	to	'$p \supset (x)Fx$',
(vii)	'$(\exists x)(Fx \supset p)$'	to	'$(x)Fx \supset p$',
(viii)	'$(x)(Fx \supset p)$'	to	'$(\exists x)Fx \supset p$'.

It will be recalled that '$(\exists x)$' was distributable only through '$Fx \lor Gx$' and not through '$Fx \cdot Gx$', and that '(x)' was distributable only through '$Fx \cdot Gx$' and not through '$Fx \lor Gx$' (cf. §19); when it is a question of confinement of the quantifier to one side rather than distribution, however, all four principles (i)–(iv) are forthcoming.

Since '$p \supset$' is just another way of writing '$\bar{p} \lor$', clearly (v)–(vi) are virtual repetitions of (i) and (iii). But when the conditional has the form '$Fx \supset p$', the confinement principles take on the curious twist shown in (vii)–(viii). This circumstance was already touched on at the end of §22 and in (5) of §24.

For the biconditional there are no confinement principles analogous to (i)–(viii). '$(x)(p \equiv Fx)$' is equivalent neither to '$p \equiv (x)Fx$' nor to '$p \equiv (\exists x)Fx$', and similarly for '$(\exists x)(p \equiv Fx)$', as may be seen by construing 'F' as 'red' and trying both a truth and a falsehood for 'p'.

Let us now establish (i), by deducing '$(\exists x)(p \lor Fx)$' and '$p \lor (\exists x)Fx$' each from the other.

Deduction 1:			*Deduction* 2:	
$\star$(1) $(\exists x)(p \lor Fx)$			$\star$(1) $p \lor (\exists x)Fx$	
$\star$(2) $p \lor Fy$	(1) y		$\star\star$(2) $(\exists x)Fx$	
$\star\star$(3) Fy			$\star\star$(3) Fy	(2) y

★★(4) $(\exists x)Fx$ (3)   ★(4) $(\exists x)Fx \supset Fy$ ★(3)
★(5) $Fy \supset (\exists x)Fx$ ★(4)   ★(5) $p \lor Fy$ (1)(4)
★(6) $p \lor (\exists x)Fx$ (2)(5)   ★(6) $(\exists x)(p \lor Fx)$ (5)

In these and previous illustrative deductions, the use of UI, EG, UG, and EI has been accompanied by an alphabetical change of variable: the variable V' of instantiation (cf. §28) has been different from the variable V of quantification. But there is no general requirement in UI, EG, UG, or EI that V' and V be distinct, and often deductions can be carried through correctly from beginning to end without any such change of variables. In Deductions 1 and 2, in particular, 'x' could have been used everywhere in place of 'y'. It is perhaps easier to proceed thus without change of variable when we can. Meaning is unaffected, for, as far as any questions of interpretation are concerned, there is no more connection between a free and a bound 'x' than between 'x' and 'y'. But we shall find that a change of variable is sometimes demanded, indirectly, by any of three considerations: by the preconceived lettering of the schema which we are trying to deduce, by the alphabetical stipulation in UG and EI, or by the restriction on UG and EI which forbids flagging a variable twice.

Both uses of TF, in line (6) of Deduction 1 and in line (5) of Deduction 2, happen to turn upon substitution in one and the same implication of truth-functional logic: '$p \lor q \,.\, q \supset r$' implies '$p \lor r$'. When in doubt as to whether a given line is truth-functionally implied by a given line or lines, the reader can decide the point by a mechanical check as noted in §26.

Given any deduction, indeed, it is a mechanical matter to check it from start to finish for conformity to the rules. If a line has no citation at the right, we have merely to make sure that it initiates a new column of stars. If a line has a citation and flagged variable at the right, we have merely to determine by inspection that the line is really subjoined to the cited line in conformity with UG or EI and that the flagged variable was never flagged before. If a line has a multiple citation at the right, we know that TF is intended and can check accordingly. If a line has a starred citation at the right, we know that Cd is intended; and we can tell by inspection whether it is correctly used. If a line has at the right a single citation without star or flagged variable, we can quickly check to see whether the line properly proceeds from the cited line by UI, EG, or TF. A moment's final inspection decides whether the deduction as a whole is "finished": the last line, and the premisses whose stars run through to the last line, must be devoid of free occurrences of flagged variables.

But whereas the checking of a presented deduction is mechanical, the discovery of a desired deduction is not. Here the best we can do is make the most of certain general strategies. When as in Deduction 1 we are starting with a quantification, the obvious strategy is to begin by dropping the quantifier by UI or EI (with or without change of variable). Conversely, when as in Deduction 2 we are hoping to get a quantification as end result, the strategy is to try to deduce the desired schema without its quantifier (and with or without change of variable); afterward the quantifier may be supplied by UG or EG. If we were trying to discover Deductions 1 and 2, these two strategies would afford us just this much: (1)–(2) of Deduction 1 and, working backward, (5)–(6) of Deduction 2.

So, if we were trying to devise Deduction 1, the initial strategy of dropping the quantifier would leave us with the problem of getting from (2) of Deduction 1 to (6). Next, since (2) and (6) are alike to the extent of 'p ∨', it would be natural to wonder whether a conditional joining the remaining parts of (2) and (6), viz., '$Fy \supset (\exists x)Fx$', might combine with (2) to imply (6) truth-functionally. A fell swoop confirms the notion: 'p ∨ q' and '$q \supset r$' in conjunction imply 'p ∨ r'. So we now know that the desired (6) can be subjoined by TF to (2) and (5); the problem remains merely of getting (5). Here an obvious strategy of the conditional comes into play: assume the desired antecedent as additional temporary premiss, try to deduce the consequent, and then get the conditional by Cd. So we assume (3), from which (4) happens to proceed without difficulty; and thus Deduction 1 has been created in full.

If we were trying to devise Deduction 2, the strategy of quantifiers would have left us with the problem of getting from (1) of Deduction 2 to (5). The reasoning which solves this problem is exactly parallel to that detailed in the preceding paragraph.

Truth-functional implications are checked easily enough once they are thought of. But when we are building a deduction, the implication has to be thought up before it can be tested. (Cf. §7). The way in which Deduction 1 was achieved illustrates a course which must often be followed. There we consulted common sense for a suggestion of obtainable lines from which the desired result (6) might follow. (2) was at hand, and common sense suggested (5) as an adequate supplementation. So then we checked the suggestion and found that (2) and (5) do in conjunction imply (6) truth-functionally. Accordingly we undertook to get (5).

Let us now turn to a new project, that of establishing the equivalence (ii) by deducing '$(\exists x)(p \cdot Fx)$' and '$p \cdot (\exists x)Fx$' from each other:

⋆(1)	$(\exists x)(p \cdot Fx)$		⋆(1)	$p \cdot (\exists x)Fx$	
⋆(2)	$p \cdot Fx$	(1) x	⋆(2)	$(\exists x)Fx$	(1)
⋆(3)	Fx	(2)	⋆(3)	Fx	(2) x
⋆(4)	$(\exists x)Fx$	(3)	⋆(4)	$p \cdot Fx$	(1)(3)
⋆(5)	$p \cdot (\exists x)Fx$	(2)(4)	⋆(5)	$(\exists x)(p \cdot Fx)$	(4)

The obvious operation of separating conjunctions by TF may often conveniently be left tacit, by stating conjunctive lines at will as bracketed pairs of lines. Thus the above two deductions may be condensed as follows:

	Deduction 3:			*Deduction 4:*	
⋆ (1)	$(\exists x)(p \cdot Fx)$		⋆ {(1)	p	
⋆ {(2)	p	} (1) x	{(2)	$(\exists x)Fx$	
{(3)	Fx		⋆ (3)	Fx	(2) x
⋆ (4)	$(\exists x)Fx$	(3)	⋆ (4)	$p \cdot Fx$	(1)(3)
⋆ (5)	$p \cdot (\exists x)Fx$	(2)(4)	⋆ (5)	$(\exists x)(p \cdot Fx)$	(4)

The strategy behind the discovery of Deduction 3 is evident. The usual strategy of quantifiers leads from (1) to (2) and (3), leaving us with the problem of getting from (2) and (3) to (5); and this problem offers little challenge to ingenuity. In Deduction 4 the strategy of quantifiers leaves us with the problem of getting (4) from (1) and (2), which again is the work of a moment.

Deductions establishing the equivalences (iii)–(vi) are left to the reader. He will find that those for (iii) and (iv) can run quite parallel, line by line, to Deductions 1–4. As for (v) and (vi), it will be found, despite the connection in meaning which has been noted between (v) and (i) and between (vi) and (iii), that deductions adapted directly to (v) and (vi) may be arrived at along lines like those followed in Deductions 5 and 6 below.

Let us now establish (vii), by deducing '$(\exists x)(Fx \supset p)$' and '$(x)Fx \supset p$' from each other.

<table>
<tr><td colspan="3">Deduction 5:</td><td colspan="3">Deduction 6:</td></tr>
<tr><td>*(1)</td><td>$(\exists x)(Fx \supset p)$</td><td></td><td>*(1)</td><td>$(x)Fx \supset p$</td><td></td></tr>
<tr><td>*(2)</td><td>$Fx \supset p$</td><td>(1) x</td><td>**(2)</td><td>Fx</td><td></td></tr>
<tr><td>**(3)</td><td>$(x)Fx$</td><td></td><td>**(3)</td><td>$(x)Fx$</td><td>(2) x</td></tr>
<tr><td>**(4)</td><td>Fx</td><td>(3)</td><td>**(4)</td><td>p</td><td>(1)(3)</td></tr>
<tr><td>**(5)</td><td>p</td><td>(2)(4)</td><td>*(5)</td><td>$Fx \supset p$</td><td>*(4)</td></tr>
<tr><td>*(6)</td><td>$(x)Fx \supset p$</td><td>*(5)</td><td>*(6)</td><td>$(\exists x)(Fx \supset p)$</td><td>(5)</td></tr>
</table>

The strategy behind the discovery of Deduction 5 is as follows. The strategy of quantifiers leads us from (1) to (2), leaving us with the problem of getting (6) from (2). According to the strategy of the conditional, in order to get (6) we assume its antecedent as (3) and try to deduce its consequent 'p'. The strategy of quantifiers leads us from (3) to (4), so that all that remains to be done is get 'p' somehow from the lines (1)–(4) which are now at our disposal. Obviously (2) and (4) serve the purpose, via TF.

The strategy behind Deduction 6 is rather as follows. Since we want (6), the strategy of quantifiers directs us to overlook its quantifier and aim for (5). According to the strategy of the conditional, in order to get (5) we assume its antecedent (2) and try to deduce its consequent 'p'. So all that remains to be done is get 'p' somehow from (1) and (2). The intervening line (3) quickly suggests itself.

It must be remembered that our rules of deduction apply only to whole lines. UI and EI serve to remove a quantifier only if the quantifier is initial to a line and covers the line as a whole; and UG and EG serve to introduce a quantifier only into such a position. It would be fallacious, e.g., to proceed to the last line '$(x)Fx \supset p$' of Deduction 5 from the earlier line '$Fx \supset p$' by UG, and it would be fallacious to proceed from the first line '$(x)Fx \supset p$' of Deduction 6 to the subsequent line '$Fx \supset p$' by UI. '$(x)Fx \supset p$' is not a quantification, but a conditional containing a quantification '$(x)Fx$'. What issues from '$Fx \supset p$' by UG, and yields '$Fx \supset p$' by UI, is not '$(x)Fx \supset p$' but '$(x)(Fx \supset p)$'.

The equivalence (viii) has already been established by less sophisticated methods, in showing (5) of §24 to be valid. But the reader may, for practice, care to reestablish (viii) by the present methods. He can do so by deductions strictly parallel, line for line, to Deductions 5 and 6.

Next let us undertake the inference about slovenly persons at the beginning of §15. Here our premisses are:

$$(x)(Gx \supset . Fx \vee Hx), \qquad (\exists x)(Gx . -Hx),$$

and what we want by way of conclusion is:

$$(\exists x)(Fx . -Hx).$$

The strategy of quantifiers reduces the problem to that of getting from '$Gx \supset . Fx \vee Hx$' and '$Gx . -Hx$' to '$Fx . -Hx$'. If by luck the conjunction of '$Gx \supset . Fx \vee Hx$' and '$Gx . -Hx$' truth-functionally implies '$Fx . -Hx$', then our deduction is complete. So we submit:

$$p \supset . q \vee r : p\bar{r} : \supset q\bar{r}$$

to a truth-value analysis, and find that luck is with us. Accordingly the finished deduction runs thus:

$$
\begin{aligned}
&\star\begin{cases}(1) & (x)(Gx \supset . Fx \vee Hx) \\ (2) & (\exists x)(Gx . -Hx)\end{cases} \\
&\star \ (3) \quad Gx \supset . Fx \vee Hx \qquad (1) \\
&\star \ (4) \quad Gx . -Hx \qquad\qquad (2) \ x \\
&\star \ (5) \quad Fx . -Hx \qquad\qquad (3)(4) \\
&\star \ (6) \quad (\exists x)(Fx . -Hx) \qquad (5)
\end{aligned}
$$

A strategy known as *reductio ad absurdum* should be noted, for its occasional utility where other strategies seem to fail. It consists in assuming the contradictory of what is to be proved and then looking for trouble. It may be illustrated by deducing '$-(\exists x)Fx$' from '$(x) -Fx$':

$$\begin{array}{lll}
\ast(1) & (x) -Fx & \\
\ast(2) & -Fx & (1) \\
\ast\ast(3) & (\exists x)Fx & \\
\ast\ast(4) & Fx & (3)\ x \\
\ast(5) & (\exists x)Fx \supset Fx & \ast(4) \\
\ast(6) & -(\exists x)Fx & (2)(5)
\end{array}$$

Here the usual strategy of quantifiers leads from (1) to (2), leaving us with the problem of proceeding thence to (6). Resorting to *reductio ad absurdum*, we assume the contradictory of the desired (6) as (3). Thence by the strategy of quantifiers we move to (4), and find the trouble we were looking for; for (4) conflicts with (2). Cd and TF then lead through (5) to (6).

EXERCISES

1. In strict analogy to the deduction last presented, deduce '$-(x)Fx$' from '$(\exists x) - Fx$'.

2. Establish (iii)–(vi) and (viii) by pairs of deductions. Note the hints in the text.

3. Establish by deduction the syllogisms in §14, including the reinforced one about Spartans. Model: the above deduction about slovenly persons.

4. Similarly for the inference about witnesses, middle of §15.

5. Deduce '$(\exists x) - Fx$' from '$-(x)Fx$'. Plan on having this intermediate line:

$$\ast(4) \quad Fx \supset (x)Fx \quad \ast(3)$$

Analogously, deduce '$(x) - Fx$' from '$-(\exists x)Fx$'.

6. Establish the equivalence of '$(x)(p \cdot Fx \supset Fx)$' to '$p$'. *Hint*: '$p$' truth-functionally implies '$p \cdot Fx \supset Fx$'.

7. Establish the equivalence of '$(\exists x)(p \cdot Fx \supset Fx)$' to '$p$'.

8. The following are excerpts from a deductive solution of Exercise 3 of §21. Complete it.

$$\begin{array}{lll}
\ast(3) & Gx \supset Hx & (1) \\
\ast\ast(4) & (\exists x)(Fx \cdot Gx) & \\
\ast\ast(5) & Fx \cdot Gx & (4)\ x \\
\ast\ast(8) & (x)(Fx \supset -Hx) \supset . Fx \supset -Hx & \ast(7) \\
\ast\ast(11) & Hy \supset -Jy . \supset (x)(Hx \supset -Jx) & \ast(10) \\
\ast\ast(12) & Hy \cdot Jy & (2)(3)(5)(8)(11)
\end{array}$$

9. Establish the inference about the class of '00, end of §15. For formulation see (4)–(6) of §17. *Warning*: This deduction is a holiday venture. None of the truth-functional implications involved is as formidable as that which leads to (12) in the preceding exercise, but the deduction runs to 21 lines (in my version anyway), some of which are not easily come by. It tends to heighten one's appreciation of the solution in § 21.

§30. POLYADIC PROBLEMS. CONVERSION OF QUANTIFIERS

The examples of deduction in the foregoing section have involved only monadic schemata; i.e., schemata in which 'F', 'G', etc., carry single variables only, in the fashion 'Fx', 'Fy', 'Gx'. But the same techniques carry over to problems involving polyadic schemata. It was problems of the latter sort that revealed, in §22, the inadequacy of the logic of uniform quantification and prompted us to turn to general quantification theory; so let us now face them. One item of unfinished business from §22 is the inference:

All circles are figures, ∴ All who draw circles draw figures.

The quantificational structure of this premiss and conclusion have already been noted (§22):

$$(x)(Fx \supset Gx), \qquad (y)[(\exists x)(Fx \,.\, Hyx) \supset (\exists x)(Gx \,.\, Hyx)].$$

Now the steps of deduction from the one to the other are dictated almost automatically by the strategies of quantifiers and the conditional. The desired conclusion being a universal quantification, we first aim for this expression minus its '(y)'. But this is a conditional; so we assume its antecedent '$(\exists x)(Fx \,.\, Hyx)$' and try for its consequent '$(\exists x)(Gx \,.\, Hyx)$'. But in order to get '$(\exists x)(Gx \,.\, Hyx)$' the strategy is to try for '$Gx \,.\, Hyx$' (or '$Gz \,.\, Hyz$', etc.). What we have to deduce this from are '$(x)(Fx \supset Gx)$' and '$(\exists x)(Fx \,.\, Hyx)$'; so the strategy of dropping quantifiers is brought to bear on these, and little proves to be left to the imagination. In full the deduction is as follows.

```
*(1)   (x)(Fx ⊃ Gx)
**(2)  (∃x)(Fx . Hyx)
**(3)  Fz . Hyz                        (2) z
```

$\star\star$(4) $Fz \supset Gz$ (1)

$\star\star$(5) Gz . Hyz (3)(4)

$\star\star$(6) $(\exists x)(Gx$. $Hyx)$ (5)

$\star$(7) $(\exists x)(Fx$. $Hyx) \supset (\exists x)(Gx$. $Hyx)$ $\star$(6)

$\star$(8) $(y)[(\exists x)(Fx$. $Hyx) \supset (\exists x)(Gx$. $Hyx)]$ (7) y

Note that the shift from 'x' to 'z', in line (3), was necessitated by the alphabetical stipulation in EI.

Next there is the example about paintings and critics in §22. The translation into quantificational notation was noted there, and the steps of deduction are wholly dictated by the strategies of quantifiers and the conditional. Let us record the deduction and afterward review its genesis.

$\star$ (1) $(\exists y)[Fy$. $(x)(Gx \supset Hxy)]$

$\star\begin{cases}(2) & Fy \\ (3) & (x)(Gx \supset Hxy)\end{cases}$ $\Big\}$(1) y

$\star$ (4) $Gx \supset Hxy$ (3)

$\star\star$ (5) Gx

$\star\star$ (6) Fy . Hxy (2)(4)(5)

$\star\star$ (7) $(\exists y)(Fy$. $Hxy)$ (6)

$\star$ (8) $Gx \supset (\exists y)(Fy$. $Hxy)$ $\star$(7)

$\star$ (9) $(x)[Gx \supset (\exists y)(Fy$. $Hxy)]$ (8) x

Lines (2)–(4) issue automatically from our strategy of dropping quantifiers. Moreover, since we want (9), the backward strategy of quantifiers directs us to aim for (8); and in order to get (8) the strategy of the conditional directs us to assume (5) and aim for (7). In order to get (7) we try for (6), according to the backward strategy of quantifiers. So now the deduction is complete if in fact (6) happens to follow from its predecessors by TF. Truth-value analysis or inspection shows that it does. Thus the truth-functional implication leading to (6) from (2), (4), and (5) did not need to be thought up; it automatically presented itself for appraisal.

In the example of §22 about philosophers, the premiss and conclusion have the respective forms:

$$(\exists y)[Fy \text{ . } (x)(Fx \supset Gxy)], \qquad (\exists x)(Fx \text{ . } Gxx).$$

Our strategies of quantifiers prompt us to derive 'Fy' and '$(x)(Fx \supset Gxy)$' from the premiss, and to aim for 'Fx' and 'Gxx'—or say 'Fy'

and 'Gyy'. So all that remains is to get 'Gyy' from 'Fy' and '$(x)(Fx \supset Gxy)$', which is easy. The full deduction, then, is this:

$$\star \quad (1) \quad (\exists y)[Fy \,.\, (x)(Fx \supset Gxy)]$$

$$\star \left\{ \begin{array}{ll} (2) & Fy \\ (3) & (x)(Fx \supset Gxy) \end{array} \right\} (1)\, y$$

$$\star \quad (4) \quad Fy \supset Gyy \qquad\qquad (3)$$
$$\star \quad (5) \quad Fy \,.\, Gyy \qquad\qquad (2)(4)$$
$$\star \quad (6) \quad (\exists x)(Fx \,.\, Gxx) \qquad (5)$$

Note that the changes of variables between (3) and (4) and between (5) and (6) are not, as in previous examples, prompted by the restrictions attending UG and EI. They are simply steps in the obvious route from (2) and (3) to (6).

By way of opening a good field for further examples of deduction involving polyadic schemata, let us acquaint ourselves with *symmetry*, *transitivity*, *reflexivity*, and related concepts—these being worth noting also in their own right. A dyadic relative term is called symmetrical, asymmetrical, transitive, intransitive, totally reflexive, reflexive, or irreflexive according as it fulfills:

$$(x)(y)(Fxy \supset Fyx) \qquad\qquad \text{(symmetry)}$$
$$(x)(y)(Fxy \supset -Fyx) \qquad\qquad \text{(asymmetry)}$$
$$(x)(y)(z)(Fxy \,.\, Fyz \,.\supset Fxz) \qquad \text{(transitivity)}$$
$$(x)(y)(z)(Fxy \,.\, Fyz \,.\supset -Fxz) \qquad \text{(intransitivity)}$$
$$(x)Fxx \qquad\qquad\qquad \text{(total reflexivity)}$$
$$(x)(y)(Fxy \supset .\, Fxx \,.\, Fyy) \qquad \text{(reflexivity)}$$
$$(x)\, -Fxx \qquad\qquad\qquad \text{(irreflexivity)}$$

The relative term 'compatriot' is symmetrical, in that if x is a compatriot of y then y is a compatriot of x. It is also transitive, if we disallow multiple nationality; for then if x is a compatriot of y and y of z, x will also be a compatriot of z. It is also reflexive, if we consider a person a compatriot of himself—as indeed we must if 'compatriot of' means 'having same nationality as'. But it is not totally reflexive, if we think of our universe as containing any things devoid of nationality. Examples of total reflexivity are rare and trivial; 'identical' and 'coexistent' are two such.

The relative term 'north' is again transitive, but it is asymmetrical and irreflexive; 'x is north of y' excludes 'y is north of x', and nothing is north of itself. The relative term 'mother' is intransitive, asymmetrical, and irreflexive.

The relative term 'loves' lacks all seven properties. Where x loves y, y may or may not love x; thus 'loves' is neither symmetrical nor asymmetrical. Where x loves y and y loves z, x may or may not love z; thus 'loves' is neither transitive nor intransitive. And, since some love themselves while others (even among those who love or are loved) do not love themselves, 'loves' is neither reflexive nor irreflexive.

The reader may wonder why, parallel to the distinction between reflexivity and total reflexivity, a distinction is not drawn between "irreflexivity" in the sense of:

$$(x)(y)(Fxy \supset . -Fxx . -Fyy)$$

and "total irreflexivity" in the sense of '$(x) -Fxx$'. The reason is that this latter distinction is illusory; the two schemata are equivalent!

$\star$(1) $(x)(y)(Fxy \supset .$		
$\qquad -Fxx . -Fyy)$		
$\star$(2) $(y)(Fxy \supset . -Fxx .$		
$\qquad -Fyy)$	(1)	
$\star$(3) $Fxy \supset . -Fxx . -Fxx$	(2)	
$\star$(4) $-Fxx$	(3)	
$\star$(5) $(x) -Fxx$	(4) x	

$\star$(1) $(x) -Fxx$		
$\star$(2) $-Fxx$	(1)	
$\star$(3) $-Fyy$	(1)	
$\star$(4) $Fxy \supset . -Fxx . -Fyy$	(2)(3)	
$\star$(5) $(y)(Fxy \supset . -Fxx .$		
$\qquad -Fyy)$	(4) y	
$\star$(6) $(x)(y)(Fxy \supset .$		
$\qquad -Fxx . -Fyy)$	(5) x	

In the former of these two deductions, just as in the preceding deduction about philosophers, a change of variable was made in connection with UI. In detail the strategy of the deduction is as follows. Wanting (5) as conclusion, we naturally head for (4). Equally naturally, starting with (1), we drop '(x)' and get (2). Now in the next step, that of dropping '(y)', we are led to the appropriate change of variable from 'y' to 'x' simply by observing that no variable but 'x' appears in our objective (4). Finally, having (3) and wanting (4), we check for truth-functional implication as a matter of course and find that it holds: '$p \supset \bar{p}p$' implies '$\bar{p}$', since '$\top \supset \perp\perp$' resolves to '$\perp$' (fell swoop).

As an example of a deduction calling for more ingenuity in the manipulation of variables, let us show that symmetry and transitivity together imply reflexivity. Our problem is to deduce '$(x)(y)(Fxy \supset$. Fxx . $Fyy)$' from the symmetry premiss '$(x)(y)(Fxy \supset Fyx)$' and the transitivity premiss '$(x)(y)(z)(Fxy$. Fyz .$\supset Fxz)$'. Backward strategy tells us to aim for '$Fxy \supset$. Fxx . Fyy', or perhaps '$Fuw \supset$. Fuu . Fww', afterward getting the desired conclusion by two applications of UG. In deductions which promise to involve serious shuffling of variables, we can often obviate awkward conflicts of variables by immediately shifting to wholly new variables in our backward strategy; so let us aim for '$Fuw \supset$. Fuu . Fww'. To get this, the strategy is to assume 'Fuw' and try for both 'Fuu' and 'Fww'. So the problem reduces to that of getting 'Fuu' and 'Fww' from 'Fuw' and the two original premisses of symmetry and transitivity. Turning then to forward strategy, we consider dropping the quantifiers from the premisses; but there remains the problem of picking new variables in suitable ways. We are well advised to pick them as 'u' and 'w' exclusively, since only these appear in the desired results 'Fuu' and 'Fww' and the intermediate premiss 'Fuw'. In the symmetry premiss the relettering '$Fuw \supset Fwu$' is more promising than '$Fwu \supset Fuw$', since our intermediate premiss 'Fuw' will combine with '$Fuw \supset Fwu$' to yield something more, 'Fwu', with which to work. So now we have 'Fuw' and 'Fwu' to go on. Therefore the two reletterings of the transitivity premiss which we seem to have to choose between, viz., 'Fuw . Fwu .$\supset Fuu$' and 'Fwu . Fuw .$\supset Fww$', will both be useful; one will yield our desired result 'Fuu', and the other will yield our other desired result 'Fww'. So our deduction uses the transitivity premiss twice, and runs as follows (subject to subsequent refinement):

$$\star\begin{cases}(1) & (x)(y)(Fxy \supset Fyx) \\ (2) & (x)(y)(z)(Fxy . Fyz .\supset Fxz)\end{cases}$$

$\star$ (3)	$(y)(Fuy \supset Fyu)$	(1)
$\star$ (4)	$Fuw \supset Fwu$	(3)
$\star$ (5)	$(y)(z)(Fuy . Fyz .\supset Fuz)$	(2)
$\star$ (6)	$(z)(Fuw . Fwz .\supset Fuz)$	(5)
$\star$ (7)	$Fuw . Fwu .\supset Fuu$	(6)
$\star$ (8)	$(y)(z)(Fwy . Fyz .\supset Fwz)$	(2)
$\star$ (9)	$(z)(Fwu . Fuz .\supset Fwz)$	(8)
$\star$(10)	$Fwu . Fuw .\supset Fww$	(9)

$$**(11) \quad Fuw$$
$$**(12) \quad Fwu \qquad\qquad (11)(4)$$
$$**(13) \begin{cases} Fuu & (11)(12)(7) \\ Fww & (12)(11)(10) \end{cases}$$
$$*(14) \quad Fuw \supset . Fuu . Fww \qquad *(13)$$
$$*(15) \quad (y)(Fuy \supset . Fuu . Fyy) \qquad (14)\ w$$
$$*(16) \quad (x)(y)(Fxy \supset . Fxx . Fyy) \qquad (15)\ u$$

Once a deduction is discovered, it is easily enough revised so as to eliminate unnecessary uses of P, TF, and Cd. A stretch of unquantified deduction such as appears in lines (4), (7), (10)–(14) is bound to embody a single truth-functional implication. In the process of discovery we built up the implication piecemeal, but now that its end points are visible we can verify mechanically that (14) is truth-functionally implied directly by the conjunction of (4), (7), and (10). So in retrospect we can refine our deduction by deleting (11)–(13) and justifying (14) directly by the citation '(4)(7)(10)'. Incidentally, for condensation we might omit (8)–(9) and just write 'similarly' after (10).

The advantage of having aimed for (14) in the form '$Fuw \supset$. Fuu . Fww', rather than in the form '$Fxy \supset . Fxx . Fyy$', may be appreciated by rewriting the above deduction with 'x' and 'y' in place of 'u' and 'w' everywhere. Difficulty will be found to arise in (8).

Sequences of deductive steps could be compressed to single steps by adopting supplementary rules. One such addition which recommends itself is a rule of *converting quantifiers* (CQ): To a line of the form '$-(x)(\cdots x \cdots)$' subjoin its correspondent of the form '$(\exists x)$ $-(\cdots x \cdots)$', or vice versa; and to a line of the form '$-(\exists x)$ $(\cdots x \cdots)$' subjoin its correspondent of the form '(x) $-(\cdots x \cdots)$', or vice versa.

CQ accomplishes nothing that could not be accomplished deviously by our existing rules, as is shown by the deduction at the end of the preceding section and those in Exercises 1 and 5 of that section. In practice CQ does not usually even save four intermediate lines such as appear in those deductions. When our premiss and our desired conclusion are not of the sort that can be linked by just a step of CQ, commonly the shortest route which avoids use of CQ will be a route which does not pass through the particular intermediate point at which CQ might have been applicable. The saving of steps afforded by CQ—and similarly for other added rules—is usually comparable to the walking you save by getting a ride to a point nearer your destination but off the direct route, or by walking to a point off the direct route to get a ride toward your destination.

Still CQ is a worthwhile addition. For, to continue the analogy, it saves steps over rocky terrain. It will be found, e.g., that the deduction in Exercise 8 of the preceding section runs to the same number of steps with CQ as without it, but, as the reader would appreciate if the hard part of Exercise 8 had not been done for him, the steps come to be more natural and easier to discover. With use of CQ, the route from (8) to (12) in that exercise is as follows:

$$\begin{array}{lll} \star\star(9) & -(x)(Hx \supset -Jx) & (2)(3)(5)(8) \\ \star\star(10) & (\exists x) -(Hx \supset -Jx) & (9) \\ \star\star(11) & -(Hy \supset -Jy) & (10)\ y \\ \star\star(12) & Hy . Jy & (11) \end{array}$$

The reason CQ is helpful is that UI, EG, UG, and EI are all geared to lines which are quantifications, not negations of quantifications.

There is no limit, of course, to the short-cut rules that could be justified and added in the same spirit as CQ. But circumspection is advisable, because the benefits of such additions are often illusory for three reasons. First, as brought out by the analogy of riding, the net saving of steps averages less than the apparent saving. Second, having to maintain oneself ready with a wide repertoire of rules involves an added labor in itself. Third, a multiplicity of rules often operates actually to impair one's strategy, by presenting a wider variety of possibly blind alleys to explore. Whether a particular added rule will bring any net advantage can be judged only on the basis of sustained experimentation.

EXERCISES

1. Prove by deduction that asymmetry implies irreflexivity, and that intransitivity implies irreflexivity.

2. Prove that transitivity and irreflexivity together imply asymmetry.

3. Show, by mutual deduction, that the schemata:

$$-(\exists x)(y)(\exists z)Fxyz, \qquad (x)(\exists y)(z)\ -Fxyz$$

are equivalent. Use CQ. Note the more general law which this equivalence suggests.

4. If Exercise 9 of the preceding section has become a hobby, try again using CQ.

§31. APPLICATION

When our deductive technique is to be brought to bear upon statements couched in ordinary language, the task of suitably paraphrasing the statements and isolating their relevant structure becomes just as important as the deductive operation for which that preliminary task prepares the way (cf. §8).

In §12 we noted a considerable variety of ways in which the categorical forms **A**, **E**, **I**, and **O** may appear in ordinary language; and in §16 we saw how to put those forms over into quantificational notation. These observations provide the beginning of a guide to the translation of words into quantificational symbols. But we saw also, from examples such as 'A lady is present', 'A Scout is reverent', 'John cannot outrun any man on the team', and 'Tai always eats with chopsticks' (§12), that it is a mistake to trust to a pat checklist of idioms. The safer way of paraphrasing words into symbols is the harder way: by a sympathetic re-thinking of the statement in context. If there are obvious ways of rectifying logically obscure phrases by rewording, it is well to do so before resorting to logical symbols at all.

Even if we had a really dependable lexicon of ordinary language in relation to **A**, **E**, **I**, and **O**, this of course would not cover all paraphrasing of verbal statements into quantificational form; on the contrary, quantification theory depends for its importance upon the very fact that it far outreaches **A**, **E**, **I**, and **O**. In paraphrasing more complex statements into quantificational form, a problem which obtrudes itself at every turn is that of determining the intended groupings. The cues to grouping which were noted at the truth-functional level in §4 continue to be useful here, but the most important single cue proves to be the additional one which was noted in connection with (20) of §16 and again in §22: *The scope of a quantifier must reach out far enough to take in any occurrence of a variable which is supposed to refer back to that quantifier.*

The technique of *paraphrasing inward* (§8), as a means of dividing the problem of interpretation into manageable parts and keeping the complexities of grouping under control, is as important here as at the truth-functional levels; more important, indeed, in proportion to the increasing complexity of the statements concerned. After each step of paraphrasing, moreover, it is well to check the whole against the original statement to make sure that the intended idea is still being reproduced.

By way of a serious venture in paraphrasing, let us try putting the following premisses and conclusion over into quantificational form preparatory to setting up a deduction.

> Premisses: The guard searched all who entered the premises except those who were accompanied by members of the firm,
> Some of Fiorecchio's men entered the premises unaccompanied by anyone else,
> The guard searched none of Fiorecchio's men;

> Conclusion: Some of Fiorecchio's men were members of the firm.

The first premiss says in effect:

> Every person that entered the premises and was not searched by the guard was accompanied by some member(s) of the firm.

Setting about now to paraphrase this premiss inward, we inspect it for its outermost structure, which obviously is '$(x)(\ldots \supset \ldots)$':

> $(x)(x$ is a person that entered the premises and was not searched by the guard $\supset x$ was accompanied by some members of the firm).

The virtue of thus paraphrasing inward a step at a time is that the unparaphrased internal segments can now be handled each as a small independent problem. The clause 'x was accompanied by some members of the firm', e.g., regardless of context, becomes:

> $(\exists y)(x$ was accompanied by y . y was a member of the firm).

The other clause, 'x is a person that entered the premises and was not searched by the guard', needs little more attention; we have merely to make it an explicit conjunction:

> x is a person that entered the premises . x was not searched by the guard.

So the whole becomes:

> (x)[x is a person that entered the premises . x was not searched by the guard .⊃ (∃y)(x was accompanied by y . y was a member of the firm)].

Care must be taken, as here, to insert dots or parentheses to indicate intended grouping.

Finally, writing 'Fx' for 'x is a person that entered the premises', 'Gx' for 'x was searched by the guard', 'Hxy' for 'x was accompanied by y', and 'Jy' for 'y was a member of the firm', we have:

$$(x)[Fx \, . \, -Gx \, .\supset (\exists y)(Hxy \, . \, Jy)]$$

as the logical form of the first premiss.

Instead of carrying the word 'person' explicitly through the above analysis, we might, as an alternative procedure, have limited the universe to persons. But in the present example this would have made no difference to the final symbolic form, since 'x is a person that entered the premises' has all been fused as 'Fx'.

The reason for representing so long a clause as this simply as 'Fx', without further analysis, is that we know that no further analysis of it will be needed for the proposed deduction. We are assured of this by the fact that 'entered' never occurs in premisses or conclusion except as applied to persons entering the premises. Similarly we were able to leave 'x was searched by the guard' unanalyzed, because 'searched' never occurs except with 'by the guard'. On the other hand it behooved us to break up 'x was accompanied by some members of the firm', since accompaniment and membership in the firm are appealed to also outside this combination in the course of the premisses and conclusion. In general, when we paraphrase words into logical notation and then introduce schematic letters as above, it is sound policy to *expose no more structure than promises to be needed for the proposed deduction.* This restraint not only minimizes the work of paraphrasing, but also minimizes the length and complexity of the schemata that are to be manipulated in the deduction.

Turning to the second premiss, and writing 'Kx' for 'x was one of Fiorecchio's men', we get this as the obvious outward structure:

$(\exists x)(Kx$. Fx . x was unaccompanied by anyone else).

It remains to paraphrase the component clause 'x was unaccompanied by anyone else'. Clearly the intended meaning is:

Anyone accompanying x was one of Fiorecchio's men,

which becomes '$(y)(Hxy \supset Ky)$', so that the second premiss as a whole becomes:

$$(\exists x)[Kx \ . \ Fx \ . \ (y)(Hxy \supset Ky)].$$

The third premiss and conclusion immediately become:

$$(x)(Kx \supset -Gx), \qquad\qquad (\exists x)(Kx \ . \ Jx).$$

The deduction, finally, proceeds as follows:

$$
\begin{aligned}
&\star\left\{\begin{array}{ll}
(1) & (x)[Fx \ . \ -Gx \ .\supset \ (\exists y)(Hxy \ . \ Jy)] \\
(2) & (\exists x)[Kx \ . \ Fx \ . \ (y)(Hxy \supset Ky)] \\
(3) & (x)(Kx \supset -Gx)
\end{array}\right. \\
&\star \ (4) \quad Fx \ . \ -Gx \ .\supset \ (\exists y)(Hxy \ . \ Jy) \qquad (1) \\
&\star\left\{\begin{array}{ll}
(5) & Kx \ . \ Fx \\
(6) & (y)(Hxy \supset Ky)
\end{array}\right\} (2) \ x \\
&\star \ (7) \quad Kx \supset -Gx \qquad\qquad\qquad\qquad (3) \\
&\star \ (8) \quad (\exists y)(Hxy \ . \ Jy) \qquad\qquad\qquad (4)(5)(7) \\
&\star \ (9) \quad Hxy \ . \ Jy \qquad\qquad\qquad\qquad\ (8) \ y \\
&\star \ (10) \quad Hxy \supset Ky \qquad\qquad\qquad\quad (6) \\
&\star \ (11) \quad Ky \ . \ Jy \qquad\qquad\qquad\qquad (9)(10) \\
&\star \ (12) \quad (\exists x)(Kx \ . \ Jx) \qquad\qquad\qquad (11)
\end{aligned}
$$

When we undertake to inject logical rigor into inferences encountered in informal discourse, we are likely to confront a second problem of interpretation over and above that of paraphrasing verbal idioms into logical notation. This second problem is that of supplying suppressed premisses; and it is occasioned by the popular practice of arguing in *enthymemes*. An enthymeme is a logical inference in which one or more of the premisses are omitted from mention on the ground that their truth is common knowledge and goes without saying; thus we argue:

Some Greeks are wise; for, some Greeks are philosophers,

omitting mention of the additional premiss 'All philosophers are wise' on the ground that this would naturally be understood by all concerned.[1]

In everyday discourse most logical inference is enthymematic. We are constantly sparing ourselves the reiteration of known facts, trusting the listener to supply them where needed for the logical completion of an argument. But when we want to analyze and appraise a logical inference which someone has propounded, we have to take such suppressed premisses into account. At this point two problems demand solution simultaneously: the problem of filling in the details of a logical deduction leading from premisses to desired conclusion, and the problem of eking out the premisses so that such a deduction can be constructed. Solution of either problem presupposes solution of the other; we cannot set up the deduction without adequate premisses, and we cannot know what added premisses will be needed until we know how the deduction is to run.

Sometimes, as in the syllogistic example above, the form of logical inference intended by the speaker suggests itself to us immediately because of its naturalness and simplicity. In such a case there is no difficulty in identifying the tacit premiss which the speaker had in mind. Sometimes, on the other hand, the form of inference itself may not be quite evident, but the relevant tacit premisses are already somehow in the air because of recently shared experiences. Such a case differs in no practical way from the case where all premisses are explicit.

Sometimes, finally, neither the intended form of inference nor the intended tacit premisses are initially evident; and in this case the best we can do is try to solve both problems concurrently. Thus we may start a tentative deduction on the basis of the explicit premisses, and then, on coming to an impasse, we may invent a plausible tacit prem-

[1]Traditionally 'enthymeme' meant, more specifically, a syllogism with suppressed premiss—like the above example; but it is natural, now that logic has so far outstripped the syllogism, to refer to a logical inference of any form as an enthymeme when some premisses are left tacit.

iss which would advance us toward the desired conclusion. Alternating thus between steps of deduction and supplementation of premisses, we may, with luck, achieve our goal. Of course the tacit premisses thus invoked must always be statements which can be presumed to be believed true by all parties at the outset; for it is only under such circumstances that a deduction using those tacit premisses would give reason for belief in the conclusion. If we were to invoke as a tacit premiss some statement which was (from the point of view of concerned parties) as much in need of proof as the conclusion itself, we should be guilty of what is known as *circular reasoning*, or *begging the question*, or *petitio principii*; any added conviction that might accrue to the conclusion through such argument would be deceptive. Deciding whether a statement is believed true by all parties at the outset is a task of applied psychology, but in most cases it offers no difficulty, there commonly being a wide gulf between the moot issues of an actual argument and the common fund of platitudes.

As an example of the kind of problem discussed in the foregoing paragraph, consider the explicit

Premisses: All natives of Ajo have a cephalic index in excess of 96,
             All women who have a cephalic index in excess of 96
             have Pima blood

and the

Conclusion: All persons both of whose parents are natives of Ajo
             have Pima blood.

Let us put these statements into logical notation, but for the present let us use obvious contractions instead of schematic letters '*F*', '*G*', etc., for we must keep the meanings of the words in mind in order to be able to think of relevant platitudes for use as tacit premisses. The following, then, are the results of translation, supposing the universe to be comprised this time of persons:

Premisses: $(x)(x \text{ is nat} \supset x \text{ has } 96)$
             $(x)(x \text{ is wom} . x \text{ has } 96 . \supset x \text{ has P bl})$
Conclusion: $(x)[(y)(y \text{ par } x \supset y \text{ is nat}) \supset x \text{ has P bl}]$

Since the conclusion is a universally quantified conditional, the strategy is to get it by UG from a result of Cd. A few more lines fall in fairly naturally by forward strategy, so that we have the following outline for our proposed deduction. The number of lines left blank for eventual tacit premisses and for intermediate steps is fixed by guess, ostensibly (by peeking, actually).

$$\star \begin{cases} (1) & (x)(x \text{ is nat } \supset x \text{ has } 96) \\ (2) & (x)(x \text{ is wom } . \ x \text{ has } 96 . \supset x \text{ has P bl}) \\ (3) & \\ (4) & \end{cases}$$

$\star\star$ (5) $(y)(y$ par $x \supset y$ is nat)

$\star\star$ (6) y par $x \supset y$ is nat   (5)

$\star\star$ (7) y is nat $\supset y$ has 96   (1)

$\star\star$ (8) y is wom . y has 96 .$\supset y$ has P bl)   (2)

.

.

.

$\star\star$ (14) x has P bl

$\star$(15) $(y)(y$ par $x \supset y$ is nat) $\supset x$ has P bl $\star$(14)

$\star$(16) $(x)[(y)(y$ par $x \supset y$ is nat) $\supset x$ has P bl]   (15) x

Now the question is how to get (14). By TF, clearly, (6)–(8) yield:

$\star\star$(9) y is wom . y par x .$\supset y$ has P bl   (6)(7)(8)

which assures us, not quite that the x of (14) has Pima blood, but that his mother does. The two platitudes wanted as tacit premisses then suggest themselves: everyone has a mother, and anyone has Pima blood if one of his parents does.

(3) $(x)(\exists y)(y$ is wom . y par $x)$

(4) $(x)(y)(y$ par x . y has P bl .$\supset x$ has P bl).

It is left to the reader to fill in lines (10)–(13) and append the proper reference numbers to (14).

For a more searching analysis of ordinary language see Reichenbach Chapter VII.

EXERCISES

1. Supply lines (10)–(13) and the references for (14).
2. Paraphrasing inward step by step, put:

Everyone who buys a ticket receives a prize

into symbols using '*Fxy*' for '*x* buys *y*', '*Gy*' for '*y* is a ticket', '*Hz*' for '*z* is a prize', and '*Jxz*' for '*x* receives *z*'. Then deduce:

> If there are no prizes then nobody buys a ticket.

3. Paraphrasing inward step by step, put:

> Every applicant who is admitted is examined beforehand

into symbols using '*Fx*' for '*x* is an applicant', '*Gxy*' for '*x* is admitted at time *y*', '*Hxz*' for '*x* is examined at time *z*', and '*Jzy*' for '*z* is before *y*'. Then deduce:

> Every applicant who is admitted is examined sometime.

4. Paraphrasing inward step by step, put:

> There is a painting which is admired by every critic who admires any paintings at all

into symbols using '*F*' for 'painting', '*G*' for 'critic', and '*H*' for 'admires'. Then add the further premiss:

> Every critic admires some painting or other

and deduce:

> There is a painting which all critics admire.

Par: seven lines besides the premisses and conclusion.

§32. NATURE OF QUANTIFICATION THEORY

It can (but will not) be shown that our present system of deduction is *complete*, in this sense: every valid quantificational schema can be reached as unstarred last line of a deduction conforming to our rules.[1] Likewise every schema implied by given schemata can be reached as last line of a deduction with those schemata as its premisses. So, however unsuccessfully we may seek to deduce a desired conclusion from

---

[1] The proof of this fact is due to Gödel (1930). The argument can be found also in Hilbert and Ackermann, pp. 74–81; Hilbert and Bernays, vol. 2, pp. 182–189; and Church, *Introduction to Mathematical Logic*. The systems shown to be complete in these various presentations of the argument differ radically from our present one, being rather of the type exemplified by the alternative system outlined a few pages hence. However, there is no difficulty in establishing co-extensiveness of the systems concerned.

given premises in quantificational theory, we may rest assured that an appropriate deduction *can* be discovered if the premises really imply the conclusion.

We saw in §28 that our rules are sound, in the sense that the validities and implications which our finished deductions purport to establish actually hold. Since also the rules are complete, we see that the valid quantificational schemata are *all and only* those quantificational schemata which can be reached as unstarred last lines of finished deductions according to our rules. This circumstance is philosophically significant for the same reason that was noted apropos of uniform quantification theory in §21. The original definition of validity of quantificational schemata (§24) appealed to a realm of classes; now, however, we see that the same totality of valid quantificational schemata can be marked out without that excursion through classes.

Despite its completeness, however, general quantification theory differs radically from the logic both of truth functions (Part I) and of uniform quantification (Part II) in that there is no mechanical test of validity or implication. At those simpler levels of logic we had mechanical routines for deciding the validity of any given schema, and for deciding, given any two schemata, whether the one implied the other. In quantification theory, on the other hand, we have in general to grope for the deduction which will establish the validity of a given schema, or which will establish a desired implication. Our strategies help us in devising desired deductions, but they fall far short of a mechanical technique which can be trusted to deliver a deduction whenever a deduction is possible. Once discovered, the deduction can be checked quite mechanically for correctness (cf. §29); nevertheless we may despite all efforts fail to assure ourselves of some validity or implication which actually holds, simply for lack of luck or ingenuity in hitting upon the appropriate deduction. Now this situation, while it might be alleviated here and there by devising supplementary strategies, is essentially one in which we must acquiesce; for, as Alonzo Church has proved, *no mechanical routine can be generally adequate to deciding validity* (or implication) *in quantification theory.*[1] In the technical phrase, quantification theory admits no

[1]Church, "A note on the Entscheidungsproblem"; see Bibliography. A more readable rendering of the argument may be found in Kleene; also in Hilbert and Bernays, vol. 2, pp. 416–421. See also Rosser, "Informal exposition."

decision procedure. This is remarkable, and that it should actually have been proved is yet more remarkable. We cannot embark upon the proof here.

So the logic of truth functions and uniform quantification differs from general quantification theory as school arithmetic differs from advanced mathematics. In school arithmetic, everything we want to know can be determined by mechanical computation. In advanced mathematics, on the other hand, proofs have in large part to be discovered by artistry and good fortune; and so it is in general quantificational theory. Hence there is a premium on so fashioning the rules of deduction as to render the discovery of deductions as easy, on the average, as we can. Such has been the objective of the system developed in the foregoing sections. Had it not been for this objective, fewer rules would have sufficed—and rules far easier to state and justify.

A simpler systematization of quantification theory, quite adequate from a theoretical point of view, is as follows. The only rules of deduction are TF and a simplified UG which says merely this: *From any line, infer any universal quantification of it.* Schemata are deduced by TF and the simplified UG from a specified class of initial schemata; viz., from schemata which are obtainable by substitution (§25) in one or other of the valid schemata:

$$(x)Fx \supset Fy, \qquad (x)(p \supset Fx) \supset . \, p \supset (x)Fx$$

(also with other variables in place of 'x' and 'y').

Thus a "proof", in this new system, consists of one or more initial schemata of the sort just described, followed by any number of further lines each of which is got from earlier lines by TF or by the simplified UG. Example:

$$(x) -Fx \supset -Fy$$
$$(y)[(x) -Fx \supset -Fy] \supset . \, (x) -Fx \supset (y) -Fy$$
$$(y)[(x) -Fx \supset -Fy]$$
$$(x) -Fx \supset (y) -Fy$$

The first two lines here are of the initial kind; the third line is derived from the first by simplified UG; and the last line is derived from the second and third by TF.

If we view existential quantifiers as mere abbreviations of universal quantifiers flanked by negation signs, this system is complete: every valid schema can be reached as last line of a proof.[1] Furthermore the system is, we see, far easier to describe than the system of the foregoing sections. It

---

[1] See first footnote of present section.

is also far easier to justify; for it could be shown, in a fraction of the space that was taken up in §§27–28 to justify our five rules, that every line of a proof in the newly described system is a valid schema. But our greater investment in §§27–28 pays off in the relative ease with which desired deductions tend to be discoverable.

So much for quantification theory in its broader aspects. Let us now pause for further examination of that special part of quantification theory in which the predicate letters are followed only by single variables. The obstacle to a decision procedure for quantification theory lies wholly in polyadic schemata, schemata in which predicate letters occur followed by multiple occurrences of variables. As long as monadic schemata are adhered to, quantification theory is essentially no richer than the logic which was treated in Part II and provided with a decision procedure. The remaining pages of the section will be devoted to clarifying and establishing this fact.

Monadic schemata are those in which the predicate letters are followed by single variables exclusively. Uniform quantificational schemata, studied in Part II, are therefore monadic schemata. The mixed schemata of §21, which were uniform schemata with an admixture of sentence letters, are likewise monadic. So also, indeed, are the purely truth-functional schemata of Part I. In short, all the schemata dealt with in Parts I–II are monadic. They may for the space of the next few pages be designated more particularly as *standard* monadic schemata, for there are other monadic schemata which they fail to include; e.g.:

(1) $(\exists x)(Fy \cdot Gx)$, $(x)(p \supset Fx)$, $(y)[Fy \supset (\exists x)Fx]$.

A uniform quantification, i.e. a quantification in the sense of Part II, consists of '(x)' or '$(\exists x)$' followed by a truth function exclusively of 'Fx', 'Gx', etc. So a standard monadic schema is describable as any truth function of components each of which is a uniform quantification or sentence letter. We know from Parts I–II how to test any standard monadic schema for validity. Now what will be shown here is that every closed monadic schema can be translated into an equivalent which is standard. As for the open ones, we know that the question of their validity is simply the question of the validity of their universal closures (§24).

In nonstandard monadic schemata, quantifications are frequently *impure* in this sense: what the quantifier governs is a truth function of components some of which show no free occurrences of the variable of quantification. Each of the three schemata (1), e.g., is an impure quantification; and so is '$(\exists x)[Fx \lor (x)Gx]$'.

Consider now an *innermost* quantification, i.e., a quantification containing no further quantifications as parts. If it is pure, this quantification must consist of a quantifier—say '(y)'—governing a truth function of components each of which shows free 'y'. So, supposing only monadic materials available, those components can only be 'Fy', 'Gy', etc. The quantification therefore has no variables but 'y'; hence no free variables.

If a monadic schema has no impure quantification in it, every quantification in it will be innermost. For, we just saw that each innermost quantification will lack free variables; hence each innermost quantification would, if used as component of a truth function governed by a new quantifier, impair the purity of that broader quantification.

So, combining the observations of the past two paragraphs, we see that if a monadic schema contains no impure quantifications, each quantification in it will consist of some quantifier, say '(y)', governing a truth function exclusively of 'Fy', 'Gy', etc. Under these circumstances, clearly we can rewrite the variable of each quantification uniformly as 'x' without fear of conflicting cross-references. Each quantification thus becomes a uniform quantification. The schema as a whole thereupon appears as a truth function of components each of which is either a uniform quantification or a sentence letter or perhaps an unquantified 'Fx', 'Fy', 'Gz', etc. No such dangling 'Fx', 'Fy', 'Gz', etc., will be present if the schema is closed; so in this event the schema meets the specifications of a standard monadic schema.

It is thus seen that any closed monadic schema which is devoid of impure quantifications is simply a standard monadic schema as it stands, or becomes so by an insignificant relettering of its variables as 'x'. The whole problem of transforming a closed monadic schema into a standard schema therefore reduces to the problem of purifying quantifications.

Consider, then, any impure existential quantification. It consists of a quantifier, say '$(\exists x)$', governing a truth function of components some of which are impurities in the sense of lacking free 'x'. In the example:

(2) $(\exists x)\{p \lor Fx . \supset -[(y)Fy . Gx]\}$

there are the impurities 'p' and '$(y)Fy$'. By dint of some of the transformations of truth-functional structure learned in §10, the impurities can be brought fairly near the surface; for, we can get rid of '$\supset$' and '$\equiv$' by translation, we can break up negations of compounds as far as we like by DeMorgan's laws, and we can distribute conjunction through alternation. E.g., (2) becomes successively:

$(\exists x)[-(p \lor Fx) \lor -(y)Fy \lor -Gx]$,

(3) $(\exists x)[\bar{p} . -Fx .\lor -(y)Fy \lor -Gx]$.

In general, in this way, the truth function governed by our quantifier can be put into such a form that the impurities come to be buried no more deeply than under alternation only (cf. '$-(y)Fy$' in (3)), or under conjunction only, or under conjunction which is under alternation (cf. '$\bar{p}$' in (3)). This done, we can bring the impurities out altogether by transformations according to (ii) of §19 and (i)–(ii) of §29. E.g., by (ii) of §19 we transform (3) into:

$$(\exists x)(\bar{p} \ . \ -Fx) \ \mathbf{v} \ (\exists x)[-(y)Fy \ \mathbf{v} \ -Gx].$$

By (ii) of §29 we transform '$(\exists x)(\bar{p} \ . \ -Fx)$' in turn into '$\bar{p} \ . \ (\exists x) \ -Fx$', so that the whole becomes:

$$\bar{p} \ . \ (\exists x) \ -Fx \ . \mathbf{v} \ (\exists x)[-(y)Fy \ \mathbf{v} \ -Gx].$$

By (i) of §29 we transform '$(\exists x)[-(y)Fy \ \mathbf{v} \ -Gx]$' into '$-(y)Fy \ \mathbf{v} \ (\exists x) \ -Gx$', so that the whole becomes finally:

(4) $\bar{p} \ . \ (\exists x) \ -Fx \ . \mathbf{v} \ -(y)Fy \ \mathbf{v} \ (\exists x) \ -Gx,$

in which the quantifications are pure.

Applied to any impure existential quantification which has no further impure quantification inside it, clearly the above procedure will turn the impure quantification into a schema in which all quantifications are pure.

Therefore, given any closed monadic schema, we can rid it of impure quantifications as follows. First we dispense with universal quantification, by changing '(x)' to '$-(\exists x) \ -$', '(y)' to '$-(\exists y) \ -$', etc. Then we purify the innermost impure quantifications by the above technique, and continue outward until no impure quantifications remain. Example:

$$(x)[Fx \ . \ p \ .\supset \ (\exists y)(Gx \supset . \ Fy \ . \ p)]$$
$$-(\exists x) \ -[-(Fx \ . \ p) \ \mathbf{v} \ (\exists y)(-Gx \ \mathbf{v}. \ Fy \ . \ p)]$$
$$-(\exists x) \ -[-(Fx \ . \ p) \ \mathbf{v} \ -Gx \ \mathbf{v} \ (\exists y)(Fy \ . \ p)]$$
$$-(\exists x) \ -[-(Fx \ . \ p) \ \mathbf{v} \ -Gx \ \mathbf{v}. \ (\exists y)Fy \ . \ p]$$
$$-(\exists x)\{Fx \ . \ p \ . \ Gx \ . \ -[(\exists y)Fy \ . \ p]\}$$
$$-\{(\exists x)(Fx \ . \ Gx) \ . \ p \ . \ -[(\exists y)Fy \ . \ p]\}$$

Finally, relettering any variables other than 'x' as 'x', we have a standard monadic schema.

In the deductive techniques of §§27–28 there was no dependence on equivalence. The transformations just now set forth, however, turn upon equivalence at each step. Their justification therefore remains incomplete until various general laws of equivalence tacitly depended upon in the above reasoning have been substantiated. The laws in question are familiar enough from Parts I–II:

(A) Substitution preserves equivalence.
(B) Interchange of equivalents yields equivalents.
(C) If S_1 is equivalent to S_2 and S_2 to S_3 then S_1 is equivalent to S_3.

But we have to show that these laws continue to hold at the level of general quantification theory. For, the transformation of monadic schemata into standard ones is a matter of general quantification theory; it is only after such transformation is complete that the logic of Parts I–II assumes control.

From §9 onward we have spoken of equivalence sometimes as mutual implication and sometimes as validity of the biconditional, observing that these two characterizations come to the same thing. It must now be shown that they continue to come to the same thing in general quantification theory. This thesis may be established in two parts.

(a) Suppose S_1 and S_2 imply each other. Then, since implication is validity of the conditional, the two conditionals joining S_1 and S_2 are valid. Then, by (v) of §26, the conjunction of those conditionals is valid. But this conjunction truth-functionally implies the biconditional of S_1 and S_2 , which then is valid by (iii) of §26.

(b) Suppose the biconditional of S_1 and S_2 is valid. Then, being truth-functionally implied by the biconditional, the two conditionals joining S_1 and S_2 are valid by (iii) of §26. I.e., S_1 and S_2 imply each other.

So we can continue to think of equivalence indifferently as mutual implication and as validity of the biconditional. Now since equivalence is validity of the biconditional, (A) follows from the fact that substitution preserves validity (§25). Again, since equivalence is mutual implication, (C) follows from its analogue for implication,- (vii) of §26.

So our remaining concern is (B). The following version of (B), though less sweeping than what could be proved, is adequate to the uses at hand: If S_1 and S_2 are equivalent quantificational schemata having just the same free variables (if any), and S_1' and S_2' are alike except that S_1' shows S_1 in some places where S_2' shows S_2 , then S_1' and S_2' are equivalent. This can be established exactly after the manner of the law of interchange in §19, for the cases where the free variables in S_1 and S_2 are none or one; and a parallel argument serves for any larger number of free variables.

PART FOUR

Glimpses Beyond

§33. EXISTENCE AND SINGULAR INFERENCE

The logic of truth functions and quantification is now under control. There are, however, some simple sorts of inference which still want discussion—notably those turning upon *singular terms* such as 'Socrates':

All men are mortal,	Socrates is a Greek,
Socrates is a man;	Socrates is wise;
∴ Socrates is mortal.	∴ Some Greeks are wise.

Furthermore the theory of identity, including such evident laws as '$x = x$' and '$x = y . \equiv . y = x$', remains untouched. A few sections will suffice to do justice to singular terms and identity. In conclusion we shall have a brief glimpse of set theory, or the theory of classes—a discipline which may be characterized both as higher logic and as the basic discipline of classical mathematics.

The logic of identity will be needed in the final treatment of the logic of singular terms, but meanwhile singular terms will be helpful in expounding the concept of identity. So let us begin with a preliminary study of singular terms.

It will be recalled that for purposes of the definition of validity in general quantification theory (§24) we understood "interpretations" of sentence letters, predicate letters, and free variables respectively as truth values, extensions, and single objects of the universe. Now the expressions that have truth values are statements, and the expressions that have extensions are predicates; and in completion of the picture the idea suggests itself that the expressions which similarly correspond to single objects are the singular terms that name them. Or to put the matter in another way: just as the sentence letters in a schema stand as dummy sentences and the predicate letters as dummy predicates, so the free variables stand as dummy singular terms. To represent the above inferences about Socrates schematically, therefore, we may simply use a free 'y' to represent 'Socrates'. The inferences then go through by our familiar deductive method:[1]

$\left\{\begin{matrix}(1) & (x)(Fx \supset Gx) \\ (2) & Fy\end{matrix}\right.$

$\star(3)$ $Fy \supset Gy$ (1)
$\star(4)$ Gy (2)(3)

$\star(1)\left\{\begin{matrix}Fy \\ Gy\end{matrix}\right.$

$\star(2)$ $(\exists x)(Fx \cdot Gx)$ (1)

Another example:

Premisses: Aldrich bribed every member of the committee,
                   Barr is a member of the committee;

Conclusion: Someone bribed Barr.

$\left\{\begin{matrix}(1) & (x)(Fx \supset Gzx) \\ (2) & Fw\end{matrix}\right.$ (z as Aldrich)
                                                                                      (w as Barr)

$\star$ (3) $Fw \supset Gzw$ (1)
$\star$ (4) Gzw (2)(3)
$\star$ (5) $(\exists x)Gxw$ (4)

These deductions establish implication and hence show that the conclusions will come out true if the premisses do, no matter what objects of the universe we choose in interpretation of 'y', 'z', and 'w'. In particular therefore we may choose Socrates, Aldrich, and Barr—provided merely that the universe contains such things.

But this last proviso is essential to the intended application of our deductive results. Singular terms do not, after all, stand to objects quite as statements and predicates stand to truth values and extensions; for whereas every statement has its truth value and every predicate its extension, empty or otherwise, a singular term may or may not name an object. A singular term always *purports* to name an object, but is powerless to guarantee that the alleged object be forthcoming; witness 'Cerberus'. The deductive techniques of quantification theory with free variables serve very well for inferences depend-

---

[1]Obviously it would be inappropriate to flag 'y' in such a deduction. But this point is already covered in the notion of a "finished deduction."

ing on singular terms when we are assured that *there are* objects such
as those terms purport to name; so this question of existence then
becomes the central question where singular terms are concerned.

I shall find no use for the narrow sense which some philosophers
have given to 'existence', as against 'being'; viz., concreteness in
space-time. If any such special connotation threatens in the present
pages, imagine 'exists' replaced by 'is'. When the Parthenon and the
number 7 are said to be, no distinction in the sense of 'be' need be
intended. The Parthenon is indeed a placed and dated object in space-
time while the number 7 (if such there be) is another sort of thing;
but this is a difference between the objects concerned and not between senses of 'be'.

In contrast to 7 and the Parthenon, there is no such thing as
Cerberus; and there is no such number as $\frac{0}{0}$. Clearly these repudia-
tions do not of themselves depend on any limitation of existence to
space-time. The meaning of the particular word 'Cerberus' merely
happens to be such that, if the word did name an object, that object
would be a physical object in space and time. The word 'Cerberus' is
like 'Parthenon' and 'Bucephalus' in this respect, and unlike '7' and
'$\frac{0}{0}$'. But the word 'Cerberus' differs from 'Parthenon' and 'Bucephalus'
in that whereas there is something in space-time such as the word
'Parthenon' purports to name (viz., at Athens for some dozens of
centuries including part or all of the twentieth), and whereas there is
(tenselessly) presumably something in space and time such as the word
'Bucephalus' purports to name (viz., at a succession of positions in
the Near and Middle East in the fourth century B.C.), on the other
hand there happens to be nothing such as the word 'Cerberus' purports to name, near or remote, past, present, or future.

It is surely a commonplace that some singular terms may, though
purporting to name, flatly fail to name anything at all. 'Cerberus'
is one example, and '$\frac{0}{0}$' is another. But, commonplace though this be,
experience shows that recognition of it is beset with persistent confusions, to the detriment of a clear understanding of the logic of singular terms. Let us make it our business in the remainder of this
section to dispel certain of these confusions.

There is a tendency to try to preserve some shadowy entity under the word 'Cerberus', for example, lest the word lose its meaning. If 'Cerberus' were meaningless, not only would poetry suffer, but even certain blunt statements of fact, such as that there is no such thing as Cerberus, would lapse into meaninglessness. Thus we may hear it said, e.g., that Cerberus exists as an idea in the mind. But this verbal maneuver conduces only to confusion. Of a tangible object such as the Parthenon, to change the subject for a moment, it would be wanton obscurantism to affirm a *double* existence: in Athens *and* in the mind. Far more straightforward to admit two (or many) objects: the tangible Parthenon in Athens, and the Parthenon-idea in the mind (or the Parthenon-ideas in many minds). 'Parthenon' names the Parthenon and only the Parthenon, whereas 'the Parthenon-idea' names the Parthenon-idea. Similarly not 'Cerberus', but 'the Cerberus-idea', names the Cerberus idea; whereas 'Cerberus', as it happens, names nothing.

This is not the place to try to say what an idea is, or what existence in the mind means. Perhaps from the point of view of experimental psychology an idea should be explained somehow as a propensity to certain patterns of reaction to words or other stimuli of specified kinds; and perhaps "existing in the mind" then means simply "being an idea." But no matter; the idea of "idea" is entertained here only as a concession to the other party. The point is that though we be as liberal about countenancing ideas and other nonphysical objects as anyone may ask, still to identify the Parthenon with the Parthenon-idea is simply to confuse one thing with another; and to try to assure there being such a thing as Cerberus by identifying it with the Cerberus-idea is to make a similar confusion.

The effort to preserve meaning for 'Cerberus' by presenting some shadowy entity for 'Cerberus' to name is misdirected; 'Cerberus' remains meaningful despite not naming. Most words, like 'and' or 'sake', are quite meaningful without even purporting to be names at all. Even when a word is a name of something, its meaning would appear not to be identifiable with the thing named.[1] Mount Everest has been known, from opposite points of view, both as Everest and as Gaurisanker;[2] here the named object was always one, yet the

---

[1]This much neglected point was well urged by Frege, "Ueber Sinn und Bedeutung."
[2]Ernst Schrödinger, *What is Life?*, last paragraph.

names can scarcely be viewed as having been alike in *meaning* or synonymous; for no insight into the combined minds of all users of 'Everest' and 'Gaurisanker' could reveal that these named the same thing, pending a strenuous investigation of nature. Again there is Frege's example of 'Evening Star' and 'Morning Star'; the named planet is one, but it took astronomy and not mere analysis of meanings to establish the fact.

Precise and satisfactory formulation of the notion of meaning is an unsolved problem of semantics. Perhaps the meaning of a word is best construed as the associated idea, in some sense of 'idea' which needs to be made precise in turn; or perhaps as the system of implicit rules in conformity with which the word is used, supposing that a criterion of "implicit rule" can be devised which is selective enough to allow sameness of meaning on the part of distinct expressions. Perhaps, indeed, the best treatment of the matter will prove to consist in abandoning all notion of so-called meanings as entities; thus such phrases as 'having *meaning*' and 'same *in meaning*' might be dropped in favor of 'significant' and 'synonymous', in hopes eventually of devising adequate criteria of significance and synonymy involving no excursion through a realm of intermediary entities called meanings. Perhaps it will even be found that of these only significance admits of a satisfactory criterion, and that all effort to make sense of 'synonymy' must be abandoned along with the notion of meaning.[1] However all this may be, the important point for present purposes is that significance of a word, even of a word which (like 'Cerberus') purports to be a name, is in no way contingent upon its naming anything; and even if a word does name an object, and even if we countenance entities called meanings, there is still no call for the named object to be the meaning.

The mistaken view that the word 'Cerberus' must name something in order to mean anything turns, it has just now been suggested, on confusion of naming with meaning. But the view is encouraged also by another factor, viz., our habit of thinking in terms of the misleading word 'about'. If there is no such thing as Cerberus, then, it is asked, what are you talking *about* when you use the word 'Cerberus' (even to say that there is no such thing)? Actually this protest could be

[1]See Goodman, "On Likeness of Meaning."

made with the same cogency (viz., none) in countless cases where no would-be name such as 'Cerberus' occurs at all: What are you talking about when you say that there are no Bolivian battleships? The remedy here is simply to give up the unwarranted notion that talking sense always necessitates there being things talked about. The notion springs, no doubt, from essentially the same confusion which was just previously railed against; then it was confusion between meanings and objects named, and now it is confusion between meanings and things talked about.

This mistaken view that 'Cerberus' must name something has been seen to evoke, as one lame effort to supply a named object, the notion that Cerberus is something in the mind. Other expedients to the same end are commonly encountered. There is, e.g., the relativistic doctrine according to which Cerberus exists in the world of Greek mythology and not in the world of modern science. This is a perverse way of saying merely that Greeks believed Cerberus to exist and that (if we may trust modern science thus far) they were wrong. Myths which affirm the existence of Cerberus have esthetic value and anthropological significance; moreover they have internal structures upon which our regular logical techniques can be brought to bear; but it does happen that the myths are literally false, and it is sheer obscurantism to phrase the matter otherwise. There is really only one world, and there is not, never was, and never will be any such thing as Cerberus.

Another such expedient which had best not detain us long, if only because of the mazes of metaphysical controversy in which it would involve us if we were to tarry, is the view that concrete individuals are of two kinds: those which are actualized and those which are possible but not actualized. Cerberus is of the latter kind, according to this view; so that there *is* such a thing as Cerberus, and the proper content of the vulgar denial of Cerberus is more correctly expressed in the fashion 'Cerberus is not actualized'. The universe in the broader sense becomes badly overpopulated under this view, but the comfort of it is supposed to be that there comes to *be* something Cerberus about which we may be said to be talking when we rightly say (in lieu of 'There is no such thing as Cerberus') 'Cerberus is not actualized'.

But this device depends on the possibility of Cerberus; it no longer applies when we shift our example from 'Cerberus' to some would-be name of complex form involving an out-and-out impossibility, e.g., 'the spherical pyramid of Copilco'. Having already cluttered the universe with an implausible lot of unactualized possibles, are we to go on and add a realm of unactualizable impossibles? The tendency at this point is to choose the other horn of the supposed dilemma, and rule that expressions involving impossibility are meaningless. Thence, perhaps, the not uncommon notion that a statement logically inconsistent in form must be reclassified as a nonstatement: not false but meaningless. This notion, besides being unnatural on the face of it, is impractical in that it rules out the possibility of tests of meaningfulness; for logical consistency, like validity (cf. preceding section), admits of no general test.

All this piling of expedients on expedients is, insofar as prompted by a notion that expressions must name to be meaningful, quite uncalled for. There need be no mystery about attributing nonexistence where there is nothing to attribute it to, and there need be no misgivings over the meaningfulness of words which purport to name and fail. To purport to name and fail is already proof of a full share of meaning.

If for *other* reasons the recognition of unactualized possibles is felt to be desirable, there is nothing in the ensuing logical theory that need conflict with it as long as essential distinctions are preserved. So-called mental ideas and so-called meanings were provisionally tolerated above; "ideas" of the Platonic stripe, including unactualized possibles, could be accommodated as well. What must be insisted on is merely that such shadowy entities, if admitted, be named in some distinguishing fashion: 'the Cerberus-possibility', or 'the Cerberus-idea', or 'the meaning of 'Cerberus' '. If we can get together on this much by way of convention, then everyone can be left to his favorite metaphysics so far as anything further is concerned. The essential message to be carried over from this section into succeeding ones is simply this: Some meaningful words which are proper names from a grammatical point of view, notably 'Cerberus', do not name anything.[1]

---

[1]For more on this theme see Russell, "On denoting," and my paper "On what there is."

EXERCISES

1. From the premisses:

> Barr and Williams did not both contribute,
> If Blake contributed then so did everybody

deduce the conclusion:

> Blake did not contribute,

allowing free variables to stand for the proper names.

2. From the premisses:

> Edith envies everyone more fortunate than she,
> Herbert is no more fortunate than any who envy him

deduce the conclusion:

> Herbert is no more fortunate than Edith.

§34.   SINGULAR TERMS VERSUS GENERAL TERMS

More remains to be said on the subject of singular inference than was covered by the simple considerations at the beginning of the preceding section. But as a tool for the further developments we shall need the theory of identity, which will be introduced in the next section. We must also render the scope and logical status of singular terms more explicit than has thus far been done; and this work will occupy the present section.

What were called "terms" in §§12, 22 and represented by '*F*', '*G*', etc., are *general terms*, as opposed to singular terms. But generality is not to be confused with ambiguity. The singular term 'Jones' is ambiguous in that it might be used in different contexts to name any of various persons, but it is still a singular term in that it purports in any particular context to name one and only one person. The same is true even of pronouns such as 'I' and 'thou'; these again are singular terms, but merely happen to be highly ambiguous pending determination through the context or other circumstances attending any given use of them. The same may be said of 'the man', or more clearly 'the President', 'the cellar'; these phrases (unlike 'man', 'president', and 'cellar' themselves) are singular terms, but the one and only one object to which they purport to refer in any given use depends on attendant circumstances for its determination.

Besides the classification of terms into singular and general, there is a cross classification into *concrete* and *abstract*. Concrete terms are those which purport to refer to individuals, physical objects, events; abstract terms are those which purport to refer to abstract objects, e.g., to numbers, classes, attributes. Thus some singular terms, e.g., 'Socrates', 'Cerberus', 'earth', 'the author of *Waverly*', are concrete, while other singular terms, e.g., '7', '3 + 4', 'piety', are abstract. Again some general terms, e.g., 'man', 'house', 'red house', are concrete (since each man or house is a concrete individual), while others, e.g., 'prime number', 'zoological species', 'virtue', are abstract (since each number is itself an abstract object, if anything, and similarly for each species and each virtue).

For attributes, as a realm of entities distinct from classes, I hold no brief; I mention them only as a concession to readers with preconceptions. If both sorts of entities are to be recognized, the one intelligible difference between them would seem to be that classes are considered identical with one another when they have the same members (e.g., the class of vertebrates and the class of creatures with hearts) whereas attributes are regarded as sometimes distinct though applying to the same objects (e.g., heartedness and vertebracy). Classes and attributes are equally abstract, but classes have the edge on attributes in point of clarity of identification and separation.

Those who draw a distinction between classes and attributes will see in 'humanity' a name of an attribute and in 'mankind' a name of a class, the class of all objects which partake of the attribute of humanity. But both terms are abstract singular terms, as opposed to the concrete general term 'man' or 'human'. This general term has the class mankind as its extension.

The correspondence exemplified between the abstract singular term 'mankind' or 'humanity' and the concrete general term 'man' is a systematic feature of our language. 'Piety' is an abstract singular term corresponding to the concrete general term 'pious person'; 'redness' is an abstract singular term corresponding to the concrete general term 'red thing'. In each such correspondence the abstract singular term purports to name an attribute (or perhaps a class) which is shared by (or embraces) all and only those individuals of which the corresponding general concrete term is true. Despite this correspondence the singular abstract term differs from the general concrete term in an important way: it purports to name one and only one object, abstract object though it be, while the general term does not purport to name at all. The general term may indeed "be true of" each of *many* things, viz., each red thing, or each man, but this kind of reference is not called naming; "naming," at least as I shall use the word, is limited to the case where the named object purports to be unique.

Occasionally, as language is ordinarily used, a word like 'man' which is normally a general concrete term may be used as a singular abstract term; e.g., 'Man is a zoölogical species'. But from a logical point of view it is well to think of such examples as rephrased using a distinctively singular abstract term (thus 'Mankind is a zoölogical species').

The division of terms into concrete and abstract is a distinction only in the kinds of objects referred to. The distinction between singular and general terms is more vital from a logical point of view. Thus far it has been drawn only in a very vague way: a term is singular if it purports to name an object (one and only one), and otherwise general. Note the key word 'purports'; it separates the question off from such questions of fact as the existence of Socrates and Cerberus. Whether a word purports to name one and only one object is a question of language, and is not contingent on facts of existence.

In terms of logical structure, what it means to say that the singular term "purports to name one and only one object" is just this: *The singular term belongs in positions of the kind in which it would also be coherent to use variables 'x', 'y', etc.* (or, in ordinary language, pronouns). Contexts like:

Socrates is wise,   Piety is a virtue,
Cerberus guards the gate, $7 = 3 + 4$,

etc., are parallel in form to open sentences:

x is wise, x guards the gate, x is a virtue, $x = 3 + 4$

such as may occur in closed statements having the form of quantifications: '$(\exists x)(x$ is wise)', etc. The terms 'Socrates', 'Cerberus', 'piety', and '7' are, in short, substitutable for variables in open sentences without violence to grammar; and it is this that makes them singular terms. Whether there is in fact such an object as Socrates (which, tenselessly, there is) or Cerberus (which there is not) or piety or 7 (on which philosophers disagree) is of course a separate question.

General terms, in contrast to singular ones, do not occur in positions appropriate to variables. Typical positions of the general term 'man' are seen in 'Socrates is a man', 'All men are mortal'; it would not make sense to write:

(1)   Socrates is an x,   All x are mortal,

or to imbed such expressions in quantifications in the fashion:

(2) $(\exists x)$(Socrates is an x),

(3) (x)(all x are mortal $\supset$ Socrates is mortal).

The 'x' of an open sentence may refer to objects of any kind, but it is supposed to refer to them one at a time; and then application of '(x)' or '$(\exists x)$' means that what the open sentence says of x is true of all or some objects taken thus one at a time.

There are indeed legitimate open sentences somewhat resembling (1) but phrased in terms of class membership, thus:

(4)   Socrates is a member of x,   All members of x are mortal.

But these do not, like (1), show 'x' in place of a general term such as 'man'; rather they show 'x' in place of an abstract singular term, 'mankind' ('class of all men'), as in 'Socrates is a member of mankind', 'All members of mankind are mortal'. The open sentences (4) may quite properly appear in quantifications:

(5) $(\exists x)$(Socrates is a member of x),

(6) (x)(all members of x are mortal $\supset$ Socrates is mortal).

Incidentally (6) can be further analyzed:

(7) $(x)[(y)(y$ is a member of $x \supset y$ is mortal) $\supset$ Socrates is mortal].

As an alternative to (4) we might also appeal to attributes instead of classes, thus:

(8)   Socrates has x,   Everything that has x is mortal.

Here 'x' appears in the position of an abstract singular term such as 'humanity' which purports to name an attribute. Quantifications analogous to (5)–(7) can then be built on (8).

It may seem pedantic to reject (1)–(3) as meaningless while accepting (4)–(8). Why not accord (1) the meanings (4) or (8), and thus construe (2)–(3) as interchangeable with the quantifications (5)–(6) or with the analogous quantifications in terms of attributes? In short, why not simply rub out the distinction between general terms and abstract singular terms? The answer is as old as William of Ockham: "Entities are not to be multiplied beyond necessity." Abstract singular terms purport to name abstract entities; and, as we saw early in the preceding section, singular inference commonly presupposes existence of the purportedly named object within the universe over which our variables of quantification range. The presupposition that our universe include abstract objects can be avoided, in much of our thinking, if we adhere to the point of view that words like 'man', in contexts like 'Socrates is a man' and 'All men are mortal', occupy positions which are inaccessible to variables—just as inaccessible as the positions occupied by '(' or 'and'. The positions occupied by general terms have indeed no status at all in a logical grammar, for we have found (§23) that for logical purposes the predicate recommends itself as the unit of analysis; thus 'Socrates is a man' comes to be viewed as compounded of 'Socrates' and '① is a man', the latter being an indissoluble unit in which 'man' stands merely as a constituent syllable comparable to the 'rat' in 'Socrates'.

If for any perverse reason we *should* want to rephrase 'Socrates is a man' or 'All men are mortal' in such a way as to make outright reference to abstract objects, the formulations:

Socrates is a member of mankind,   Socrates has humanity,
All members of mankind are mortal,   All having humanity are mortal,

are at our disposal. These versions do contain singular terms which purport to name abstract objects. But we keep the record straight by reserving recognizably singular terms like 'mankind' and 'humanity' for such naming of abstract objects. Then, so long as we are minded to proceed independently of the question of the existence of abstract objects, we can eschew such idioms as the above in favor of 'Socrates is a man' and 'All men are mortal'. Eventually the question of abstract objects has to be faced anyway; it will be recalled, in fact, that classes were already appealed to in defining validity (cf. §§18, 24, but also §§21, 32). More of this later. But it is sound policy to keep as much of our logic clear of the question as we can.

The distinction between general terms and abstract singular terms is a remnant of medieval logic which some modern logicians do not share my concern to preserve. Actually the significance of the distinction is clearer since the rise of quantification theory than it had traditionally been; singular terms are accessible to positions appropriate to quantifiable variables, while general terms are not. In the foregoing paragraphs it has accordingly been urged that general terms have the virtue, as against abstract singular terms, of letting us avoid or at least postpone the recognition of abstract objects as values of our variables of quantification. Some logicians, however, attach little value to such avoidance or postponement. This attitude may be explained in some cases by a Platonic predilection for abstract objects; not so in other cases, however, notably Carnap's. His attitude is rather that quantification over abstract objects is a linguistic convention devoid of ontological commitment; see his "Empiricism, semantics, and ontology."

§35. IDENTITY

Identity is such a simple and fundamental idea that it is hard to explain otherwise than through mere synonyms. To say that x and y are identical is to say that they are the same thing. Everything is identical with itself and with nothing else. But despite its simplicity, identity invites confusion. E.g., it may be asked: Of what use is the notion of identity if identifying an object with itself is trivial and identifying it with anything else is false?

This particular confusion is cleared up by reflecting that there are really not just two kinds of cases to consider, one trivial and the other false, but three:

Cicero = Cicero,   Cicero = Catiline,   Cicero = Tully,

The first of these is trivial and the second false, but the third is neither trivial nor false. The third is informative, because it joins two different terms; and at the same time it is true, because the two terms are names of the same object. For truth of a statement of identity it is necessary only that '=' appear between names of the same object; the names may, and in useful cases will, themselves be different. For it is not the names that are affirmed to be identical, it is the things named. Cicero is identical with Tully (same man), even though the name 'Cicero' is different from the name 'Tully'. To say anything about given objects we apply the appropriate verb or predicate to *names of* the objects; but there is no reason to expect that what is thereby said of the objects will be true also of the names themselves. The Nile, e.g., is longer than the Tuscaloosahatchie, but the names are oppositely related.

Still, since the useful statements of identity are those in which the named objects are the same and the names are different, it is only because of a peculiarity of language that the notion of identity is needed. If our language were so perfect a copy of its subject matter that each thing had but one name, then statements of identity would indeed be useless.[1] But such a language would be radically different from what we have. To rid language of redundant nomenclature of the simple type, e.g., 'Tully' and 'Cicero', would be no radical departure; but to eliminate redundancies among complex names, e.g., '7 × 5' and '27 + 8', or 'twenty-fifth President of U.S.' and 'first President of U.S. to be inaugurated at 42', or 'mean temperature at Tuxtla' and '93°F', would be to strike at the roots. The utility of language lies partly in its very failure to copy reality in any one-thing-one-name fashion. The notion of identity is then needed to take up the slack.

But to say that the need of identity derives from a peculiarity of language is not to say that identity is a relation of expressions in language. On the contrary, as lately emphasized, what are identical are the objects with themselves and not the names with one another; the names stand in the statement of identity, but it is the named objects that are identified. Moreover, no linguistic investigation of the names in a statement of identity will suffice, ordinarily, to determine whether the identity holds or fails. The identities:

---

[1]Thus it was that Hume had trouble accounting for the origin of the identity idea in experience. See *Treatise of Human Nature*, Bk. I, Pt. IV, Sec. II.

Everest = Gaurisanker   (cf. §33),
Evening Star = Morning Star,
25th President of U.S. = first President of U.S. inaugurated at 42,
Mean temperature at Tuxtla = 93°F

all depend for their substantiation upon inquiry into extra-linguistic matters of fact.

A popular riddle, so commonly associated with identity that it should be touched on here, is this: How can a thing that changes its substance be said to remain identical with itself? How is it, e.g., that one's body may be spoken of as the same body over a period of years? The problem dates from Heraclitus, who said "You cannot step into the same river twice, for fresh waters are ever flowing in upon you." Actually the key to this difficulty is to be sought not in the idea of identity but in the ideas of thing and time. A physical thing— whether a river or a human body or a stone—is at any one moment a sum of simultaneous momentary states of spatially scattered atoms or other small physical constituents. Now just as the thing at a moment is a sum of these spatially small parts, so we may think of the thing over a period as a sum of the temporally small parts which are its successive momentary states. Combining these conceptions, we see the thing as extended in time and in space alike; the thing becomes a sum of momentary states of particles, or briefly particle-moments, scattered over a stretch of time as well as space. All this applies as well to the river or human body as to the stone. There is only a difference of detail in the two cases: in the case of the stone the constituent particle-moments pair off fairly completely from one date to another as momentary states of the same particles, whereas in the case of the river or human body there is more heterogeneity in this respect. The river or human body will regularly contain some momentary states of a particle and exclude other momentary states of the same particle, whereas with the stone, barring small peripheral changes or ultimate destruction, this is not the case. Here we have a distinction reminiscent of the distinction in traditional philosophy between "modes" and "substances". But things of both kinds are physical things in one and the same sense: sums of particle-moments. And each thing is identical with itself; we *can* step into the same river twice. What we cannot do is step into the same temporal part of the river twice, where the part is temporally shorter than a stepping-while. Diversity among the parts of a whole must not be allowed to obscure the identity of the whole, nor of each part, with itself.

Thus far we have been thinking of statements of identity composed of '=' flanked by singular terms. But '=' is an ordinary relative term, and so may be flanked as well by variables; e.g.:

$(x)(y)(x$ is a god . y is a god . $\supset$. $x = y)$,
$(\exists x)[x$ is a god . $(y)(y$ is a god $\supset$. $x = y)]$,
$(\exists x)(\exists y)(x$ is a god . y is a god . $x \neq y)$,
$(x)(y)(z)(x$ is a god . y is a god . z is a god . $\supset$: $x = y$ .v. $x =$
z .v. $y = z)$.

(The notation '$x \neq y$' is a convenient abbreviation for '$-(x = y)$'.) As the reader can verify on a little reflection, these four statements amount respectively to the following:

> There is one god at most,[1]
> There is exactly one god,
> There are at least two gods,
> There are two gods at most.

Statements of identity consisting of '=' flanked by singular terms are needed, we saw, because language includes a redundancy of names. But the need of '=' flanked by variables arises from a different peculiarity of language; viz., from its use of multiple variables of quantification (or their pronominal analogues in ordinary language). Two variables are allowed to refer to the same object, and they are also allowed to refer to different objects; and thus the sign of identity comes to be needed when, as in the above four examples, there arises the question of sameness or difference of reference on the part of the variables. From a logical point of view it is the use of the identity sign between variables, rather than between singular terms, that is fundamental. We shall see, indeed (§37), that the whole category of singular terms is theoretically superfluous, and that there are logical advantages in thinking of it as theoretically cleared away.

The logic of identity is a branch not reducible to the logic of

---

[1] This, according to a quip of the late Professor Whitehead's, is the creed of the Unitarians.

quantification. Its notation may be thought of as comprising that of the logic of quantification plus the one additional sign '='. Thus the schemata of the logic of identity are the same as the quantificational schemata except that they may contain, along with the clauses 'p', 'q', 'Fx', 'Gxy', etc., additional clauses of the form of identities: '$x = y$', '$x = z$', etc. Validity may be defined for schemata of the logic of identity precisely as it was defined for quantificational schemata (§24). Thus there are valid schemata such as:

$$(\exists y)(x = y \,.\, Fy) \supset (\exists y)(x = y)$$

which are like valid quantificational schemata except that '$x = x$', '$x = y$', etc., turn up instead of schematic clauses 'Gxx', 'Gxy', etc. These are valid still by virtue simply of their quantificational structure, and independently of any peculiarities of identity. But there are further valid schemata whose validity depends specifically on the meaning of identity; one such is:

(I) $Fx \,.\, x = y \,.\supset Fy.$

For, consider any choice of universe, any interpretation of 'F' therein, and any assignment of objects to the free variables 'x' and 'y'. If the object assigned to 'x' is the same as that assigned to 'y', and is an object of which 'F' is interpreted as true, then (I) comes out true through truth of its consequent 'Fy'; and in any other case (I) comes out true through falsity of its antecedent.

Through having added the identity sign to our logical notation we find ourselves able, for the first time, to write genuine sentences without straying from our logical notation. Hitherto, schemata were the best we could get; extra-logical materials had to be imported from ordinary language when, for the sake of illustration, a genuine sentence was wanted. In '$x = x$' and '$(x)(x = x)$', however, we have sentences—the first open, the second closed and true.

Any schemata obtained by putting identities '$x = x$', '$x = y$', etc., in place of say 'Gxx', 'Gxy', etc., in valid quantificational schemata are, it has been explained, valid schemata of the logic of identity. But such putting of identities for schematic clauses can, when thorough, yield a sentence instead of a schema, e.g.:

$$x = x \,.\supset (\exists y)(x = y).$$

It is convenient to allow the concept of validity to apply to such sentences along with schemata. The extension, indeed, is quite automatic. A schema has been explained as valid when it comes out true under every nonempty choice of universe and every interpretation therein of its schematic letters and free variables; and this characterization carries over unchanged to sentences such as the above, except that the provision for schematic letters becomes irrelevant. When furthermore the sentence has no free variables, the definition of validity reduces to 'true for every nonempty choice of universe'.

The example '$x = x . \supset (\exists y)(x = y)$' above is a sentence which is valid by virtue simply of its quantificational structure. Of those whose validity depends specifically on the meaning of identity, on the other hand, the simplest is:

(II) $x = x.$

Another, truth-functionally implied by the two foregoing sentences, is '$(\exists y)(x = y)$'.

Substitutions may be made for 'F' in (I) just as explained in §25, except that the substituted expressions may now contain identity signs instead of predicate letters. Reflection on the general mechanics of substitution (§25) reveals that, in (I) in particular, 'Fx' and 'Fy' may in effect be directly supplanted respectively by any schemata S_x and S_y which differ only in that S_x has free 'x' in some places where S_y has free 'y'. (For, the predicate or predicate-schema theoretically substituted for 'F' would then be simply S_x with '①' in the particular places where S_x and S_y are to differ). Thus one result of substitution in (I) is:

$$w = x . x = y . \supset . w = y$$

—the law of transitivity of identity (cf. §30).

The universal closures of (I) and (II), viz:

$$(x)(y)(Fx . x = y . \supset Fy), \qquad (x)(x = x),$$

together with the universal closures of any results of substituting for 'F' in (I), will be called *axioms of identity*. Now the technique of deduction in quantification theory carries over to the logic of identity; we simply deduce the valid schemata and statements of the logic of identity from the axioms as premisses.[1] E.g., the law of symmetry of identity '$x = y . \supset . y = x$' may be deduced from two axioms of identity as follows:[2]

$$
\star\begin{cases}
(1) & (x)(y)(x = x . x = y . \supset . y = x) \\
(2) & (x)(x = x)
\end{cases}
$$

$$
\begin{array}{lll}
\star\ (3) & (y)(x = x . x = y . \supset . y = x) & (1) \\
\star\ (4) & x = x . x = y . \supset . y = x & (3) \\
\star\ (5) & x = x & (2) \\
\star\ (6) & x = y . \supset . y = x & (4)(5)
\end{array}
$$

A convenient condensed notation for deductions from axioms is obtained by suppressing the axioms as premisses, and suppressing also the steps of UI which get rid of the initial quantifiers of the axioms. Under this plan we would justify (4) of the above deduction simply by writing '(I)' to the right of it—thus referring back beyond the actual axioms to the convenient open schema (I). Similarly a line '$z = z$', if wanted, would be justified simply by writing '(II)' to the right of it. (I) and (II) themselves, when they are to be used as actual lines without substitution for 'F' or changes of variables, need not be written in as lines at all; for we can always refer back to them simply as (I) and (II). Thus line (5) above drops out, and the citation '(5)' in the next line changes to '(II)'. Condensed accordingly, the above deduction appears as follows.

$$
\begin{array}{lll}
(1) & x = x . x = y . \supset . y = x & (I) \\
(2) & x = y . \supset . y = x & (1)(II)
\end{array}
$$

The extension of the concept of validity to the logic of identity carries with it, as usual, an extension of implication and equivalence; for implication is validity of the conditional, and equivalence is mutual implication. Thus '$x = y$' implies '$y = x$'. Moreover, since the

---

[1] The axioms are complete, in the sense that every valid schema or statement of the logic of identity can be reached as last line of a finished deduction with only axioms as premisses. This follows from the completeness of quantification theory (§32) together with the analysis of identity theory which is contained in Hilbert and Bernays, vol. 1, pp. 164–209.

[2] Note that (1) here is not a legitimate result of substitution in the axiom of identity '$(x)(y)(Fx . x = y . \supset Fy)$'. Cf. §25, second restriction. But (1) is the universal closure of a legitimate result of substitution in (I); and as such it is an axiom of identity.

reverse implication likewise holds (by mere change of variables), '$x = y$' is equivalent to '$y = x$'.

For further illustration let us establish the equivalence of '$(y)(x = y . \supset Fy)$' to 'Fx', by mutual deduction in the condensed style.

$\star$(1) $(y)(x = y . \supset Fy)$ $\star$(1) Fx

$\star$(2) $x = x . \supset Fx$ (1) $\star$(2) $x = y . \supset Fy$ (1)(I)

$\star$(3) Fx (II)(2) $\star$(3) $(y)(x = y . \supset Fy)$ (2) y

EXERCISES

1. Rewrite the last two deductions without condensation, showing the appropriate axioms explicitly as premises.

2. Writing 'F' for 'cross-fertile' ('is cross-fertile with'), put this statement into logical form:

> Some zoölogical species are cross-fertile.

Note that 'distinct' is understood after 'Some' here. Does the resulting statement call for abstract entities as values of its variables?

3. Writing 'y' for 'Barr', 'z' for 'the cashier', and 'F' for 'had a key', put the statement:

> None but Barr and the cashier had a key

into logical notation with help of identity. From this and:

> Someone who had a key took the briefcase

deduce the conclusion:

> Barr or the cashier took the briefcase

with help of (I). This can be done in four lines in addition to the premises and conclusion; but such condensation need not be insisted upon.

4. Establish the equivalence of:

$$(\exists x)(Fx . x = y), \qquad\qquad Fy$$

by deducing each from the other.

§36. DESCRIPTIONS

Since Peano it has been customary in logic to write '$(\imath x)$', with an inverted iota, to mean 'the object x such that'. Thus the complex singular terms 'the author of *Waverley*' and 'the prime number between 5 and 11' become:

$$(\imath x)(x \text{ wrote } Waverley), \qquad (\imath x)(x \text{ is prime} . 5 < x < 11).$$

Singular terms are called *descriptions* when written in this form. The singular terms of ordinary language which may be represented thus as descriptions begin typically with the singular 'the', but by no means necessarily so, as these examples show:

what he went after,	$(\imath x)(\text{he went after } x)$;
where he was born,	$(\imath x)(\text{he was born at } x)$;
John's mother,	$(\imath x)(x \text{ bore John})$;
Smith's house,	$(\imath x)(x \text{ is a house} . x \text{ is Smith's})$.

In general a singular term purports to name one and only one object, and in particular a singular term of the form '$(\imath x)Fx$' purports to name the one and only object of which the predicate represented by 'F' is true. Thus, if y is the object $(\imath x)Fx$, then y must be such that

$$Fy . F \text{ nothing-but-}y.$$

This conjunction amounts to saying that, for each thing x, 'F' is true of x if $x = y$, and false of x otherwise. In short:

(1) $\qquad\qquad (x)(Fx \equiv . x = y)$.

E.g., to say that Scott is $(\imath x)(x \text{ wrote } Waverley)$ is to say that

$$(x)(x \text{ wrote } Waverley \equiv . x = \text{Scott}).$$

If 'F' is true of nothing or of many things, then there is no such thing as $(\imath x)Fx$. Actually the predicate appearing in the rôle of the 'F' of '$(\imath x)Fx$' in verbal examples from ordinary discourse very frequently needs supplementary clauses to narrow it down to the point of being true of only one object, but this situation can commonly be viewed merely as a case of the familiar practice of depending on context or situation to resolve ambiguities of ordinary language.

We saw in §33 that arguments involving a singular term can be carried through by straight quantification theory with a free variable, say 'y', for the singular term, but that the application of the results depends on construing y as the object named by the singular term, and hence is contingent on existence of such an object. This construing of *y*, and the existence assumption on which it rests, figured nowhere in the schematism of the deduction, but only in the informal step of application. Now the beauty of descriptions is that here the construing of *y* as the named object can itself be schematized quite explicitly as an additional premiss, of the form (1) above. So our technique for deductions involving descriptions is as follows: we use free variables for the descriptions as for any singular terms, but we also add a *descriptional premiss* of the form (1) for each description. Then the deduction proceeds not by pure quantification theory but by identity theory, in view of the '=' in the descriptional premisses. Thus let us try this example:

Premiss: The broker who hired John hired only honors graduates,
Conclusion: John was an honors graduate.

Here we have two singular terms, the simple one 'John' and the complex one 'the broker who hired John'. Let us represent them by free variables '*w*' and '*y*' respectively. Writing '*F*' for 'broker' and '*G*' for 'hired', we may also render the complex singular term as a description '$(\imath x)(Fx \cdot Gxw)$'; so the corresponding descriptional premiss is:

$$(x)(Fx \cdot Gxw .\equiv. x = y).$$

So from this and the original premiss, which is '$(x)(Gyx \supset Hx)$' where '*H*' represents 'honors graduate', our problem is to deduce '*Hw*'.

$$
\left\{
\begin{array}{lll}
\text{(1)} & (x)(Gyx \supset Hx) & \\
\text{(2)} & (x)(Fx \cdot Gxw .\equiv. x = y) & \\
\end{array}
\right.
$$

* (3) $Gyw \supset Hw$ (1)
* (4) $Fy \cdot Gyw .\equiv. y = y$ (2)
* (5) $y = y$ (II)
* (6) Hw (3)(4)(5)

Whether a proposed deduction is to enjoy the benefits of a descriptional premiss depends, evidently, on whether a given singular term can fairly be translated into the form of a description. Now fairness of translation is a vague matter, hinging as it does on the concept of synonymy which was so dimly regarded in §33. 'The author of *Waverley*' seems fairly translatable as '$(\imath x)(x$ wrote *Waverley*)', but 'Scott' and 'the author of *Ivanhoe*' do not, despite the fact that all of these name the same object; for it is felt that 'the author of *Waverley*' is connected with '$(\imath x)(x$ wrote *Waverley*)' by sheer meaning, whereas 'Scott' and 'the author of *Ivanhoe*' are connected with it through accidental matters of fact.

At the same time it seems that singular terms can depart widely in form from the singular 'the' idiom and still be fairly deemed translatable into descriptions; witness 'John's mother'. Indeed, even so simple a term as 'Socrates', Russell has argued,[1] is for each of us synonymous with some description, perhaps '$(\imath x)(x$ was a philosopher *x* drank hemlock)' or perhaps another depending on how each of us first learned of Socrates. Are then all singular terms to be considered capable of fair translation into descriptions, except for those very few names which we may be supposed to have learned by direct confrontation with name and object? Must a separate category then be kept open for these few hypothetical exceptions?

Happily, we can isolate such epistemological considerations from the logic of singular terms by a very simple expedient: by insisting on the primacy of predicates. We may insist that what are learned by ostension, or direct confrontation, be never names but solely predicates. This we may insist on at the level strictly of logical grammar, without prejudice to epistemology or ontology. Without prejudice to ontology because the same things remain, whether as things which names name or as things which predicates are true of. Without prejudice to epistemology because we may grant the epistemologist any of the words which he traces to ostension; we merely parse them differently. Instead of treating the ostensively learned word as a *name of* the shown object to begin with, we treat it to begin with as a predicate *true* exclusively of the shown object; then we construe the name, as such, as amounting to '$(\imath x)Fx$' where '*F*' represents that primitive predicate. No matter to epistemology, but much to the smoothness of logical theory.

So there is no longer an obstacle to treating all singular terms as descriptions. Given any singular term of ordinary language, more-

[1] E.g., in "Knowledge by acquaintance."

over, say 'Socrates' or 'Cerberus' or 'the author of *Waverley*', the proper choice of '*F*' for translation of the term into '$(\imath x)Fx$' need in practice never detain us. If a pat translation such as '$(\imath x)(x$ wrote *Waverley*)' lies ready to hand, very well; if not, we need not hesitate to admit a version of the type of '$(\imath x)(x$ is-Socrates)' or '$(\imath x)(x$ is-Cerberus)', since any less lame version would, if admissible as a translation at all, differ at most in expository value and not in meaning.

Deductions of the type of the broker example set forth above are in no way facilitated by thus trivially transforming simple singular terms into descriptions. Construing 'John' in the broker example as a description '$(\imath x)(x$ is-John)', or '$(\imath x)Jx$', would entitle us to a further descriptional premiss '$(x)(Jx \equiv_. x = w)$', but this is neither necessary nor useful for the progress of the deduction. The advantage of treating all singular terms as descriptions is of a more theoretical kind: that of sparing us having to admit into the framework of our technical theory a distinction between a category of descriptions and a category of non-descriptive singular terms. It is theoretically important not to have to admit this distinction because, as we have seen, the question of there being essentially nondescriptive singular terms at all, and if so what, was shrouded in the theory of knowledge and meaning. We have segregated that issue from our concerns, by shifting it from the realm of singular terms into that of predicates. Every singular term can now, trivially if not otherwise, be handled as a description; what had been an issue over names learned ostensively versus names learned discursively now becomes an issue over predicates learned ostensively versus predicates learned discursively. In this form the issue ceases to cut across any of our schematism of logical forms and categories, and can be left to other minds.

There is a yet more striking benefit to be gained from treating all singular terms as descriptions, but it must await the next section.

EXERCISES

1. Express 'the tallest man in town' in the form '$(\imath x)(\cdots x \cdots)$', using 'taller than' but not 'tallest'.

2. From:

The author of *Waverley* wrote *Ivanhoe*

and a descriptional premiss, deduce:

Someone wrote both *Waverley* and *Ivanhoe*.

§37. ELIMINATION OF SINGULAR TERMS

Let us next take up the problem, which has been looming for some time, of the truth value of such statements as 'Cerberus barks'. Falsity, as a sweeping answer covering all statements containing 'Cerberus', would be over-hasty: first, because the statement 'There is no such thing as Cerberus', at least, is true; and second, because whatever statements we adjudge false must admit of compounds, e.g., their negations, which will be true. Truth, as a sweeping answer, would encounter parallel difficulties.

Our deductive methods for singular terms throw no light on the question; for we already assume that the singular term names an object when we represent the singular term by a free variable, and we make the same assumption again when we adopt a descriptive premiss for a description. Failing a named object, our methods show nothing, for what they purport to show rests then on a contrary-to-fact assumption. Common usage, moreover, likewise leaves us in the dark; for, excepting such contexts as 'There is no such thing as Cerberus', a singular term is ordinarily used only when the speaker believes or cares to pretend that the object exists.   .

Under ordinary usage, we saw (§3), truth values attach not to indicative conditionals as wholes but only to the consequents contionally upon truth of the antecedents. Analogously, under ordinary usage truth values attach to contexts of singular terms for the most part only conditionally upon existence of the objects. But if we are to have a smooth logical theory we must fill such gaps, even though arbitrarily, in such a way that every statement comes to have a truth value. Thus it was that we conventionally extended the concept of the conditional, in §3, so as to allow truth values generally to conditionals as wholes. An extension in the same spirit is needed now on the score of singular terms that do not name.

We cannot, we have seen, accomplish this extension by any blanket decision that all contexts of a term such as 'Cerberus' are to be false, or all true. We can, however, decide the simple contexts and then let the truth values of the compounds follow from those decisions. Let us speak of a predicate as *simple*, for our purposes, when it does not explicitly have the form of a quantification, negation, conjunction, alternation, conditional, or biconditional of shorter components. When any such simple predicate is applied to a singular term which fails to name, let us classify the resulting sentence as false (for all values of any free variables it may have). Thus 'Cerberus barks', formed as it is by applying the simple predicate '① barks' to 'Cerberus', is adjudged false.

This rule is suited for use only upon sentences which are considered to be fully analyzed in point of logical structure. If the sentences are still to be subject to further paraphrasing of words into symbols, we must be wary of treating a predicate as "simple" in the above sense and then paraphrasing it into a complex one.

For illustration let us re-examine the statement:

(1)   The broker who hired John hired only honors graduates.

If we use 'F' for 'broker' and 'G' for 'hired', then 'the broker who hired John' may be rendered '$(\imath x)(Fx \,.\, G x \text{ John})$'. To say that this alleged person hired u is then to say:

(2) $G\,(\imath x)(Fx \,.\, G x \text{ John})\,u,$

so that (1) becomes:

(3) $(u)[G\,(\imath x)(Fx \,.\, G x \text{ John})\,u \supset Hu]$

where 'H' means 'honors graduate'. Now let us suppose that no broker or several hired John, so that there is no such thing as *the* broker who hired John. According to the decision which we have newly adopted to cover such cases, the simple context (2) of '$(\imath x)(Fx \,.\, G x \text{ John})$' is then to be classified as false for all choices of u. Thereupon the conditional in (3) becomes true for all choices of u through falsity of antecedent, so (3) becomes true. The outcome is therefore that (1) becomes true, independently of any consideration of honors graduates, in case John was hired by no broker or several. This particular outcome is the merest curiosity, neither welcome nor unwelcome, since ordinary usage leaves cases such as this undecided.

Even when a singular term fails to name, however, we do have very proper preconceptions about the truth value of the special context 'There is [or: is not] such a thing as $\cdots$'. But statements of this form call for a separate analysis, along lines which are already pretty evident from these past observations:

(a) We may take '$(\imath x)Fx$' as the general form for singular terms.

(b) '$(\imath x)Fx$' purports to name the one and only·object of which 'F' is true (supposing any particular predicate for 'F' here).

(c) '$(x)(Fx \equiv. x = y)$' amounts to saying that y is the one and only object of which 'F' is true.

To say that there is such a thing as $(\imath x)Fx$ is to say, in view of (b), that there is one and only one object of which 'F' is true; and this may, in view of (c), be said as follows:

$$(4) \qquad\qquad (\exists y)(x)(Fx \equiv. x = y).$$

Here, then, is an adequate formulation of 'there is such a thing as '$(\imath x)Fx$'; and no more can be wanted, in view of (a), in formulation of the general idiom 'There is such a thing as $\cdots$'.

Curiously enough, the translation (4) of 'There is such a thing as $(\imath x)Fx$' is devoid of the singular term '$(\imath x)Fx$'. Now elimination of '$(\imath x)Fx$' from other contexts can also be accomplished. For, think of 'G' as representing any predicate which is "simple" in the recently defined sense. Then '$G (\imath x)Fx$', which attributes 'G' to $(\imath x)Fx$, may be paraphrased as:

$$(5) \qquad\qquad (\exists y)[Gy . (x)(Fx \equiv. x = y)].$$

This is seen as follows. First suppose (Case 1) that there is such a thing as $(\imath x)Fx$. Then the clause '$(x)(Fx \equiv. x = y)$' identifies y with $(\imath x)Fx$, and accordingly (5) as a whole becomes true or false according as 'G' is true or false of $(\imath x)Fx$. Next suppose (Case 2) that there is no such thing as $(\imath x)Fx$. Then '$(x)(Fx \equiv. x = y)$' becomes false for all choices of y; so (5) becomes false. But '$G (\imath x)Fx$' likewise is to be false in this case, according to our recent agreement about simple predicates in application to singular terms that do not name.

We are now in a position to eliminate singular terms everywhere. Given any sentence involving singular terms, we begin by paraphrasing the sentence into the explicit notation of quantification and truth functions as fully as we can, leaving the singular terms undisturbed as components but putting each in the form of a description. Then we supplant each simple context of each description by its equivalent of the form (5)—or by (4) if it happens to have the form 'there is such a thing as $(\imath x)Fx$'.[1]

For simplicity we have been imagining always *closed* singular terms, as opposed to open ones such as '$x + 5$' or 'the eldest son of x' or '$(\imath x)(x$ wrote $z)$'. Clearly, however, the open ones admit of elimination by the same procedure; the fact that a free variable is being carried along alters nothing essential to the reasoning.

To see how the elimination of singular terms proceeds in practice, let us return to (1) and eliminate the singular terms 'John' and 'the broker who hired John'. As a first step we may eliminate the description from the simple context (2). The general method of doing this was seen in the translation of '$G (\imath x)Fx$' into (5); but what we have to deal with now in place of '$G (\imath x)Fx$' is (2), which is of the form of '$G (\imath x)Fx$' with '$F\textcircled{1}$. $G\textcircled{1}$ John' for 'F' and '$G\textcircled{1}u$' for 'G'. These same substitutions in (5) give:

(6) $(\exists y)[Gyu . (x)(Fx . G x \text{ John} . \equiv . x = y)]$,

then, as the translation of (2). But 'John' has yet to be dealt with. Writing 'J' for 'is-John', we render 'John' as a description '$(\imath z)Jz$', so that '$G x$ John' in (6) becomes '$Gx(\imath z)Jz$'. This clause is of the form '$G(\imath x)Fx$' with 'z' for 'x', 'J' for 'F', and '$Gx\textcircled{1}$' for 'G'. Corresponding changes in (5) give:

(7) $(\exists w)[Gxw . (z)(Jz \equiv . z = w)]$,

then, as translation of '$Gx(\imath x)Jz$'. Now we have eliminated both singular terms. It remains only to assemble the pieces, by putting (7) for '$G x$ John' in (6) and then putting the result for (2) in (3). We thus get:

$(u)[(\exists y)(Gyu . (x)\{Fx . (\exists w)[Gxw . (z)(Jz \equiv . z = w)] . \equiv . x = y\})$
$\supset Hu]$

---

[1]This method of eliminating descriptions is due to Russell (1905). But he did not take the further step of treating all singular terms as descriptions.

as our final paraphrase of (1). But by now it begins to appear that the elimination of descriptions is of essentially theoretical interest, and that in practice the alternative handling of the broker problem which was noted in the preceding section recommends itself highly.

Nevertheless, the theoretical eliminability of singular terms—the dispensability of all names—is so startling that its importance scarcely needs dwelling upon, except in the negative fashion of pointing out what it does not mean. It does not mean that our language loses all means of talking about objects; on the contrary, the foregoing considerations show that the extrusion of singular terms is unaccompanied by any diminution in the power of the language. What the disappearance of singular terms does mean is that all reference to objects of any kind, concrete or abstract, is narrowed down now to one specific channel: variables of quantification. We can still say anything we like about any one object or all objects, but we say it always through the idioms of quantification: 'There is an object x such that $\cdots$' and 'Every object x is such that $\cdots$'. The objects whose existence is implied in our discourse are finally just the objects which must, for the truth of our assertions, be acknowledged as "values of variables"— i.e., be reckoned into the totality of objects over which our variables of quantification range. To be is to be a value of a variable. There are no ultimate philosophical problems concerning terms and their references, but only concerning variables and their values; and there are no ultimate philosophical problems concerning existence except insofar as existence is expressed by the quantifier '$(\exists x)$'. Except when we are concerned with philosophical issues of linguistic reference and existence, on the other hand, there is no point in depriving ourselves of the convenience of singular terms; and accordingly the techniques of inference hitherto developed for singular terms are not to be thought of as abandoned.

EXERCISE

Put the statement:

The woman who lives above us is German and loves flowers

into symbols, using 'Fx' for 'x is a woman', 'Gx' for 'x lives above us', 'Hx' for 'x is German', and 'Jx' for 'x loves flowers'. Then transform the whole so as to eliminate use of description.

§38. CLASSES

The evident analogy between variables 'x', 'y', etc., and schematic letters 'F', 'G', etc., tempts us to try using the latter in quantifiers, e.g., thus:

(1) $(F)[(x)Fx \supset (\exists x)Fx]$,

(2) $(\exists F)[(\exists x)Fx \ . \ -(x)Fx]$.

However, let us not be hasty in supposing that we understand (1) and (2). We have been reading the quantifiers '(x)' and '$(\exists x)$' in the fashion 'each thing x is such that' and 'something x is such that', but how are we to read '(F)' and '$(\exists F)$'? May we read '(F)' in the fashion 'each general term (or predicate) F is such that', and '$(\exists F)$' correspondingly? No, this is a confusion. 'F' has never been thought of as referring to general terms (and thus as standing in place of *names of* general terms), but only as standing in place of general terms. If there were objects of a special sort, say gimmicks, of which general terms were names, then the proper readings of '(F)' and '$(\exists F)$' would be 'each gimmick F is such that' and 'some gimmick F is such that'. But the difficulty is that general terms are not names at all.

From time to time we have, however, associated certain abstract entities, viz., classes, with general terms. We have never treated general terms as names of classes, but we have spoken of general terms as having classes as their so-called extensions. So classes recommend themselves as objects for the newly quantified variable 'F' to range over. We can read '(F)' and '$(\exists F)$' in (1) and (2) as 'each class F is such that' and 'some class F is such that', provided that we also reread 'Fx' for present purposes as 'x is a member of the class F'.

But we have now strained 'F' away from its former usage in two important respects. The new reading of 'Fx' involves use of 'F' in positions appropriate no longer to general terms, but to abstract singular terms, viz. class names; and the use of 'F' in quantifiers changes the status of 'F' from schematic letter to variable. It is more conducive to clarity to renounce this altered usage of 'F' and adopt instead a fresh notation for the new purposes: variables 'α', 'β', 'γ', $\cdots$ for classes, and 'ε' for 'is a member of'. (1) and (2) then give way to:

(3) $(\alpha)[(x)(x \text{ ε } \alpha) \supset (\exists x)(x \text{ ε } \alpha)]$,

(4) $(\exists \alpha)[(\exists x)(x \text{ ε } \alpha) \, . -(x)(x \text{ ε } \alpha)]$.

Such sentences combine variables which range over two distinct universes. The variables 'x', 'y', etc., range over some unspecified universe U, while the variables 'α', 'β', etc., range over a distinct but related universe U_1 composed of the subclasses of U: the classes whose members belong to U. The simplest sentences of this class-theory notation consist of 'ε' with an ordinary variable on its left and a class variable on its right, in the manner '$x \text{ ε } \alpha$'; and all further sentences are built up by quantification and truth functions from these simple ones.

Up to a point, despite its overt reference to a new realm of entities called classes, this new branch of logic can be created by definition in terms merely of the concepts of validity and consistency of quantificational schemata. To say that the schema '$(x)Fx \supset (\exists x)Fx$' is valid is, we know, to say that it comes out true under all choices of classes as extensions of 'F'; hence to affirm the statement (3) or (1) of class theory as true amounts merely to affirming the validity of the schema '$(x)Fx \supset (\exists x)Fx$'. Similarly to affirm (4) or (2) as true amounts to affirming the consistency of the quantificational schema '$(\exists x)Fx \, . -(x)Fx$'. Such an account of (3) and (4) is interesting in that, within its limits, it explains statements about classes without presupposing classes. Use is made merely of the concepts of quantificational validity and consistency. These concepts were themselves explained in turn in terms of classes at one stage, indeed, but we ultimately found that they could be specified also in terms of decision procedures or deductive rules, without dependence on the class concept.

Let us speak of a quantifier as *prenex* in a sentence when, like '(α)' and '$(\exists \alpha)$' in (3) and (4), it is initial (except perhaps for other quantifiers) and its scope reaches to the end of the sentence. Now in general a statement in our new class-theory notation can be explained in terms of validity or consistency, as was done for (3) and (4) above, as long as the statement is of the following sort: its class variables all refer back to prenex quantifiers, and furthermore all the quantifiers, up to the last class quantifier, are uniformly universal or uniformly existential. if they are universal, truth of the statement amounts to validity of the corresponding quantificational schema; if they are existential, truth of the statement amounts to consistency of the schema. E.g., truth of the statements:

$$(x)(\alpha)[x \; \varepsilon \; \alpha \; . \supset \; (\exists y)(y \; \varepsilon \; \alpha)],$$

$$(\exists\alpha)(\exists\beta)(x)(x \; \varepsilon \; \alpha \; . \equiv . \; x \; \varepsilon \; \beta)$$

of class theory amounts to validity and consistency of the respective schemata:

$$Fx \supset (\exists y)Fy, \qquad\qquad (x)(Fx \equiv Gx)$$

of quantification theory.

This expedient can be pushed a bit. Quantifiers internal to a statement can be brought into prenex position by writing them with distinct variables and applying (i)–(viii) of §29. Thus the statement:

$$(\exists\alpha)[(\beta)(x)(x \; \varepsilon \; \beta \; . \supset . \; x \; \varepsilon \; \alpha) \supset (\exists\gamma)(\exists x)(x \; \varepsilon \; \gamma \; . \; x \; \varepsilon \; \alpha)],$$

with buried class quantifiers '(β)' and '$(\exists\gamma)$', can be transformed by (vii) and (v) of §29 through the stages:

$$(\exists\alpha)(\exists\beta)[(x)(x \; \varepsilon \; \beta \; . \supset . \; x \; \varepsilon \; \alpha) \supset (\exists\gamma)(\exists x)(x \; \varepsilon \; \gamma \; . \; x \; \varepsilon \; \alpha)],$$

$$(\exists\alpha)(\exists\beta)(\exists\gamma)[(x)(x \; \varepsilon \; \beta \; . \supset . \; x \; \varepsilon \; \alpha) \supset (\exists x)(x \; \varepsilon \; \gamma \; . \; x \; \varepsilon \; \alpha)],$$

and this last can be explained as merely affirming, in effect, the consistency of the quantificational schema:

$$(x)(Gx \supset Fx) \supset (\exists x)(Hx \; . \; Fx).$$

If all statements constructible in our class-theory notation could thus be equated to consistencies and validities of quantification theory, we could regard our theory of classes merely as a picturesquely transcribed account of quantification theory; classes would not need to be acknowledged as seriously presupposed entities. However, the situation is otherwise. Statements of class theory cannot be explained away in the above fashion when their prenex quantifiers are mixedly universal and existential as in the examples:

(5) $(\alpha)(\exists\beta)(x)(x \; \varepsilon \; \alpha \; . \equiv . \; x \; \varepsilon \; \beta),$

(6) $(x)(y)(\exists\alpha)(x \; \varepsilon \; \alpha \; . \equiv . \; y \; \varepsilon \; \alpha).$

It is in such statements that the irreducible substance of class theory is to be sought. Similarly for statements containing buried class quantifiers which, when brought into prenex position by (i)–(viii) of §29, become mixedly universal and existential; e.g.:

(7) $(x)(y)[(\alpha)(x \; \varepsilon \; \alpha \; . \supset . \; y \; \varepsilon \; \alpha) \supset (\beta)(y \; \varepsilon \; \beta \; . \supset . \; x \; \varepsilon \; \beta)]$,

which, transformed by (vii) and (vi) of §29, becomes:

$(x)(y)(\exists\alpha)(\beta)(x \; \varepsilon \; \alpha \; . \supset . \; y \; \varepsilon \; \alpha \; : \supset : y \; \varepsilon \; \beta \; . \supset . \; x \; \varepsilon \; \beta)$.

That (5)–(7) are true is a point of higher logic, not expressible in terms merely of validity of quantificational schemata. Thus the general adoption of class variables of quantification ushers in a theory whose laws were not in general expressible in the antecedent levels of logic. The price paid for this increased power is ontological: objects of a special and abstract kind, viz., classes, are now presupposed. Formally it is precisely in allowing quantification irreducibly over class variables 'α', 'β', etc., that we assume a range of values for these variables to refer to. To be assumed as an entity is to be assumed as a value of a variable.

But this power of expressing irreducibly new logical laws would of itself justify little interest in class theory, were it not accompanied by a corresponding increase of power on the side of application. Quantification over classes brings new power of expression also when used as an auxiliary to extra-logical discourse. A good example of this effect may be seen in the definition of the predicate or relative term 'ancestor' on the basis of 'parent'. To simplify the situation let us understand 'ancestor' in a slightly broadened sense, thereby counting as a person's ancestors not only his parents, grandparents, and so on, but also the person himself. Let us represent 'parent' by 'F', so that 'Fxy' means 'x is a parent of y'. Now the problem is to write 'x is an ancestor of y' using only 'F' and our various logical symbols.

An important feature of the class of y's ancestors is that all parents of members of the class are members of it in turn. Another feature of it is that y himself belongs to it. But these two features do not yet fix the class of y's ancestors uniquely; there are larger classes which also contain y and contain all parents of members. One such class is the class of the ancestors of y's grandsons. Another such class is the combined class of y's ancestors and neckties; for, neckties being parentless, their inclusion does not disturb the fact that all parents of members are members. But clearly every class which contains y and all parents of members will have at least to contain all y's ancestors, no matter what extra things it may happen to contain. Moreover, *one* of these classes contains nothing but y's ancestors. Hence to be an ancestor of y it is necessary and sufficient to belong to every class which contains y and all parents of members. Therefore 'x is an ancestor of y' can be written thus:

x belongs to every class which contains y and all parents of members;

i.e.:

$(\alpha)(y \; \varepsilon \; \alpha \; . \;$ all parents of members of α belong to $\alpha \; . \supset . \; x \; \varepsilon \; \alpha)$;

i.e.:

(8) $(\alpha)[y \; \varepsilon \; \alpha \; . \; (z)(w)(w \; \varepsilon \; \alpha \; . \; Fzw \; \dot{.} \supset . \; z \; \varepsilon \; \alpha) \; . \supset . \; x \; \varepsilon \; \alpha]$.

This ingenious construction, due to Frege but often attributed to Dedekind or to Peirce, admits of many applications besides this genealogical one. An application to number will be encountered in the next section. But what is significant about the construction for present purposes is that it makes essential use of quantification of a class variable 'α'.

A simpler but still important illustration of our new access of power may be seen in the fact that the sign '$=$' of identity now becomes superfluous; for instead of writing '$x = y$' we may say that x and y belong to just the same classes, thus:

$$(\alpha)(x \; \varepsilon \; \alpha \; . \equiv . \; y \; \varepsilon \; \alpha).$$

Identity of classes, '$\alpha = \beta$', may be explained in a somewhat opposite way, as meaning that α and β have just the same members. So the convenient sign '$=$' may now be viewed as a mere abbreviation, according to these "definitions" or conventions of abbreviation:

'$x = y$'   for   '$(\alpha)(x \; \varepsilon \; \alpha \; . \equiv . \; y \; \varepsilon \; \alpha)$',

'$\alpha = \beta$'   for   '$(x)(x \; \varepsilon \; \alpha \; . \equiv . \; x \; \varepsilon \; \beta)$'.

So, while we may continue to use the sign '=' as a convenience, it is superfluous and may always be imagined eliminated as above.

Once the notation of identity is thus at hand, we can also allow ourselves the further luxury of the notation of *description* without having to reckon it into our inventory of basic notation. For we know from the preceding section how, with help of identity, to eliminate a description from any statement in which it occurs.

Occasion continually arises in class theory to speak of the class of all and only the objects fulfilling a given condition. The notation for this purpose is a variable with circumflex accent, used as prefix to the condition in question; thus $\hat{x} - (x \ \varepsilon \ \alpha)$ is the class of all objects x such that $-(x \ \varepsilon \ \alpha)$, or in other words the class of all non-members of α. The prefix '$\hat{x}$' may be read, in general, 'the class of all objects x such that'. Class names formed by use of such a prefix are called *abstracts*. Now the main utility of description, in class theory, is as a means of introducing this important notation of abstraction; for, where 'Fx' represents any open sentence involving 'x', clearly we can explain '$\hat{x}Fx$' as an abbreviation of a description thus:

$$\text{'}\hat{x}Fx\text{'} \qquad \text{for} \qquad \text{'}(\imath\alpha)(x)(x \ \varepsilon \ \alpha \ . \equiv Fx)\text{'},$$

The special abbreviations '$\bar{\alpha}$', '$\alpha\beta$', and '$\alpha \ \vee \ \beta$', or others to the same purpose, are commonly adopted for the three abstracts:

$$\hat{x} - (x \ \varepsilon \ \alpha), \qquad \hat{x}(x \ \varepsilon \ \alpha \ . \ x \ \varepsilon \ \beta), \qquad \hat{x}(x \ \varepsilon \ \alpha \ . \vee . \ x \ \varepsilon \ \beta).$$

The classes $\bar{\alpha}$, $\alpha\beta$, and $\alpha \ \vee \ \beta$ are spoken of respectively as the complement of the class α, the logical product (or common part) of α and β, and the logical sum of α and β. In terms primarily of these notions an "algebra of classes" is developed which embraces such laws as:

$$\alpha\beta = \beta\alpha, \qquad -(\alpha\beta) = \bar{\alpha} \ \vee \ \bar{\beta}, \qquad \alpha(\beta \ \vee \ \gamma) = \alpha\beta \ \vee \ \alpha\gamma.$$

In large part this algebra goes back to Boole (1854), along with truth-functional logic—to which, indeed, the algebra of classes is close kin.

Taken by itself, the algebra of classes does no more than reproduce in another form the content of uniform quantification theory, as of Part II. We could, if we liked, apply the notations of the algebra to schematic predicate letters in quantification theory by adopting conventions of abbreviations as follows:

$$\text{'}\bar{F}x\text{'} \quad \text{for} \quad \text{'}-Fx\text{'}, \qquad\qquad \text{'}(F \ \vee \ G)x\text{'} \quad \text{for} \quad \text{'}Fx \ \vee \ Gx\text{'},$$

$$\text{'}(FG)x\text{'} \quad \text{for} \quad \text{'}Fx \ . \ Gx\text{'}, \qquad \text{'}F = G\text{'} \quad \text{for} \quad \text{'}(x)(Fx \equiv Gx)\text{'}.$$

The notations '$\bar{F}$', '$F \vee G$', and 'FG' are indeed reminiscent of a shorthand which was actually used in §§19 ff.

So, though the algebra of classes is the most familiar manifestation of class theory, it is in essential respects independent of the whole assumption of classes. The serious motivation for assuming classes is to be found rather in constructions such as that of 'ancestor'.

EXERCISES

1. Using the above definitions, and the method of the preceding section for eliminating descriptions, expand '$y \; \varepsilon \; \hat{x}(x \; \varepsilon \; \alpha)$' step by step into unabbreviated class-theory notation.

2. If we were developing theorems for class theory, we should certainly want '$\alpha = \hat{x}(x \; \varepsilon \; \alpha)$' as one. Expand this into unabbreviated class-theory notation. Concerning the appropriate order of steps see fifth paragraph of §37.

§39. NUMBER

We say the Apostles are twelve, but not in the sense in which we say they are pious; for we attribute piety, but not twelveness, to each. 'The Apostles are pious' has the form '$(x)(Fx \supset Gx)$', with 'F' for 'Apostle' and 'G' for 'pious'; but 'The Apostles are twelve' has no such form, and is more nearly comparable to the mere existential quantification '$(\exists x)Fx$'. This familiar quantification may be read 'The Apostles are at least one'; and we might analogously think of 'The Apostles are twelve' as written '$(\exists x)Fx$', using what is called a numerically definite quantifier. The notation is Tarski's.

Numerically definite quantifiers can be introduced on the basis purely of the theory of quantification and identity, as of §35; there is no need here of assuming classes as in §38. For, we can begin by explaining '$(\exists x)$' easily enough:

$$'(\exists x)Fx' \quad \text{for} \quad '-(\exists x)Fx'.$$

Then we can explain each succeeding numerical quantifier in terms of its predecessor in a uniform way:

$$'(\exists x)Fx' \quad \text{for} \quad '(\exists x)[Fx \, . \, (\exists y)(Fy \, . \, y \neq x)]',$$

$$'(\exists x)Fx' \quad \text{for} \quad '(\exists x)[Fx \,.\, (\exists y)(Fy \,.\, y \neq x)]',$$
$$_{2} \qquad\qquad\qquad\quad _{1}$$

$$'(\exists x)Fx' \quad \text{for} \quad '(\exists x)[Fx \,.\, (\exists y)(Fy \,.\, y \neq x)]',$$
$$_{3} \qquad\qquad\qquad\quad _{2}$$

and so on. The general pattern is this: for anything to be true of $n + 1$ things is for it to be true of something other than which it is true of n things. By a dozen steps of successive expansion according to these definitions, '$(\exists x)Fx$' goes over into a schema of pure identity

theory as of §35. Similarly for any other numerically definite quantification. However, we still have no expansion for '$(\exists x)Fx$' with variable 'n'. Thus, though we can easily say there are twelve Apostles and twelve Muses, in the form:

$$(\exists x)Fx \,.\, (\exists x)Gx,$$
$$_{12} \qquad\quad _{12}$$

we find difficulty if we want to say simply 'There are just as many Apostles as Muses' without saying how many. The plan:

$$(\exists n)[(\exists x)Fx \,.\, (\exists x)Gx]$$
$$_{n} \qquad\quad\;\; _{n}$$

is of no avail, for no definitions are at hand for expanding this expression into the notation of §35, nor even into that of §38.

All high school students appreciate the persistence, and some the utility, of number variables in algebra. The above example and such related ones as 'There are twice as many eyes as faces' suggest that quantifiable number variables have a place also in the analysis of virtually unmathematical discourse.

If we are to have quantified variables for numbers we must find entities in our universe to view as numbers—or else expand our universe to include such entities. As a step toward a reasonable theory of numbers, consider the adjective 'twelvefold'. If we are to recognize such a predicate (and not merely a corresponding type of quantifier '$(\exists x)$'), we must recognize it as a predicate which is true not of persons, e.g., Apostles, but rather of classes, e.g., the class of Apostles. Thus we may define '12-fold α' as short for '$(\exists y)(y \,\varepsilon\, \alpha)$'; 'is twelvefold' means 'has twelve members'. Now the remaining step to the number

12 as an entity is a short one; for it is natural to construe 12 as the extension of 'twelvefold'. Thus 12 becomes identified with the class of all twelvefold classes.[1]

Now we find ourselves exceeding the basis both of the theory of identity (§35) and of our present theory of classes. Variables ranging over numbers are going to have to be of a new category 'κ', 'λ', etc., taking as values classes of classes. The range U_2 of these new variables has as members the subclasses of U_1, just as U_1 has as members the subclasses of U. This supplementation of our theory of classes brings with it a new form of simple sentence, '$\alpha \ \varepsilon \ \kappa$'. Also we have now to add a third part to our definition of identity (see preceding section):

$$\text{'}\kappa = \lambda\text{'} \qquad \text{for} \qquad \text{'}(\alpha)(\alpha \ \varepsilon \ \kappa \ .\equiv. \ \alpha \ \varepsilon \ \lambda)\text{'}.$$

The notation of descriptions may likewise be extended now to include the form '$(\imath\kappa)F\kappa$'; for, now that identity and quantification are at hand for variables of the type 'κ', a procedure parallel to that in §37 enables us to eliminate '$(\imath\kappa)F\kappa$' at will from any statement in which it occurs. The abstraction notation '$\hat{\alpha}F\alpha$', for the class of all classes α such that $F\alpha$, is then forthcoming as well. (See end of preceding section.)

The singular terms '0', '1', '2', etc., as names of numbers, may be construed in the form of abstracts. 0, to begin with, is the class of all and only those classes α which have no members.

$$\text{'0'} \qquad \text{for} \qquad \text{'}\hat{\alpha} - (\exists x)(x \ \varepsilon \ \alpha)\text{'}.$$

In other words, 0 is the class whose sole member is *the* empty class. 1 is the class of all those classes α which have exactly one member y apiece:

$$\text{'1'} \qquad \text{for} \qquad \text{'}\hat{\alpha}(\exists y)(x)(x \ \varepsilon \ \alpha \ .\equiv. \ x = y)\text{'}.$$

'2', '3', etc. may be explained in turn as '1 + 1', '1 + 2', etc., once we get a definition of '+'.

Addition of numbers κ and λ is easily definable in the light of this circumstance: a class α has $\kappa + \lambda$ members if and only if α is breakable into two parts β and γ such that β has κ members and γ has λ members. Now to say that β has κ members, where κ is a number, is simply to

[1]This way of construing numbers dates from Frege (1884).

say that $\beta \, \varepsilon \, \kappa$. So we can define $\kappa + \lambda$ as the class of all classes α such that α is breakable into two parts β and γ such that $\beta \, \varepsilon \, \kappa$ and $\gamma \, \varepsilon \, \lambda$.

$$\text{`}\kappa + \lambda\text{'} \quad \text{for} \quad \text{`}\hat{\alpha}(\exists\beta)(\exists\gamma)[\beta \, \varepsilon \, \kappa \, . \, \gamma \, \varepsilon \, \lambda \, . \, (x) - (x \, \varepsilon \, \beta \, . \, x \, \varepsilon \, \gamma) \, .$$
$$(x)(x \, \varepsilon \, \alpha \, . \equiv : x \, \varepsilon \, \beta \, .\text{v.} \, x \, \varepsilon \, \gamma)]\text{'}.$$

Definition of multiplication involves a more complicated train of thought, but the primary consideration is obvious: a class α has $\kappa \cdot \lambda$ members if and only if α is breakable into κ parts each of which has λ members. Thus, tentatively:

$\text{`}\kappa \cdot \lambda\text{'}$     for     $\text{`}\hat{\alpha}(\exists\mu)[\mu$ is a class of mutually exclusive classes $.\ \alpha$
is the class of all members of members of $\mu \, . \, \mu$ has κ members $.$
$(\beta)(\beta \, \varepsilon \, \mu \, . \supset . \, \beta \, \varepsilon \, \lambda)]$.

The clause 'μ is a class of mutually exclusive classes' goes into symbols in turn easily enough:

$$(\beta)(\gamma)(x)(\beta \, \varepsilon \, \mu \, . \, \gamma \, \varepsilon \, \mu \, . \, x \, \varepsilon \, \beta \, . \, x \, \varepsilon \, \gamma \, . \supset . \, \beta = \gamma).$$

So does the clause 'α is the class of all members of members of μ':

$$(x)[x \, \varepsilon \, \alpha \, . \equiv (\exists\beta)(x \, \varepsilon \, \beta \, . \, \beta \, \varepsilon \, \mu)].$$

It remains to put 'μ has κ members' into symbols. This cannot be rendered '$\mu \, \varepsilon \, \kappa$', because a class κ of classes admits as members only classes of individuals, not classes μ of classes. But we can express the matter indirectly, as follows:

($\exists\beta)(\beta \, \varepsilon \, \kappa \, . \, \beta$ is composed of one member apiece from each class belonging to μ).

I.e.:

($\exists\beta)\{\beta \, \varepsilon \, \kappa \, . \, (x)(x \, \varepsilon \, \beta \, . \supset . \, x \, \varepsilon \, \alpha) \, . \, (\gamma)[\gamma \, \varepsilon \, \mu \, . \supset \, (\exists x)(x$ is the one and only common member of β and $\gamma)]\}$.

Finally the clause 'x is the one and only common member of β and γ' becomes:

$$(y)(y \, \varepsilon \, \beta \, . \, y \, \varepsilon \, \gamma \, . \equiv . \, y = x).$$

Assembling the pieces, we have our definition of '$\kappa \cdot \lambda$'.

Numbers are classes of classes, but not all classes of classes are numbers. The class of all twelvefold classes is a number; on the other hand a class of classes which has some but not all twelvefold classes as members is not a number, nor is a class of classes which has both fivefold and twelvefold classes as members. So the problem is still before us of setting up a formal definition of what it means to say that a class of classes κ is a number.

It may seem from the expository references to number in the foregoing discussions of '$\kappa + \lambda$' and '$\kappa \cdot \lambda$' that the notion of being a number was already presupposed in defining '$\kappa + \lambda$' and '$\kappa \cdot \lambda$'; inspection of those formal definitions shows, however, that there is no such presupposition. The definitions of '$\kappa + \lambda$' and '$\kappa \cdot \lambda$' are adopted regardless of whether κ and λ are numbers, though the definitions are of interest only where κ and λ are numbers.

Numbers as spoken of in these pages are just 0, 1, 2, $\cdots$; that is, 0 and the positive integers. These are known as the *natural numbers*. Negative numbers, fractions, irrationals, and imaginaries do not come in for present consideration, not being of the sort used in measuring class size. So our present problem is to define 'NNκ', 'κ is a natural number', in such a way that it will come out true when and only when κ is 0 or 1 or 2, etc. A means of accomplishing this is suggested by the treatment of 'ancestor' in the preceding section. Just as 'ancestor of y' means 'y or parent of y or parent of parent of y or $\cdots$', so 'natural number' means 0 or $1 + 0$ or $1 + (1 + 0)$ or $\cdots$'. So 'NNκ' receives the following definition, in close analogy to (8) of the preceding section:

'NNκ'   for   '$(\phi)[0 \; \varepsilon \; \phi \; . \; (\lambda)(\lambda \; \varepsilon \; \phi \; . \supset . \; 1 + \lambda \; \varepsilon \; \phi) \; . \supset . \; \kappa \; \varepsilon \; \phi]$'.

In words: to be a natural number is to belong to every class to which 0 belongs and $1 +$ each member belongs.[1]

But this definition exceeds the materials at hand, by quantifying over classes ϕ of classes of classes. It presupposes another supplementation of our logic, quite like the recent supplementation whereby the variables 'κ', 'λ', etc., were introduced.

Where α and β are the classes respectively of Apostles and Muses, we can now say that they have the same number of members:[2]

(1) $(\exists \kappa)(\text{NN}\kappa \; . \; \alpha \; \varepsilon \; \kappa \; . \; \beta \; \varepsilon \; \kappa)$.

---

[1]This also stems from Frege.

[2]Readers less gifted than yourself may feel at this point that the Muses are being treated more tolerantly than Cerberus (§33), thus failing to appreciate that our example is none the worse for being false.

But in order to say this we have had to exceed the logic of quantification and identity, and enter upon the theory of classes; moreover we have had to exceed the most basic theory of classes and enter upon that which quantifies over classes of classes; and we have had even to exceed that level and ascend to the level of quantification over classes of classes of classes, for the clause 'NNκ' occurring in (1) conceals within it a quantifier '(ϕ)'.

Our progressively accrued quasi-universes U, U_1, U_2, and U_3, and any others that might be added in the same spirit, have been known since Russell (1908) as *logical types*. Each is the range of a special category of variables. Each succeeding type in the series is the class of all the subclasses of the preceding type; or, to say the same thing differently, the things of each succeeding type are the classes of the things of the preceding type.

We have not decided how many things there are to be in our basic type U, nor, therefore, how big a class of such things can be; but we may be sure that if there are just, say, 71 things in U, then this is the biggest class size we can hope for in U_1. Thereupon all natural numbers beyond 71, having as alleged members classes which are too big to exist, will turn out to be empty and thus identical with one another. So, though our definitions of '0', '1', '2', etc., and of 'NNκ' may be held to unconditionally, they will deliver the unending series of numbers of classical arithmetic only in case U is infinite. It is only through infinity of U that U_1 can supply classes in all natural-number sizes. Yet once all such sizes are at hand, there will also necessarily be odd sizes to burn; for, if U is infinite, then some of the classes in U_1 will themselves be infinite and thus unmeasured by any natural number.

EXERCISE

Translate the following three sentences into symbols, making use of '+' and any other symbols defined in the foregoing pages:

$$\kappa > \lambda, \qquad \alpha \text{ has more members than } \beta,$$

$$\alpha \text{ has twice as many members as } \beta.$$

Hint: '$\kappa \geq \lambda$' may be rendered '$(\exists\mu)(\text{NN}\mu \ . \ \kappa = \mu + \lambda)$'.

§40. RELATIONS

In its unsupplemented state as of §38, class theory was conceived in a certain analogy to monadic quantification theory. The class variables 'α', 'β', etc. ranged over the extensions of the one-place predicates represented by monadic 'F', 'G', etc., in quantification theory. Now we might extend the analogy to polyadic quantification theory by adding a category of variables 'Q', 'R', etc., to range over the extensions of two-place predicates, and another category to range over the extensions of three-place predicates, and so on. Let us content ourselves with a brief consideration of the two-place supplementation, this being the most characteristic and important of the series.

Whereas the class variables 'α', 'β', etc., range over the type U_1 of subclasses of U, the variables 'Q', 'R', etc., are to range over $_1U_1$, whose members are classes of pairs of members of U; for such were conceived to be the extensions of two-place predicates. Such pair-classes are spoken of in modern logic as *dyadic relations* or briefly *relations*. To say that x *bears* the relation R to y, or in other words that the pair of x and y belongs to R, we write 'xRy'. So the simple sentences of our new theory are of two forms, '$x \ \varepsilon \ \alpha$' and 'xRy'; and the rest of the sentences are built from these by truth functions and quantification.

Parallel to the definition of class identity in §38, we can define identity of relations thus:

$$'Q = R' \qquad \text{for} \qquad '(x)(y)(xQy \equiv xRy)'.$$

The form of description '$(\imath R)FR$' then becomes available, being eliminable along the usual lines. Now just as in class theory the main utility of the description notation '$(\imath\alpha)F\alpha$' was as a basis for the abstraction notation '$\hat{x}Gx$', so in relation theory the main utility of the description notation '$(\imath R)FR$' is as a basis for a notation of relational abstraction:

$$'\hat{x}\hat{y} \ Gxy' \qquad \text{for} \qquad '(\imath R)(x)(y)(xRy \equiv Gxy)'.$$

The prefix '$\hat{x}\hat{y}$' may be read 'the relation of anything x to anything y such that'; thus

$$\hat{x}\hat{y}(\exists z)(x \text{ is brother of } z \ . \ z \text{ is parent of } y)$$

is the uncle relation.

Analogues of '$\bar{\alpha}$', '$\alpha\beta$', and '$\alpha \vee \beta$' (cf. end of §38) can now be defined for relations in obvious fashion:

$$'\bar{R}' \quad \text{for} \quad '\hat{x}\hat{y} - (xRy)', \qquad\qquad 'QR' \quad \text{for} \quad '\hat{x}\hat{y}(xQy \ . \ xRy)',$$

$$'Q \vee R' \qquad \text{for} \qquad '\hat{x}\hat{y}(xQy \vee xRy)'.$$

But of more interest are the peculiarly relational notions which are now definable, notably the *converse* $\breve{R}$ of a relation R, the *relative product* $Q \mid R$ of a relation Q into a relation R, and the *image* $R''\alpha$ of a class α by a relation R. The definitions are these:

$$
\begin{array}{lll}
\text{`}\breve{R}\text{'} & \text{for} & \text{`}\hat{x}\hat{y}\, yRx\text{',} \\
\text{`}Q \mid R\text{'} & \text{for} & \text{`}\hat{x}\hat{y}(\exists z)(xQz \,.\, zRy)\text{',} \\
\text{`}R''\alpha\text{'} & \text{for} & \text{`}\hat{x}(\exists y)(xRy \,.\, y \,\varepsilon\, \alpha)\text{'.}
\end{array}
$$

Examples: Where R is the relation of teacher to pupil, $\breve{R}$ is the relation of pupil to teacher. Where Q is the relation of father and R is the relation of mother, $Q \mid R$ is the relation of maternal grandfather and $R \mid Q$ is the relation of paternal grandmother. Where R is the relation of father and α is the class of honors students, $R''\alpha$ is the class of fathers of honors students.

We can also define the relation of identity:

$$
\text{`}I\text{'} \qquad \text{for} \qquad \text{`}\hat{x}\hat{y}(x = y)\text{'.}
$$

'xIy' and '$x = y$' are equivalent, but 'I' and '$=$' figure differently in them. 'xIy' is a case of 'xRy', like 'Cicero R y' or 'Cicero I Tully'; 'I' is a singular term (ultimately a description) naming one of the objects over which the variable 'R' ranges. On the other hand '$x = y$' bears only a misleading notational resemblance to 'xRy'; the sign '$=$' is no name of a value of 'R', not having been introduced as a singular term at all. 'I' names a relation, viz. the extension of the predicate '① $=$ ②' (as applied to individuals), whereas '$=$' does not name. Note that there is no definable relation which corresponds to 'ε' as I does to '$=$'; we cannot write '$\hat{x}\hat{\alpha}(x \,\varepsilon\, \alpha)$', for the mixed type of prefix '$\hat{x}\hat{\alpha}$' has been introduced by none of our definitions. There is indeed no such relation in ${}_1U_1$, for the relations in ${}_1U_1$ pair members of U only with members of U, not with members of U_1.

Readers acquainted with the branch of mathematics known as group theory will recognize in '$\breve{R}$', '$Q \mid R$', and 'I' the basic notions of that discipline. Some sample laws governing these and the other notions just now defined are:

$$
\begin{array}{ll}
\breve{\breve{R}} = R, & (Q \vee R)''\alpha = (Q''\alpha) \vee (R''\alpha), \\[4pt]
I''\alpha = \alpha, & R''(\alpha \vee \beta) = (R''\alpha) \vee (R''\beta), \\[4pt]
I \mid R = R \mid I = R, & Q \mid (R \mid S) = (Q \mid R) \mid S, \\[4pt]
\breve{(Q \mid R)} = \breve{R} \mid \breve{Q}, & Q''(R''\alpha) = (Q \mid R)''\alpha.
\end{array}
$$

These laws and concepts are typical of the *algebra of relations*, a branch of logic dating from DeMorgan and Peirce, 1860–70 (and in part from Cayley's group theory, 1854). Of itself this algebra, like the algebra of classes (see end of §38), does no more than reproduce in another form the content of quantification theory—or, when I is included, quantification theory and identity theory (§35). Coming as it did before Frege's founding of quantification theory (1879), the algebra of relations had its importance; and indeed there remains some utility in its notations and much beauty in its laws. But the problems capable of being worked out purely in these terms tend to submit to easier treatment in straight quantification theory (plus, occasionally, the theory of identity).

The theory of classes and relations has its special power in connection with problems and constructions which make crucial use of the added ontological assumptions; crucial use, in other words, of quantification over classes and relations. There is indeed use of such quantification in defining (or eliminating) the notation of description which underlies class abstraction and relational abstraction, and the notations of abstraction are used in turn in the above definitions of the notations '$\breve{R}$', '$Q \mid R$', etc., of the algebra of relations; but that substructure is still not essential to these notions, for we could, if we liked, import the same notions directly into the schematism of quantification theory as follows:

'$\breve{F}xy$'   for   'Fyx',   '$(F \mid G)xy$'   for   '$(\exists z)(Fxz \, . \, Gzy)$',
        '$(F^{\prime\prime}G)x$'   for   '$(\exists y)(Fxy \, . \, Gy)$'.

But quantification theory is on the whole simpler to think with when not thus encumbered.

A construction stressed in recent sections, in which crucial use was made of quantification over classes, was that of 'ancestor' from 'parent'. Incidentally, now that relations as objects are at hand, we can carry over that construction as a definition of the so-called *ancestral of* a relation R:

'$*R$'   for   '$\hat{x}\hat{y}(\alpha)[y \, \varepsilon \, \alpha \, . \, (z)(w)(w \, \varepsilon \, \alpha \, . \, zRw \, . \supset . \, z \, \varepsilon \, \alpha) \, . \supset . \, x \, \varepsilon \, \alpha]$'.

This construction could not be duplicated in the schematism of quantification theory. The nearest we can come is to define '$*Fxy$' as an abbreviation of (8) of §38; but there is no eliminating 'α' and 'ε' from (8) of §38 by putting a schematic letter 'G' for 'α', because of the quantifier '(α)'.

The respect in which this construction goes essentially beyond quantification theory is, we see, in quantification over classes, not relations. Now an example making essential use of quantification over relations may be seen by recurring to the problem of defining what it means to say that α and β are alike in size. This problem was already solved in the preceding section (for finite sizes only) at the cost of ascending through type U_2 to U_3; but we shall see now that it can also be solved in a different way by quantification over relations, type $_1U_1$, without ascending even to U_2. We may explain likeness of size on the part of α and β as consisting in the possibility of *correlating* the members of α with those of β, in such a way that each member of α is correlated with exactly one of β and each member of β

has exactly one of α correlated with it. So we first define a relation R to be a *correlation* if no two objects bear it to the same object and no one object bears it to two.

'Crln R'   for   '$(x)(y)(z)(xRz \cdot yRz \cdot\!\mathbf{.v.}\; zRx \cdot zRy :\!\supset. x = y)$'.

Now 'α sim β', meaning that α is like β in size, may be defined to mean that there is a correlation R which relates each member of α to some member of β, and to each member of β some member of α.[1] I.e., in symbols:

$$(\exists R)\{\text{Crln } R \cdot (x)[x \;\varepsilon\; \alpha \cdot\!\supset\; (\exists y)(y \;\varepsilon\; \beta \cdot xRy)] \cdot$$
$$(y)[y \;\varepsilon\; \beta \cdot\!\supset\; (\exists x)(x \;\varepsilon\; \alpha \cdot xRy)]\}.$$

Here the quantification over a relation variable 'R' is essential.

Note that there is nothing essential about the use of 'α' or 'β' in the above construction. We could write 'Fx' and 'Gy' in place of '$x \;\varepsilon\; \alpha$' and '$y \;\varepsilon\; \beta$', and reconstrue the whole performance in terms of schematic letters as an account not of 'α sim β', but of the idiom:

Fx for exactly as many objects x as Gx.

But the work even when thus reconstrued ventures necessarily beyond schematic letters into relation variables, in view of the quantifier '$(\exists R)$'.

According to the preceding section, a natural number is the class of all the classes of some one finite size. Now a *cardinal number*, so-called in modern mathematics, is the class of all the classes of some one size, be that size finite or not. Having defined 'α sim β', therefore, we are now in a position to define 'κ is a cardinal number':

'NCκ'   for   '$(\exists \beta)[\kappa = \hat{\alpha}(\alpha \text{ sim } \beta)]$'.

One might suppose that the cardinal numbers, if they are not simply the natural numbers under another name, will differ from the latter only to the extent of there being one extra, an infinite cardinal number representing the size of all infinite classes. But to suppose this is to suppose that all infinite classes are alike in size; and this in turn is to suppose that the members of any two infinite classes can be correlated. But this, far from being obvious, can for generous universes be disproved. The disproof dates from Cantor, who in consequence of it founded a substantial branch of mathematics having to do with the infinite varieties of infinite cardinal numbers.

Curiously enough, despite the fact that the cardinal numbers allow for these recondite infinites in addition to the familiar natural numbers, the above definition of 'NCκ' does not demand as high types as did the definition of 'NNκ' in the preceding section. For 'NCκ' we have to go beyond

[1]This construction dates from Cantor (1890).

U_1 and $_1U_1$ into U_2, of course, simply because κ itself lies there; but the definition of 'NNκ' reached into U_3. On the other hand the definition of 'NCκ' does make inroads on $_1U_1$ (through the definition of 'α sim β'), while that of 'NNκ' did not.

Once we are prepared to ascend to U_3, however, the type $_1U_1$ is altogether dispensable for every purpose, as Wiener has shown (1914). His reasoning is as follows. We have been thinking of relations of type $_1U_1$ as somehow classes of pairs of objects of type U, though without making any precise sense of the notion of pair. Now any arbitrary notion of a pair of objects x and y will serve our purposes perfectly so long as these conditions are met: (i) for any objects x and y of U there is such a pair; (ii) as soon as a pair is given, its first object x is thereby uniquely determined, and so is its second object y. (Thus the pair of x and y is different from the pair of y and x, unless $x = y$.) It happens that these conditions are met when the pair of x and y, written '$x;y$', is defined arbitrarily in the following way. First we explain $\{x\}$ as the class whose sole member is x, and $\{x, y\}$ as the class whose sole members are x and y, thus:

$$\text{`}\{x\}\text{'} \quad \text{for} \quad \text{`}\hat{z}(z = x)\text{',} \qquad\qquad \text{`}\{x, y\}\text{'} \quad \text{for} \quad \text{`}\hat{z}(z = x \textbf{ .v. } z = y)\text{'.}$$

Then we construe the so-called pair $x;y$ as

$$\{\{x\}, \ \{x, y\}\}$$

—hence as the class of classes which has as members just the class $\{x\}$ and the class $\{x, y\}$.[1] So a pair $x;y$ is of type U_2; accordingly relations, as classes of such pairs, become classes of type U_3. The once fundamental notation 'xRy' disappears now in favor of '$x;y \ \varepsilon \ \phi$'.

Relations of type $_2U_2$, relating no longer objects of type U but classes of type U_1, could be reduced in parallel fashion to classes of type U_4; and so on up. We can consequently dismiss the complications of relation types, and countenance only the series U, U_1, U_2, $\cdots$ of class types. This is seen to be an important simplification when we reflect that it does away not only with such relation types as $_1U_1$, $_2U_2$, etc., but also with a jungle of types of classes of relations, classes of classes of relations, classes of relations of classes, and so on. The whole logic of relations of any types reduces to the logic of classes, provided merely that the latter is carried into high enough types.

The theory of triadic relations can be reduced to the theory of classes by a fairly obvious extension of the above treatment of dyadic relations. Similarly for tetradic relations and higher.

---

[1] In detail this definition differs from Wiener's, and comes rather from Kuratowski.

§41. CLASS THEORY, MATHEMATICS, AND THE THEORY OF PROOF

We have been seeing how various familiar expressions, mainly having to do with number, can be translated into the notation of the theory of classes. Our concern in the theory of classes has thus been with questions of definition and not of proof. Let us now turn briefly to the latter topic. The general method of proof in the theory of classes is as in identity theory: deduction of theorems from axioms by the deductive methods of quantification theory. In identity theory the axioms gave laws for the special predicate '='. In the theory of classes, correspondingly, the starting point consists of axioms giving laws for the special predicate 'ε'.

The most notable set of such axioms consists of results of substituting for 'F' (and universally quantifying any free variables) in:

(A) $(\exists \alpha)(x)(x \; \varepsilon \; \alpha \; . \equiv Fx)$.

This is called the *principle of abstraction*. Its content, for cases without free variables, is simply that *every monadic predicate has a class as extension*.

For the sake of one sample proof in the theory of classes let us prove (I) of §35, viz., '$Fx \, . \, x = y \, . \supset Fy$', which was a schema for axioms of identity. We now construe '$x = y$' therein as '$(\alpha)(x \; \varepsilon \; \alpha \; . \equiv . \, y \; \varepsilon \; \alpha)$', in conformity with §38.

$\left.\begin{array}{l} \text{(1)} \quad Fx \\ \text{(2)} \quad (\alpha)(x \; \varepsilon \; \alpha \; . \equiv . \, y \; \varepsilon \; \alpha) \end{array}\right\}$

* (3) $(x)(x \; \varepsilon \; \alpha \; . \equiv Fx)$ (A) α
* (4) $x \; \varepsilon \; \alpha \; . \equiv Fx$ (3)
* (5) $y \; \varepsilon \; \alpha \; . \equiv Fy$ (3)
* (6) $x \; \varepsilon \; \alpha \; . \equiv . \, y \; \varepsilon \; \alpha$ (2)
* (7) Fy (1)(4)(5)(6)
  (8) $Fx \, . \, (\alpha)(x \; \varepsilon \; \alpha \; . \equiv . \, y \; \varepsilon \; \alpha) \, . \supset Fy$ *(7)

We had to define '$x = y$' and '$\alpha = \beta$', in §38, in opposite ways:

$(\alpha)(x \; \varepsilon \; \alpha \; . \equiv . \, y \; \varepsilon \; \alpha)$, $(z)(z \; \varepsilon \; \alpha \; . \equiv . \, z \; \varepsilon \; \beta)$, because '$x$' and '$y$' could not meaningfully follow 'ε', and 'α' and 'β' could not meaningfully precede 'ε'. But as soon as we ascend beyond the limits of §38 and into the type U_2 , *both* ways of construing '$\alpha = \beta$' come to be meaningful; and consequently this *axiom of extensionality* then comes to be needed to connect the two:

(E) $(z)(z \;\varepsilon\; \alpha \;.\equiv.\; z \;\varepsilon\; \beta) \;.\; \alpha \;\varepsilon\; \kappa \;.\supset.\; \beta \;\varepsilon\; \kappa.$[1]

This says that any classes α and β which are alike in members are identical in the sense of belonging in turn to the same classes.

Ascent into U_2 also calls for a repetition of (A) with 'x' and 'α' changed to 'α' and 'κ'; and each continuation of the theory of classes into higher types—U_3 , U_4 , etc.—calls for a further repetition of both (A) and (E) with upward revision of the types of variables.

How such ascents of type may be called for has already been seen in the course of constructing a few basic ideas of number theory. We were lured as far as U_3 . If we were to go on to fractions, and then to the theory of real numbers generally (rational and irrational), and to the theory of functions of real numbers, and to the theory of functions of complex numbers (real and imaginary), we should find need of variables of quantification of higher and higher types.

It is a remarkable fact that the concepts of all such branches of pure mathematics can be defined within the meager notation of the theory of classes, just as strictly as has thus far been done for the simple arithmetical concepts '0', '1', '$\kappa + \lambda$', '$\kappa \cdot \lambda$', '$\alpha \;sim\; \beta$', 'NCκ', and 'NNκ'.[2] But it is significant that the construction of these higher branches calls for the introduction of higher and higher types of variables of quantification. Even very elementary parts of arithmetic, we have seen, call for some quantification over abstract entities, and hence for

---

[1] The actual axiom is rather the universal closure of this, but the prenex universal quantifiers '$(\alpha)(\beta)(\kappa)$' are dropped for ease in reading. This way of stating axioms will be usual hereafter.

[2] The reduction of the theory of natural numbers to the theory of classes and relations is Frege's (1893). The reduction of ratios is due to Peano, and that of reals is due chiefly to Dedekind (1872). The execution of the whole reduction program in full detail came with Whitehead and Russell's monumental *Principia Mathematica* (1911–13), except for Wiener's step (1914) of reducing relation theory in turn to that of classes. For a readable survey of the reduction of real number theory and other branches of mathematics to logic, see Russell's *Introduction to Mathematical Philosophy*. A briefer sketch appears in Chapter 6 of my *Mathematical Logic*.

abandonment of the ontological agnosticism which remained tenable until §38. (Our theory of validity assumed classes and relations even prior to §38, but the logical statements and schemata themselves did not.) So it may be said that classical mathematics reduces to logic, but it may be said also, in a different and equally defensible sense of the word 'logic', that logic stopped and mathematics began with §38.

But be it logic or be it mathematics, the general theory of classes constitutes an impressive reduction and consolidation of the foundations of classical mathematics. Mathematical theorems come on translation to contain nothing but class-theory notation, and hence to be deducible from the basic laws of 'ε': the laws (A) and (E) and whatever further ones there may be. So the question of completeness of (A) and (E), or of completion of them, suddenly looms as a question of a general codification of mathematical truth. But there is a startling result due to Gödel (1931) to which, lest false hopes be aroused, we must now turn.

Let us consider to begin with the question of a general codification not of class theory, nor of mathematics generally, but of so-called *elementary number theory*. In elementary number theory the variables of quantification are all of one type, viz., the usual 'x', 'y', 'z', etc., but these are construed now as referring exclusively to the natural numbers. The notation of elementary number theory is just that of identity theory (§35) supplemented by the notations '$x + y$' and '$x \cdot y$' of sum and product. Typical truths expressible in this notation are:

$$(\exists x)(y)(x + y = y), \qquad (x)(y)(x \cdot y = y \cdot x),$$

$$(x)[(\exists y)(x + y = y) \supset (y)(x \cdot y = x)].$$

In effect the notation includes also all numerals, and the power notation 'x^y'; for these can be paraphrased away (Gödel, 1931).

It will be recalled that in §6 and again in §21 we found mechanical test of validity of certain categories of schemata. An ideal treatment of elementary number theory would consist, correspondingly, in a mechanical test of truth for all statements expressible in the notation described above. It happens, however, that this ideal is unattainable. Elementary number theory is in this respect like general quantification theory (cf. pp. 190f.): it lacks a decision procedure.

Given the impossibility of a decision procedure for quantification theory (Church), the corresponding result for elementary number theory can be established along the following lines. Paraphrasing 'v', '⊃', and '≡' in terms of conjunction and negation, and paraphrasing existential quantifiers in the fashion '−(x)−', and rendering the variables and schematic letters as:

$$x, \ x', \ x'', \ \cdots \ ; \ F, \ F', \ F'', \ \cdots \ ; \ p, \ p', \ p'', \ \cdots \ ,$$

we can couch all quantificational schemata in this eight-sign alphabet:

$$- \quad . \quad (\quad) \quad x \quad F \quad p \quad '$$

We can also treat any finite sequence of schemata as a single string of signs of this same alphabet, by just laying the schemata end to end and interposing some otherwise useless combination of signs, say '( )', to mark the end of each. Now let us assign the numbers 1, 2, $\cdots$, 8 to the eight signs of our alphabet. To each string of those signs let us assign, as its so-called *Gödel number*, the number which is designated by the corresponding string of digits; the Gödel number of the schema '(x) −Fx', e.g., is 354,165. Following Gödel (1931), one can then proceed (and here is the laborious part, which I shall skip) to construct an open sentence, '$\cdots x \cdot \cdot y \cdots$' say, purely in the notation of elementary number theory, which is true of any numbers x and y if any only if x is the Gödel number of a sequence of schemata which is a "proof," in the sense say of the lower part of p. 191, of the schema whose Gödel number is y. But then '$(\exists x)(\cdots x \cdot \cdot y \cdots)$' is true of exactly those numbers y which are the Gödel numbers of valid quantificational schemata (for, all and only the valid schemata have proofs). So, if we had a decision procedure for elementary number theory, we could (contrary to Church's theorem) decide the validity of any quantifitional schema by testing '$(\exists x)(\cdots x \cdot \cdot y \cdots)$' for truth, with 'y' supplanted by a numeral designating the Gödel number of the schema.

The impossibility of a decision procedure is less surprising in the case of elementary number theory than in the case of quantification theory. For, various unsolved problems of long standing, notably the celebrated one of Fermat, can be formulated within the notation of elementary number theory, and a decision procedure for that domain would have made a clean sweep of them all. Yet the lack of a decision procedure for elementary number theory, however unsurprising, can be quickly shown to have a startling consequence. Quantification theory, though lacking a decision procedure, has its complete proof procedure; but elementary number theory cannot even have that. For, suppose there were a procedure whereby each true sentence written in the notation of elementary number theory could be proved. Then there would also be this complete disproof procedure: to disprove a false sentence, prove its negation. But then, combining the proof procedure and the disproof procedure as at the top of p. 191, we would have a decision procedure.

Quantification theory was capable of lacking a decision procedure and still possessing a complete proof procedure. This is because a complete procedure for proving validity does not carry with it a complete procedure for disproving validity; and this is because nonvalid schemata do not always have valid negations. On the other hand a complete procedure for proving truth does carry with it a complete procedure for disproving truth (if negation is available), and hence also a decision procedure.

The discovery of the undecidability and incompletability of elementary number theory is due to Gödel (1931). Since it antedated Church's theorem, Gödel's proof did not take the line of p. 245. Anyway, that line is pretty roundabout if one counts in the proof of Church's theorem itself, which I have omitted. Gödel's way was to argue directly to the incompletability of elementary number theory, by showing how, for any given proof procedure $\mathfrak{P}$ for elementary number theory, a statement $S_\mathfrak{P}$ of elementary number theory can be constructed which will be true if and only if it is not provable by the procedure $\mathfrak{P}$. Either $S_\mathfrak{P}$ is provable, in which case it is false and so the general proof procedure $\mathfrak{P}$ is discredited, or else $S_\mathfrak{P}$ is true and not provable, in which case the proof procedure $\mathfrak{P}$ is incomplete.

In broadest outlines, Gödel's construction of $S_\mathfrak{P}$ is as follows. He assigns Gödel numbers to the sentences that can be written in the notation of elementary number theory, and then shows that, given $\mathfrak{P}$, it is possible within the notation of elementary number theory to formulate an open sentence, '$\cdots x \cdots$' say, which is true of any number x if and only if x is the Gödel number of a statement provable by $\mathfrak{P}$. If we put for 'x' in '$-(\cdots x \cdots)$' the actual numeral designating some particular number n, clearly the resulting statement, schematically '$-(\cdots n \cdots)$', will be true if and only if that chosen n is not the Gödel number of a statement provable by $\mathfrak{P}$. But Gödel shows that n can be so chosen as to turn out to be the Gödel number of '$-(\cdots n \cdots)$' itself. The statement '$-(\cdots n \cdots)$' produced by that sly choice of n is the sought $S_\mathfrak{P}$, true if and only if not provable by $\mathfrak{P}$.[1]   ʎ an equivalent of

---

[1]Fuller details of Gödel's argument may be found not only in his 1931 paper but also in his 1934 English presentation, and in Carnap's *Logical Syntax* (esp. pp. 129–134), and in Chapter 7 of my *Mathematical Logic*. For a less detailed survey of the argument, together with useful indications of related results, see Rosser's "Informal exposition". The spirit of Gödel's argument is cleverly conveyed in a non-technical vein by Findlay.

Gödel's discovery came as a shock to preconceptions. Common sense had been on the side of supposing that complete methods of proof for elementary number theory and indeed for mathematics generally not merely were possible in principle, but were even already at hand in at least a rough and ready form. Wherein does mathematical truth lie if not in the possibility of proof? Puzzling though the situation be, however, we must face the fact that Gödel's result is established beyond peradventure. We may well rephilosophize in the light of it, but we cannot philosophize it away.

From Gödel's result there follows the corresponding conclusion regarding the theory of classes. Since elementary number theory is translatable into the notation of the theory of classes (cf. §39), the incompletability of elementary number theory entails, *a fortiori*, the incompletability of the theory of classes. So the fact is that (A) and (E) and their analogues for higher types are inadequate to the theory of classes, and can never be adequately eked out by adding even an infinity of further axioms. The only qualifications to which this sweepingly defeatist conclusion is subject are of a kind from which no comfort is to be drawn: it is assumed that the added axioms, if not actually listed, will at least be specified in such a way as to be recognizable by a mechanical process; and it is assumed that they will not be such as to enable us to deduce falsehoods.

So whereas the concepts of the general logic of classes are adequate to classical mathematics, any effort toward a complete deductive theory of classes and therewith of classical mathematics is doomed to failure. It is doomed to failure as soon as it aspires to encompass even that well-behaved infinity of objects called natural numbers. One can do no better, from that point forward, than add special axioms now and again to strengthen the system for specific purposes.

Presburger and Skolem have shown that when elementary number theory is further limited to the extent of dropping multiplication and keeping just addition, or vice versa, the resulting theory does admit of a decision procedure. What is more surprising, Tarski has shown that the elementary algebra of real numbers likewise admits of a decision procedure. The notation of this elementary algebra is precisely the same as that described above for elementary number theory, including both addition and multiplication; the only difference is that the variables are construed now as referring to real numbers generally rather than to natural numbers. Despite the seemingly greater complexity of its subject matter, elementary algebra is completable and mechanically decidable while elementary number theory is not.

Now if in view of Gödel's result our knowledge about class and number is subject to unexpected limitations, the very opposite is true of our knowledge about such knowledge. One of the few things more surprising than the incompletability of elementary number theory is the fact that such incompletability can actually have become known to us. Gödel's result brings a new branch of mathematical theory to maturity, a branch known as "metamathematics" or proof theory, whose subject matter is mathematical theory itself.

Much remains to be discovered regarding the limits of completable theories, and the essential structural features which set such theories apart from those which are incompletable. But the reader who would acquire the key concepts and techniques of this crucial new field of study, metamathematics or the theory of proof, must look beyond the bounds of this logic book. See Tarski, *Undecidable Theories*; Hilbert and Bernays; Kleene.

EXERCISES

1. Can there be a complete disproof procedure for elementary number theory? Or a decision procedure adequate to all but a finite number of the statements in the notation of elementary number theory?

2. Using (A), devise formal proofs of the theorems:

$$(\exists\alpha)(x)(x \; \varepsilon \; \alpha), \qquad (\exists\alpha)(x) \; -(x \; \varepsilon \; \alpha).$$

§42. VARIANT THEORIES OF CLASSES

The practice of distinguishing the logical types U, U_1, U_2, etc. by the use of distinctive styles of variables is due to Russell (1908). An essential point of the procedure is that forms like '$x \; \varepsilon \; x$', '$x \; \varepsilon \; y$', '$\alpha \; \varepsilon \; \alpha$', '$\alpha \; \varepsilon \; x$', etc., are rejected as meaningless; 'ε' is declared grammatically admissible between variables only of consecutive ascending types.

The obvious alternative to this procedure would be to pool the types and use the single style of variables 'x', 'y', etc., to represent entities of all sorts. Five considerations count in favor of this alternative.

(1) The notation is simpler.

(2) The application of quantification theory to class theory comes to be more direct: 'ε' comes to represent simply a particular interpretation of a two-place predicate letter of quantification theory. Supplementary adjustments of styles of variables cease to be called for.

(3) Principles such as (A) and (E) no longer need to be repeated for each type.

(4) A curious reduplication of constants is obviated. E.g., as long as we keep the logical types apart the number 12 to which the class α of Apostles belongs is not identifiable with the number 12 to which some class κ of a dozen classes belongs; for the one number 12 is of type U_2 while the other is of type U_3 . Each succeeding type, correspondingly, demands a fresh number 12 of its own. When on the other hand we pool the types, this multiple mirroring ceases; all dozens, whatever their texture, come to be members of a single number 12.

(5) The distinct existence of the full quota of natural numbers ceases to depend upon there being infinitely many individuals, or non-classes (cf. end of §39). Once types are pooled, infinitely many entities are bound to be available for simultaneous membership in classes; for we then have at our disposal not only some few individuals but also classes of them, classes of such classes, and so on, all on an equal footing.

Despite these five considerations, however, Russell had a good reason for his type restrictions. As soon as we waive his type distinctions, and read (A) simply as:

(A′) $$(\exists y)(x)(x \ \varepsilon \ y \ .\equiv \ Fx),$$

we find ourselves in trouble. For, introducing '$-(\text{①} \ \varepsilon \ \text{①})$' at the occurrence of '$F$', we can deduce a palpable falsehood as follows:

(1)	$(\exists y)(x)[x \ \varepsilon \ y \ .\equiv \ -(x \ \varepsilon \ x)]$		
(2)	$(x)[x \ \varepsilon \ y \ .\equiv \ -(x \ \varepsilon \ x)]$	(1)	y
(3)	$y \ \varepsilon \ y \ .\equiv \ -(y \ \varepsilon \ y)$	(2)	
(4)	$(\exists y)[y \ \varepsilon \ y \ .\equiv \ -(y \ \varepsilon \ y)]$	(3)	

This difficulty is called *Russell's paradox*, for its discoverer (1901).

In addition to (1) there are an infinite variety of other cases of (A′) which lead to contradiction just as surely, if less quickly. But it happens that all such cases, like (1), cease to be expressible once variables are distinguished as to type and 'ε' is held to positions between variables of consecutive ascending types.

However, there are also other ways of avoiding the contradictions. In the same year (1908) in which Russell's theory of types appeared, a different expedient was suggested by Zermelo. Further alternatives, departing from Zermelo's and Russell's in varying degrees, have appeared down the years. In the Zermelo tradition (A′) is restricted not by complicating the notation of class theory so as to render such cases as (1) inexpressible, but more directly: by treating (A′) as holding for some open sentences in the 'Fx' position and failing for others. According to this theory some predicates have classes as extensions while others, notably the '$-(\text{①} \; \varepsilon \; \text{①})$' of (1), do not. The task of a foundation of class theory in the Zermelo line then comes to be the setting up of conditions under which a predicate is to be viewed as having an extension; in other words, the setting up of conditions on 'Fx' under which (A′) is to be regarded as holding. Different sets of conditions to this end yield the different class theories in the Zermelo line. In Zermelo's own theory, (A′) is assumed for the case where the sentence put for 'Fx' has the form of a conjunction '$x \; \varepsilon \; z \;.\; Gx$'; in other words, Zermelo adopts not (A′) itself but:

$$(\exists y)(x)(x \; \varepsilon \; y \;.\equiv.\; x \; \varepsilon \; z \;.\; Gx).^1$$

Given any class z, this law furnishes other classes y all of which are subclasses of z; but of itself it furnishes no nonempty classes z to begin with. So Zermelo then goes on to assume various additional and still more special cases of (A′) individually:

$$(\exists y)(x)(x \; \varepsilon \; y \;.\equiv:\; x = z \;.\lor.\; x = w),$$
$$(\exists y)(x)[x \; \varepsilon \; y \;.\equiv\; (\exists z)(x \; \varepsilon \; z \;.\; z \; \varepsilon \; w)],$$
$$(\exists y)(x)[x \; \varepsilon \; y \;.\equiv\; (z)(z \; \varepsilon \; x \;.\supset.\; z \; \varepsilon \; w)].$$

This combination of principles can be shown to guarantee the existence of any class whose existence would be guaranteed under the theory of types by assuming (A) for each type.[2]

In class theories not involving types, the extensionality law (E) becomes:

(E′) $(z)(z \; \varepsilon \; x \;.\equiv.\; z \; \varepsilon \; y) \;.\; x \; \varepsilon \; w \;.\supset.\; y \; \varepsilon \; w.$

This gives rise to a certain perplexity where x and y are not classes; for in this case '$z \; \varepsilon \; x$' and '$z \; \varepsilon \; y$' are felt to be trivially false for everything z, so that '$(z)(z \; \varepsilon \; x \;.\equiv.\; z \; \varepsilon \; y)$' comes true regardless of identity or diversity of x and y. An exception to (E′) thus seems called for where x and y are not classes. This gives rise to a further problem of distinguishing between nonclasses and the empty class, which share the peculiarity of memberlessness.

<hr>

[1] See first footnote of preceding section. This is what Zermelo called the *Aussonderungs-axiom*. But I have stated it in an adapted form due to Skolem (1930).

[2] For a detailed development of Zermelo's system, with modifications, see Fraenkel (1919 et seq.). For other variants see my "Set-theoretic foundations for logic" (1936) and Ackermann's "Mengentheoretische Begründung der Logik" (1937). More radical departures are noted below.

However, all these difficulties are conveniently resolved by treating so-called non-classes not as memberless, but as having themselves as sole members.[1] (E′) can then be held to in its full generality. Moreover the notation '$x = y$' comes to be definable as an abbreviation for '$(z)(z \varepsilon x .\equiv. z \varepsilon y)$' without restriction to cases. (This definition has to be preferred to '$(z)(x \varepsilon z .\equiv. y \varepsilon z)$' when we come to systems in the von Neumann branch of the Zermelo line, touched on below.)

The Zermelo tradition and the Russell tradition become fused in the class theory of my "New foundations" (1937). Here, in keeping with the Zermelo tradition, (A′) is preserved subject to special restriction of 'Fx'; but the condition on 'Fx' is itself derived now from the theory of types, in the following way. A sentence S is called *stratified* if its variables, though all of the single style 'x', 'y', 'z', $\cdots$, are so disposed that there is a way of assigning types to them which will cause 'ε' to appear only between variables of consecutively ascending types. Thus the theory of types is not actually adopted, but sentences are merely classified as stratified or otherwise according as their forms are such as could or could not be adapted to the theory of types. Unstratified sentences, e.g. '$x \varepsilon x$' and '$-(x \varepsilon x)$', are admitted as meaningful on a par with stratified ones. But (A′), in particular, is assumed true only for cases where the statement put for 'Fx' is stratified.

Every one of the advantages (1)–(5) noted at the beginning of this section is enjoyed by the theory just described, or, indeed, any other theory in the Zermelo line. It should be stressed, however, that the theory of types has virtues of its own. This fact is evident in the naturalness with which we found ourselves led up through U_1 , U_2 , etc., in the course of the past few sections.

In a class theory of the Zermelo line due essentially to von Neumann (1927),[2] certain things called *elements* are viewed as capable of belonging to classes, while other things are not. We can express elementhood of x by '$(\exists z)(x \varepsilon z)$'. Now (A′) gives way to:

(A″) $(\exists y)(x)[x \varepsilon y .\equiv. (\exists z)(x \varepsilon z) . Fx]$.

The definition of class abstraction (§38) needs correspondingly to be modified:

'$\hat{x}Fx$'   for   '$(\imath y)(x)[x \varepsilon y .\equiv. (\exists z)(x \varepsilon z) . Fx]$'.

Thus $\hat{x}Fx$ is now construed as the class of all *elements* x such that Fx.

When the general theory of classes is developed along these lines, the

---

[1]See my *Mathematical Logic*, pp. 122–123, 135–137. This expedient was not used by Zermelo.

[2]Von Neumann's system has been reformulated and extensively developed by Bernays, "A system of axiomatic set-theory." But the ensuing sketch departs in certain theoretical respects from both von Neumann and Bernays.

great burden of further axioms comes in specifying what sorts of classes are to count as elements—i.e., as capable of membership in further classes. It can be proved from (A''), by an argument related to Russell's paradox itself, that $\hat{x} - (x \; \varepsilon \; x)$ is not an element; and various other proofs of non-elementhood are likewise forthcoming. But elementhood can be proved of nothing, pending special assumptions for the purpose. Varied assurances of elementhood will be needed, however, if familiar laws of arithmetic and higher branches of mathematics are to be derivable from the theory of classes. So we must add some axioms of elementhood.

Knowing as we do from Gödel's result that a complete system is not to be hoped for, we may reasonably incline to either of two attitudes in the adding of axioms: we may favor either strength or weakness. There is much to be said for a conveniently powerful set of axioms, incomplete though it be.[1] But it is also illuminating to minimize the assumptions from which a given familiar body of theorems of classical mathematics can be derived. Weakness as an objective is principally attractive on account of the lingering risk, in strong systems, of undetected contradiction.

In this spirit of minimization, the most interesting offering is perhaps Wang's "A new theory of element and number" (1948). His single meager axiom of elementhood is the following, which assures him of no elements with more than two members:

$$(\exists z)(\{x, y\} \; \varepsilon \; z). \qquad \text{(See §40 for notation.)}$$

His prior assumptions are just (A'') and (E'). On this basis, by dint of redefining natural numbers along lines other than those which were followed in §39 but equally justifiable, he is able to construct the theory of natural numbers and derive all the usual theorems. More, he is able to develop the theory of real numbers, rational and irrational, and derive the classical body of theorems for that domain. For the theory of functions of real numbers, however, or the Cantorian theory of infinite cardinal numbers, axioms need to be added. Such times as further blocks of theorems in further reaches of mathematics come thus to be wanted, the axioms may be supplemented to the necessary minimum for the purpose; and each such supplementation is a record of the added risk of contradiction.

---

[1]Such was the spirit of the too sweeping assumption of elementhood which I adopted in *Mathematical Logic*. This assumption was shown by Rosser to lead to contradiction; see *Mathematical Logic*, second printing, p. 154, where a makeshift repair is made. Wang has lately devised a more skillful repair, which restores much of the freedom of operation of the original system; see his "A formal system of logic" (1950), and the third printing of *Mathematical Logic*.

Bibliography

This list includes only such logical and nearly logical works as happen to have been alluded to, by title or otherwise, in the course of the book. For a comprehensive register of the literature of mathematical logic to the end of 1935 see Church's *Bibliography*. This work, which is helpfully annotated and thoroughly indexed by subjects, is invaluable to logicians. Subsequent literature is covered by the Reviews section of the *Journal of Symbolic Logic*, which is indexed by subjects every five years and by authors every two.

ACKERMANN, Wilhelm. "Mengentheoretische Begründung der Logik." *Mathematische Annalen*, vol. 115 (1937), pp. 1–22.

———. *Grundzüge*. See Hilbert.

BEHMANN, Heinrich. "Beiträge zur Algebra der Logik, insbesondere zum Entscheidungsproblem." *Mathematische Annalen*, vol. 86 (1922), pp. 163–229.

BERNAYS, Paul. "A system of axiomatic set-theory." *Journal of Symbolic Logic*, vol. 2 (1937), pp. 65–77; vol. 6 (1941), pp. 1–17; vol. 7 (1942), pp. 65–89, 133–145; vol. 8 (1943), pp. 89–106; vol. 13 (1948), pp. 65–79.

———. *Grundlagen*. See Hilbert.

BOOLE, George. *The Mathematical Analysis of Logic*. London and Cambridge, England, 1847. Reprinted in *Collected Logical Works*, Chicago and London, 1916.

———. *An Investigation of the Laws of Thought*. London, 1854. Reprinted ibid.

CANTOR, Georg. "Ueber eine elementare Frage der Mannigfaltigkeitslehre." *Jahresberichte* der deutschen Mathematiker-Vereinigungen, vol. 1 (1890–1), pp. 75–78. Reprinted in *Gesammelte Abhandlungen*, Berlin, 1932.

CARNAP, Rudolf. *The Logical Syntax of Language*. London and New York, 1937.

———. *Meaning and Necessity*. Chicago, 1947.

———. "Empiricism, semantics, and ontology." *Revue Internationale de Philosophie*, vol. 4 (1950), pp. 20–40.

CARROLL, Lewis. *Symbolic Logic*. London, 1897.

CAYLEY, Arthur. "On the theory of groups as depending on the symbolical equation $\theta^n = 1$." *Philosophical Magazine*, vol. 7 (1854), pp. 40–47, 408–409. Reprinted in *Collected Mathematical Papers*, Cambridge, England, 1895.

CHURCH, Alonzo. *A Bibliography of Symbolic Logic*. Providence, 1938. Reprinted from *Journal of Symbolic Logic* (1936, 1938).

———. *Introduction to Mathematical Logic*. Part I. Princeton, 1944.

———. "A note on the Entscheidungsproblem." *Journal of Symbolic Logic*, vol. 1 (1936), pp. 40–41, 101–102.

COOLEY, J. C. *A Primer of Formal Logic*. New York, 1942.

DEDEKIND, Richard. *Stetigkeit und irrationale Zahlen*. Braunschweig, 1872. Later editions 1892, 1905, 1912.

———. *Was sind und was sollen die Zahlen?* Braunschweig, 1887.

DEMORGAN, Augustus. *Formal Logic*. London, 1847.

———. "On the syllogism." *Transactions* of the Cambridge Philosophical Society, vol. 8 (1849), pp. 379–408; vol. 9 (1856), pp. 79–127; vol. 10 (1864), pp. 173–230, 331–358, 428–487.

FEIGL, H., and W. SELLARS, editors. *Readings in Philosophical Analysis*. New York, 1949.

FINDLAY, J. "Goedelian sentences: a non-numerical approach." *Mind*, vol. 51 (1942), pp. 259–265.

FRAENKEL, Adolf. *Einleitung in die Mengenlehre*. Berlin, 1919. Later editions 1923, 1928.

FREGE, Gottlob. *Begriffsschrift*. Halle, 1879.

———. *Die Grundlagen der Arithmetik*. Breslau, 1884. Reprinted 1934.

———. *Grundgesetze der Arithmetik*. Vol. 1, 1893; vol. 2, 1903. Jena.

———. "Ueber Sinn und Bedeutung." *Zeitschrift für Philosophie und philosophische Kritik*, vol. 100 (1892), pp. 25–50. Translated in Feigl and Sellars.

GENTZEN, Gerhard. "Untersuchungen über das logische Schliessen." *Mathematische Zeitschrift*, vol. 39 (1934–5), pp. 176–210, 405–431.

GERGONNE, J. D. "Essai de dialectique rationelle." *Annales de mathématiques pures et appliquées*, vol. 7 (1816–17), pp. 189–228.

GÖDEL, Kurt. *On Undecidable Propositions of Formal Mathematical Systems.* Mimeographed. Princeton, 1934.

———. "Die Vollständigkeit der Axiome des logischen Funktionenkalküls." *Monatshefte für Mathematik und Physik,* vol. 37 (1930), pp. 349–360.

———. "Ueber formal unentscheidbare Sätze der Principia Mathematica und verwandter Systeme." *Ibid.,* vol. 38 (1931), pp. 173–198.

GOODMAN, Nelson. "The problem of counterfactual conditionals." *Journal of Philosophy,* vol. 44 (1947), pp. 113–128.

———. "On likeness of meaning." *Analysis,* vol. 10 (1949–50), pp. 1–7.

HERBRAND, Jacques. *Recherches sur la théorie de la démonstration.* Warsaw, 1930.

HILBERT, David, and W. ACKERMANN. *Grundzüge der theoretischen Logik.* Berlin, 1928. 2d edition, 1938.

——— and P. BERNAYS. *Grundlagen der Mathematik.* Vol. 1, 1934; vol. 2, 1939. Berlin. 2d printing, Ann Arbor, 1944.

JAŚKOWSKI, Stanisław. "On the rules of suppositions in formal logic." *Studia Logica,* no. 1 (Warsaw, 1934).

KLEENE, S. C. "Recursive predicates and quantifiers." *Transactions of the American Mathematical Society,* vol. 53 (1943), pp. 41–73.

KURATOWSKI, Casimir. "Sur la notion de l'ordre dans la théorie des ensembles." *Fundamenta Mathematicae,* vol. 2 (1921), pp. 161–171.

LEWIS, C. I. *A Survey of Symbolic Logic.* Berkeley, 1918.

LÖWENHEIM, Leopold. "Ueber Möglichkeiten im Relativkalkül." *Mathematische Annalen,* vol. 76 (1915), pp. 447–470.

ŁUKASIEWICZ, Jan. "O logice trójwartościowej." *Ruch Filozoficzny,* vol. 5 (1920), pp. 169–171.

———. "Zur Geschichte der Aussagenlogik." *Erkenntnis,* vol. 5 (1935–6), pp. 111–131.

NEUMANN, J. von. "Eine Axiomatisierung der Mengenlehre." *Journal für reine und angewandte Mathematik,* vol. 154 (1925), pp. 219–240. Correction in vol. 155, p. 128.

PARRY, W. T. "Zum Lewisschen Aussagenkalkül." *Ergebnisse eines mathematischen Kolloquiums,* No. 4 (1933), pp. 15–16.

PEANO, Giuseppe. *Arithmetices Principia.* Turin, 1889.

――――. *Formulaire de Mathématiques.* Introduction, 1894; vol. 1, 1895; vol. 2, 1897–9. Turin. Vol. 3, 1901, Paris. Vol. 4, 1902–3; vol. 5 (s.v. *Formulario Mathematico*), 1905–8. Turin.

PEIRCE, C. S. *Collected Papers.* 6 vols. Cambridge, Mass., 1931–5.

POST, E. L. "Introduction to a general theory of elementary propositions." *American Journal of Mathematics,* vol. 43 (1921), pp. 163–185.

PRESBURGER, M. "Ueber die Vollständigkeit eines gewissen Systems der Arithmetik." *Sprawozdanie z I Kongresu Matematyków Krajów Słowańskych* (Warsaw, 1930), pp. 92–101, 395.

QUINE, W. V. *Mathematical Logic.* New York, 1940. 2d printing, Cambridge, Mass., 1947. Revised 3d printing pending.

――――. *Elementary Logic.* Boston, 1941.

――――. *O Sentido da Nova Lógica.* São Paulo, 1944.

――――. "New foundations for mathematical logic." *American Mathematical Monthly,* vol. 44 (1937), pp. 70–80.

――――. "Set-theoretic foundations for logic." *Journal of Symbolic Logic,* vol. 1 (1936), pp. 45–57.

――――. "On the logic of quantification." *Ibid.,* vol. 10 (1945), pp. 1–12.

――――. "On what there is." *Review of Metaphysics,* vol. 2 (1948), pp. 21–38.

REICHENBACH, Hans. *Elements of Symbolic Logic.* New York, 1947.

ROSSER, Barkley. "An informal exposition of proofs of Gödel's theorems and Church's theorem." *Journal of Symbolic Logic,* vol. 4 (1939), pp. 53–60.

――――. "The Burali-Forti paradox." *Ibid.,* vol. 7 (1942), pp. 1–17.

RUSSELL, Bertrand. *The Principles of Mathematics.* Cambridge, England, 1903. 2d edition, New York, 1938.

――――. *Introduction to Mathematical Philosophy.* London, 1919.

――――. "On denoting." *Mind,* vol. 14 (1905), pp. 479–493. Reprinted in Feigl and Sellars.

――――. "Mathematical logic as based on the theory of types." *American Journal of Mathematics,* vol. 30 (1908), pp. 222–262.

――――. "Knowledge by acquaintance and knowledge by description." *Proceedings* of the Aristotelian Society, vol. 11 (1911), pp. 108–128. Reprinted in *The Problems of Philosophy,* London and

New York, 1912 and in *Mysticism and Logic*, New York, 1918.

———. *Principia*. See Whitehead.

SCHRÖDER, Ernst. *Der Operationskreis des Logikkalküls*. Leipzig, 1877 (37 pp.).

———. *Vorlesungen über die Algebra der Logik*. Vol. 1, 1890; vol. 2, 1891–1905; vol. 3, 1895. Leipzig.

SHEFFER, H. M. "A set of five independent postulates for Boolean algebras." *Transactions* of the American Mathematical Society, vol. 14 (1913), pp. 481–488.

SKOLEM, Thoralf. "Einige Bemerkungen zu der Abhandlung von E. Zermelo: 'Ueber die Definitheit in der Axiomatik.' " *Fundamenta Mathematicae*, vol. 15 (1930), pp. 337–341.

———. "Ueber einige Satzfunktionen in der Arithmetik." *Skrifter* utgitt av Det Norske Videnskaps-Akademi i Oslo, I. Mat.-naturv. Kl. 1930, no. 7 (1931).

TARSKI, Alfred. *Introduction to Logic*. New York, 1941.

———. *A Decision Method for Elementary Algebra and Geometry*. Santa Monica, 1948.

———. "Remarques sur les notions fondamentales de la méthodologie des mathématiques." *Rocznik* Polskiego Towarzystwa Matematycznego, vol. 7 (1929), pp. 270–272.

VENN, John. *Symbolic Logic*. London, 1881. 2d edition, 1894.

———. "On the diagrammatic and mechanical representations of propositions and reasoning." *The London, Edinburgh, and Dublin Philosophical Magazine and Journal of Science*, vol. 10 (1880), pp. 1–18.

WANG, Hao. "A new theory of element and number." *Journal of Symbolic Logic*, vol. 13 (1948), pp. 129–137.

———. "A formal system of logic." *Ibid.*, vol. 15 (1950), pp. 25–32.

WHITEHEAD, A. N., and B. RUSSELL. *Principia Mathematica*. Vol. 1, 1910; vol. 2, 1912; vol. 3, 1913. Cambridge, England. 2d edition 1925–7.

WIENER, Norbert. "A simplification of the logic of relations." *Proceedings* of the Cambridge Philosophical Society, vol. 17 (1912–14), pp. 387–390.

WITTGENSTEIN, Ludwig. *Tractatus Logico-Philosophicus*. New York and London, 1922. Reprint of "Logisch-philosophische Abhandlung" (*Annalen der Naturphilosophie*, 1921) with English translation in parallel.

WRIGHT, G. H. von. *Form and Content in Logic*. Cambridge, England, 1949 (35 pp.).

ZERMELO, Ernst. "Untersuchungen über die Grundlagen der Mengenlehre." *Mathematische Annalen*, vol. 65 (1908), pp. 261–281.

Index

See Universal . generalization
Existential . instantiation

Appendix

Completeness of Quantification Theory. Löwenheim's Theorem

What is to be shown is that

(I) Each valid quantificational schema is obtainable as the unstarred last line of a finished deduction.

From this it obviously follows also that, if schemata S_1, ..., S_n together imply a schema S, then S is deducible from S_1, ..., S_n in a finished deduction. (For, if we can get as an unstarred line the valid conditional formed of S_1, ..., S_n as antecedent and S as consequent, we can then subjoin S to it and S_1, ..., S_n by TF. Not that this is the likely order of events.)

But it will suffice, for (I), to prove:

(II) Each valid closed quantification schema is obtainable as the unstarred last line of a deduction.

The 'closed' is no real restriction. For, if an open schema is valid, so is its universal closure (p. 139); and if we can get this closed schema as last line of a deduction, we can get the open one too, just by adding some steps of UI. (If these added steps happen to free any old flagged variables, thus making for an unfinished deduction, we can easily mend matters by rewriting the deduction of the closed schema with a happier choice of letters for the flagged variables.)

Note that in (II) itself we did not have to say 'finished'. A deduction with unstarred closed last line is of necessity finished; cf. definitions.

But it will suffice, for (II), to prove:

(III) From any inconsistent closed premiss a truth-functionally inconsistent combination of schemata can be deduced.

For, we know from p. 174 how to frame a deduction of a valid schema once we have deduced truth-functionally inconsistent consequences from its negation.

But it will suffice, for (III), to prove:

(IV) From any inconsistent closed prenex premiss a truth-functionally inconsistent combination of schemata can be deduced.

We know how, given any schema, to find a prenex equivalent (cf. p. 227); and, furthermore, there is no difficulty, starting with the former schema, in actually deducing the prenex one under our deductive rules. Pp. 168–172 and 180f may make this plausible enough.

Actually we shall find that something stronger than (IV) can be proved, viz.:

(V) From any inconsistent closed prenex premiss a truth-functionally inconsistent combination of schemata can be deduced using only EI and UI.

We shall thus be assured of the completeness not only of our regular method of deduction, but also of a more economical one, which runs as follows: to show a schema valid, just take its universal closure, negate it, get the prenex equivalent, and go to work on this last with EI and UI until you accumulate a truth-functional inconsistency. This method is certainly worth knowing on its own account, so simple is it to state and justify. Apart from inessentials of its outward form, it is due to Herbrand. §§27ff could have been made much briefer by adopting it originally in place of the elaborate apparatus there introduced. However, that elaborate apparatus has real practical advantages, as the reader will appreciate if he tries some comparative exercises. It is well to know both.

(V) may be rephrased thus: If S is a closed prenex schema, then either we can deduce a truth-functionally inconsistent combination of consequences from S by continued use of EI and UI, or else S is consistent. 'Consistent' here means true under some interpretation in some non-empty universe. Actually, though, something yet stronger will be proved, viz.:

(VI) If S is a closed prenex schema, then either (a) we can deduce a truth-functionally inconsistent combination of schemata from S by continued use of EI and UI, or else (b) some interpretation in a non-empty universe of positive integers makes S true.

As an aid to proving (VI), I shall first prove this **law of infinite conjunction**: If C is a class (finite or infinite) of truth-functional schemata, there is some assignment of truth values to the sentence letters that makes all members of C true unless some (finite) conjunction of members of C is inconsistent.

Let us refer to the sentence letters in some fixed order as P_1, P_2, ... For any given number i, let us speak of a given assignment of truth values to P_1, P_2, ..., P_i as *condemning* a given conjunction of members of C if it makes that conjunction come out false for all values of P_{i+1}, P_{i+2}, ... Then let t_i, for each number i, be one or other of the truth values, $\top$ or $\bot$, according to this rule:

(i) t_i is $\top$ if assignment of t_1, ..., t_{i-1}, and $\top$ respectively to P_1, ..., P_i condemns no conjunction of members of C; otherwise it is $\bot$.

Thus t_1, by (i), is $\top$ if assignment of $\top$ to P_1 condemns no conjunction of members of C; otherwise $\bot$. The rule (i) then fixes t_2 in turn, and t_3, and so on. Now what will be shown, as proof of the law of infinite conjunction, is that if assignment of t_1, t_2, ... to P_1, P_2, ... falsifies a member S of C, then some conjunction of members of C is inconsistent. For, let j be a number great enough so that none of P_{j+1}, P_{j+2}, ... is in S. Then assignment of t_1, ..., t_j respectively to P_1, ..., P_j is sufficient to falsify S. Then there is a least number h ($\leq j$) such that

(ii) Assignment of t_1, ..., t_h to P_1, ..., P_h condemns a conjunction (say K) of members of C.

By (i) and (ii),

(iii) $t_h = \bot$.

By (ii) and (iii),

(iv) Assignment of t_1, ..., t_{h-1}, $\bot$ to P_1, ..., P_h condemns K.

By (i) and (iii),

(v) Assignment of t_1, ..., t_{h-1}, $\top$ to P_1, ..., P_h condemns some conjunction K' of members of C.

If $h > 1$, then, by (iv) and (v), assignment of t_1, ..., t_{h-1} to P_1, ..., P_{h-1} condemns the conjunction of K and K', contrary to the leastness of h. So

(vi) $h = 1$.

By (iv), (v), and (vi), assignment of $\bot$ to P_1 condemns K and assignment of $\top$ to P_1 condemns K'. Then the conjunction of K and K' is inconsistent, q.e.d.

Our task now is to prove (VI). Suppose, then, a closed prenex schema S. So as to have an ordered and limitless stock of instantial variables for EI and UI, let us take 'z_1', 'z_2', 'z_3', ..., declaring these alphabetically later than all in S. Now let us subjoin lines to lines by EI and UI, beginning with S and proceeding according to the following rigid plan. When the latest line at hand begins with an existential quantifier, immediately subjoin a line to it by EI, using as instantial variable the earliest of 'z_1', 'z_2', ... not yet used. When the latest line at hand does not begin with an existential quantifier, enter as the next line something that can be got from some past universally quantified line by UI, using some one of 'z_1', 'z_2', ... as the instantial variable. For this step the chosen one of 'z_1', 'z_2', ... is to be no later than the one last flagged; and the new line resulting by UI is to be no mere duplicate of a line already at hand. The variable chosen from among 'z_1', 'z_2', ... is, moreover, to be as early a one as it can be compatibly with the foregoing requirements; and, given the variable, the universally quantified line used is to be as early a one as it can be.

Here is an example. '$\Phi vwxy$' in it is to be conceived as any quantificational schema, say '$Fv . Gwx .\mathbf{v}. Fy . Gvw$', containing the four variables and no quantifiers.

$*(1)\ (\exists v)(\exists w)(x)(y)\Phi vwxy$
$*(2)\ (\exists w)(x)(y)\Phi z_1 wxy$ $(1)\ z_1$
$*(3)\ (x)(y)\Phi z_1 z_2 xy$ $(2)\ z_2$
$*(4)\ (y)\Phi z_1 z_2 z_1 y$ (3)
$*(5)\ \Phi z_1 z_2 z_1 z_1$ (4)
$*(6)\ (y)\Phi z_1 z_2 z_2 y$ (3)
$*(7)\ \Phi z_1 z_2 z_2 z_1$ (6)
$*(8)\ \Phi z_1 z_2 z_1 z_2$ (4)
$*(9)\ \Phi z_1 z_2 z_2 z_2$ (6)

Here the process ends. But the next example goes on forever.

$*(1)\ (v)(w)(\exists x)(y)\Phi vwxy$
$*(2)\ (w)(\exists x)(y)\Phi z_1 wxy$ (1)

$*(3)\ (\exists x)(y)\Phi\zeta_1\zeta_1 xy$ (2)

$*(4)\ (y)\Phi\zeta_1\zeta_1\zeta_2 y$ (3) ζ_2

$*(5)\ \Phi\zeta_1\zeta_1\zeta_2\zeta_1$ (4)

$*(6)\ (w)(\exists x)(y)\Phi\zeta_2 wxy$ (1)

$*(7)\ (\exists x)(y)\Phi\zeta_2\zeta_1 xy$ (6)

$*(8)\ (y)\Phi\zeta_2\zeta_1\zeta_3 y$ (7) ζ_3

$*(9)\ \Phi\zeta_2\zeta_1\zeta_3\zeta_1$ (8)

$*(10)\ (\exists x)(y)\Phi\zeta_1\zeta_2 xy$ (2)

$*(11)\ (y)\Phi\zeta_1\zeta_2\zeta_4 y$ (10) ζ_4

$*(12)\ \Phi\zeta_1\zeta_2\zeta_4\zeta_1$ (11)

$*(13)\ \Phi\zeta_1\zeta_1\zeta_2\zeta_2$ (4)

and so on.

Let all the lines that proceed from S by the described process be called *sequents* of S. If there is any conjunction of them that is truth-functionally inconsistent, then (a) of (VI) is fulfilled. To complete the proof of (VI), therefore, it will be sufficient to assume that no conjunction of sequents of S is inconsistent, and then produce an interpretation as promised in (b) of (VI).

Let $A_1, A_2, \ldots$ be, in an arbitrary order, all the expressions obtainable by applying predicate letters of S to 'ζ_1', 'ζ_2', etc. Thus, if the predicate letters of S are just a monadic 'F' and a dyadic 'G', then $A_1, A_2, \ldots$ might be '$F\zeta_1$', '$G\zeta_1\zeta_1$', '$F\zeta_2$', '$G\zeta_1\zeta_2$', '$G\zeta_2\zeta_1$', '$G\zeta_2\zeta_2$', '$F\zeta_3$', and so on. Clearly all the unquantified sequents of S are truth functions of various of $A_1, A_2, \ldots$. Moreover, under our assumption, no conjunction of sequents is truth-functionally inconsistent. By the law of infinite conjunction, then (with $A_1, A_2 \ldots$ in place of P_1, $P_2, \ldots$), there is an assignment of truth values $t_1, t_2, \ldots$ to $A_1, A_2, \ldots$ that makes all unquantified sequents of S true. Now let us interpret the free variables 'ζ_1', 'ζ_2', $\ldots$ as naming the respective integers 1, 2, $\ldots$. Since $A_1, A_2, \ldots$ show the predicate letters applied to 'ζ_1', 'ζ_2', $\ldots$ in all combinations, any full assignment of truth values to A_1, $A_2, \ldots$ now amounts simply to an interpretation of those predicate letters in the universe of positive integers. In particular, therefore, the assigning of $t_1, t_2, \ldots$ to $A_1, A_2, \ldots$ determines an interpretation $\mathfrak{I}$ of the predicate letters of S, in the universe of positive integers, that verifies all unquantified sequents of S.

Case 1: All of 'z_1', 'z_2', ... without end turn up in sequents of S. It is evident from our general method of generating sequents that, given any sequent Q (of S) whose first quantifier is universal, an instantiation of Q with respect to each of 'z_1', 'z_2', ... will eventually occur. So, given the universe of positive integers and the stated interpretation of 'z_1', 'z_2', ..., it follows that Q will count as true if all sequents with fewer quantifiers than Q count as true. But also any sequent Q' whose first quantifier is existential will be true if all sequents with fewer quantifiers are true, for these latter will include an instance of Q'. So, to sum up, *any* sequent with quantifiers will count as true if all sequents with fewer quantifiers do. But $\mathfrak{I}$ makes all unquantified sequents true. Hence it also makes all singly quantified sequents true; hence also all doubly quantified sequents; and so on. Hence finally, S itself; q.e.d.

Case 2: 'z_1', 'z_2', ... up to only some finite number n turn up in sequents of S. Then take the universe as comprising only the integers up to n, and argue as before.

This ends the proof of (VI) and, therewith, of the completeness of our deductive method in quantification theory.

It was Gödel who, in 1930, first proved the completeness of a deductive method in quantification theory. The deductive method which he proved complete was very different from ours and more like the one on p. 191. But this difference is of little moment, since a completeness proof for one method of quantification theory can be adapted fairly easily to others. In the above adaptation, actually, I have depended partly on Gödel's original argument and partly on a variant due to Dreben.

(VI) has as corollary a celebrated theorem which, antedating Gödel, goes back to Löwenheim: *Any consistent quantificational schema comes out true under some interpretation in the universe of positive integers.* For, consider any consistent quantificational schema S. Let S' be its prenex equivalent, closed by existential quantification of any free variables. Then S', like S, is consistent. Then certainly, in view of the soundness of EI and UI (§28), no truth-functional inconsistencies can be got by EI and UI from S'. Then, by (VI), S' is true under some interpretation in a non-empty universe of positive integers.

But then, by the reasoning of p. 97n, S' will be true also under some interpretation in the full universe of positive integers. Then so will S.

The notion of consistency admits of a natural extension from schemata to classes of schemata. A class of schemata is consistent if, under some interpretation in a non-empty universe, all its members come out true together. (If some of the schemata of the class contain 'F' monadically, say, and others contain 'F' dyadically, what sense is there in speaking of a joint interpretation? Let us settle this point by treating the monadic 'F' and the dyadic 'F' as if they were different letters.) Now Löwenheim's theorem admits immediately of this superficial extension: If a finite class of quantificational schemata is consistent, all its members come out true together under some interpretation in the universe of positive integers. For, we have merely to take the schema in Löwenheim's theorem as a conjunction of all the schemata in the finite class.

Actually this limitation to finite classes can be lifted, as Skolem showed in 1920. The result is the Löwenheim-Skolem theorem: *If a class of quantificational schemata is consistent, all its members come out true together under some interpretation in the universe of positive integers.* The proof is omitted here.[1]

Consider any non-empty universe U and any assortment of predicates, all interpreted in that universe. Consider, further, the whole infinite totality of truths, known and unknown, that are expressible with help of those predicates together with the truth functions and quantification over U. Then the Löwenheim-Skolem theorem assures us that there is a reinterpretation of the predicates, in the universe of positive integers, that preserves the whole body of truths.

E.g., taking U as the universe of real numbers, we are told that the truths about real numbers can by a reinterpretation be carried over into truths about positive integers. This consequence has been viewed as paradoxical, in the light of Cantor's proof that the real numbers cannot be exhaustively correlated with integers. But the air of paradox may be dispelled by this reflection: whatever disparities between real numbers and integers may be guaranteed in

---

[1] For a version of the proof, see my "Interpretations of sets of conditions." *Journal of Symbolic Logic*, vol. 19 (1954), pp. 97–102.

those original truths about real numbers, the guarantees are themselves revised in the reinterpretation.

In a word and in general, the force of the Löwenheim-Skolem theorem is that the narrowly logical structure of a theory—the structure reflected in quantification and truth functions, in abstraction from any special predicates—is insufficient to distinguish its objects from the positive integers.